The Chindit War

Shelford Bidwell is the author and editor of several books, including the recent and controversial *World War III*. He is a Member of Council of the Royal United Services Institute for Defence Studies and a Fellow of the Royal Historical Society.

The Chindit War

*Stilwell, Wingate,
and the Campaign in Burma: 1944*

Shelford Bidwell

With an Introduction by John Masters

Macmillan Publishing Co., Inc.
New York

To

Michael Calvert,

Soldier and Student of War

Macmillan Publishing Co., Inc.
866 Third Avenue, New York, N.Y. 10022

First American Edition 1980

Printed in the United States of America

Library of Congress Cataloging in Publication Data
Bidwell, Shelford.
The Chindit war.
Bibliography: p.
Includes index.
1. World War, 1939-1945—Campaigns—Burma.
2. Burma—History—Japanese-occupation, 1942-1945.
I. Title.
D767.6.B52   1980   940.54′25   79-25696
ISBN 0-02-510600-7

Acknowledgments

I WAS FIRST attracted to the campaign fought in Burma by Generals Stilwell and Wingate as the subject for a study in contrasting methods of warfare. Then, as I collected information and began to put the story together, I was drawn away from strategy to the predicament of men in combat. I have adhered to my original theme, but I have also attempted to show how rival strategic theories, decisions of great men in conferences, and the dry work of operational planning staffs affected the fate of ordinary soldiers, whose hard task it was to realise the overall plan in a brutal war fought in a brutal environment.

My debt of gratitude to those who have so generously provided me with information on both levels is immense. I was exceptionally fortunate in being allowed to see so many narratives as yet unpublished. They are listed under Sources at the end of this book. In this connection I must thank, first and foremost, Brigadier P. W. Mead, both for allowing me to use his written record and for his advice, based on his unrivalled knowledge of the staff side of the whole Chindit venture, during the course of which he made repeated visits to the brigades in the field. He has since made an expert historical study of the whole affair. To him I am particularly indebted.

Of those who took a leading part in those events and to whom I must express my gratitude for their kindness and patience in answering endless questions I must first mention Admiral of the Fleet Earl Mountbatten of Burma; the late Major-General H. T. Alexander, Brigadier the Lord Ballantrae (Brigadier B. E. Fergusson in these pages), Brigadier Michael Calvert, Mr. D. C. Herring, Lieutenant-Colonel John Masters, Major-General A. H. G. Ricketts, Major-General F. D. Rome and Major-General G. W. Symes.

The American side of the operation has been amply covered in published works, and I should like to acknowledge my use of Carlton Ogburn's *The Marauders*, Charles N. Hunter's *Galahad* and, above all, *Stilwell's Command Problems* by C. F. Romanus and R. Sunderland. In addition I was greatly helped by the late Major-General Haydon C.

Boatner, U.S. Army, whose personal testimony, and the views he so candidly expressed to me have, I hope, enabled me to portray the fraught relationship between the Chindit command and the Americans in a fair and balanced way.

Lieutenant-Colonel A. J. Barker, author of *The March on Delhi*, referred me to Mr. James C. Wade, Jnr., an industrious and enthusiastic student of the Chindit campaign. I am deeply grateful to him for putting the fruits of his researches at my disposal, and also for a stimulating correspondence.

I wish to express my gratitude to Ronald Lewin, not only for imparting to me useful information from his store of knowledge and understanding of the Burma campaign but also for encouraging me in my task.

My published request for information produced an overwhelming response, both from those who served on the staff of Special Force or marched and fought in its ranks and from many others who supplied relevant details. Among those who answered questions, lent me maps and diaries, or gave me interviews were:

Terence S. Ahern, O. Ainscough, Major D. K. Ashton, N. P. Aylen, Lieutenant-Colonel A. J. Barker, Lieutenant-Colonel K. I. Barlow, Dr. S. Binnie, C. G. Birt, Dr. D. M. Bower, Colonel T. Brennan, Major-General R. S. Broke, Lieutenant-Colonel the Revd. P. Cane, Lieutenant-Colonel C. C. A. Carfrae, A. C. Cormack, G. N. Dennis, Dr. Norman F. Dixon, Norman Durant, Dr. Hugh L'Etang, Dr. W. M. Foreman, Colonel W. G. S. Foster, Lieutenant-Colonel M. A. Freshney, J. R. Gardiner, R. H. Gibbins, G. P. Gladman, Brigadier P. H. Graves-Morris, Robert W. Hampton, Lieutenant-Colonel A. Harper, L. W. Hart, Major H. Hart, Major H. Hayward-Surry, Guy F. Hepburn, Ian V. Hogg, J. Hesketh, A. A. H. Hopkinson, Brigadier P. M. Hughes, W. S. Hughes, G. R. Jellicoe, Major J. S. Lancaster (Hon. Secretary, the Chindit Association), Professor Sir Edmund Leach, Lieutenant-Colonel J. H. Marriott,Lieutenant-Colonel D. S. McCutcheon, R. Moffat, The Revd. W. H. Miller, R. Needham, Major-General C. A. R. Nevill and Mrs. Nevill, S. R. Nicholls, Lieutenant-Colonel H. K. N. Patterson, Major-General F. J. C. Piggott, R. W. Quickfall, Richard Rhodes-James, Lieutenant-Colonel W. A. Robinson, Colonel V. F. Royle, Brigadier W. Scott, J. R. Sealy, Major-General A. M. Sethna, Lieutenant-Colonel A. C. Simonds, Lieutenant-Colonel Ian Simpson, Major H. W. Swannell, Rodney Tatchell, Sir Robert Thompson, Major-General D. N. H. Tyacke, Mrs. J. Wallen, B. Whitehead, Dr. Desmond Whyte, D. W. Wilson, and Major-General G. F. Upjohn.

Ian V. Hogg gave me expert advice on the Japanese artillery.

Having made these acknowledgments I must emphasise that I am solely responsible for opinions expressed in this book together with any errors of fact.

I have been greatly assisted by Mr. Roderick Suddaby, Keeper of Documents in the Imperial War Museum, and also by the staff of the library of the Royal United Services Institution and the Ministry of Defence (Army), and offer them my grateful thanks.

I have always been lucky in my editors, and never more so than with Rivers Scott, of Hodder and Stoughton.

I must thank Mrs. Conrad Nazio for undertaking so capably research on my behalf.

Mrs. Jean Walter expertly typed an often chaotic manuscript with an unerring sub-editorial eye.

Lastly, but first in all other respects, I must thank my wife for her unlimited patience, encouragement and much useful criticism of work in progress.

Introduction

HOWEVER THIS BOOK came into your hands, unless it was thrown at you, you will enjoy reading it. It is about that part of the 1944 campaign of World War II in Burma that took part behind the Japanese lines, where many thousands of British, Gurkha, African, and American troops were flown and supplied by the Allied air forces. Some famous personalities took part—'Vinegar Joe' Stilwell, Lord Louis Mountbatten, 'Uncle Bill' Slim, and Philip Cochran, the original of Milton Caniff's Flip Corkin, not to mention such lesser lights as Merrill of Merrill's Marauders, Joe Lentaigne, 'Mad Mike' Calvert, Bernard Fergusson, and myself—each circling, while he was alive, round the enigmatic figure of Orde Wingate.

Seen in the large it was merely an adjunct to the great battle between Slim and Mutaguchi for Imphal, Kohima, and the eastern gates of India but it has aroused far more than its share of controversy and heated debate for two reasons. because it was an extremely bold and interesting concept; and because of those characters I have mentioned, and the clash of their ideas, wills, and personalities. Many previous books about the campaign have made dull reading because they have concentrated on what happened, or did not happen, or should or should not have been done, instead of focussing on the characters themselves.

Brigadier Bidwell does indeed tell us what happened, and why, but he does not allow himself to be suffocated by events: *The Chindit War* is about people—people at war. The narrative flows fast and strong. The tension builds and with it a foreboding sense of inevitable tragedy; but the strength of the book is in its re-creation, the bringing back to life, of those personalities in those days. Bidwell's skill here is in avoiding the 'dead fish' scientific approach: 'This fish has a three-inch dorsal fin and nineteen scales along the median line.' Perhaps, but who cares? The fish is clearly long dead. Bidwell's characters are as alive as Macaulay's Clive. Here and there he may miscount a scale or two, but by God his fish are alive, their eyes gleam, and they bite. Take this vignette:

9

Carfrae's sharp but sensitive attention was caught by the reaction of his burly African company sergeant-major to his first sight of the dead, not an African but two Japanese. . . . Both were horribly maimed; the arm of one had been severed by a grenade and the guts of the other were trailing out of his belly.

In peace the C.S.M. was the ornament of the ceremonial parade; he roared like a bull on the barrack-square and was the terror of the private soldiers. Here, confronted with the reality of war, he stood rigid, as motionless as the dead at whom he stared. . . . Such is the effect of that powerful reagent, battle, on the chemistry of the human personality.

Such, too, is the style of this book—vivid and analytical. I could quote much more about Stilwell and his 'acidulous qualities'; Wingate and the 'laser beam of his demonic stare'; Calvert, 'a fierce old boar of the jungle' . . . but better you find and enjoy these things for yourself. Read on!

—John Masters
Santa Fe, New Mexico

Contents

Maps

Illustrations

Lieut. George Albert Cairns[2]
Calvert and Lt-Col. Shaw[2]
Wingate in close-up

Acknowledgments

1 Lt-Col. H. K. N. Patterson
2 The Imperial War Museum
3 Major-General G. W. Symes
4 Brigadier The Lord Ballantrae
5 Brigadier Michael Calvert
6 Lt-Col. John Masters
7 Major-General A. H. G. Ricketts
8 Brigadier P. H. Graves-Morris
9 Brigadier P. W. Mead
10 The Institution of Royal Engineers
11 Lt-Col. A. Harper

The Chindit War

I

Prelude

EARLY IN 1944, when the war between the Allies and Japan was three years old, some twenty thousand élite troops, trained for guerrilla warfare, invaded enemy-held Burma. Some marched in by secret routes, some descended in gliders, others were flown in transport aircraft to airfields hacked out by United States engineers deep in the jungles behind the Japanese lines. Three thousand, the 'Marauders' as they came to be called, were Americans. The 'Chindits' were mainly British. In fact the whole operation was the brainchild of a British general, Orde C. Wingate, but in the Chindit ranks also marched Gurkha riflemen from Nepal, Nigerians of the Royal West African Frontier Force, Chinese from Hong Kong and men of the Burma Rifles. They were backed by another élite force detached from the United States Army Air Force: the First Air Commando. The reason for committing this unique airborne, air-sustained army to a remote wilderness in South-East Asia was because the Japanese were there, and had cut off the only land route by which the flow of aid from America could reach China.

By 1944 the United States was fighting two wars at once: one against the Axis powers in Europe and the other against Japan at sea, while at the same time its mighty arsenals were providing tanks, aircraft, ships and guns for its allies on a scale that strained even its vast resources. It was, therefore, one of the planks of United States strategy to keep China in the war to share the burden of fighting the Japanese. Military aid was being flown to China from India, but this was only a trickle compared with what she needed. The solution the Americans hit upon was typical of their national genius: bold and spectacular, they accepted difficulties as only a challenge to determination and ingenuity.

The plan was for an army of American-trained Chinese to advance from India, clearing the trace of a route through the tangle of forests and mountains and over the great rivers of the extreme north of Burma as far as the Chinese frontier. This operation was code-named ALBACORE. Behind this force would follow another army of United States military engineers who would build a road fit for heavy

17

transport and a pipe-line for oil. The whole was to be commanded by Lieutenant-General Joseph Warren Stilwell, United States Army. The task of the Chindits and Marauders was to operate in scattered groups deep in the rear of Stilwell's opponent, Lieutenant-General Tanaka, and his Japanese 18th Division, and so help the Chinese advance by ambushing his reinforcements and supply columns and destroying his dumps of stores, fuel and munitions. In addition they were to set up a blocking position on his main railway supply route. This operation, which came to be called THURSDAY, was to be commanded by the British Major-General Orde Charles Wingate.

It must be understood that for all its remoteness from the main theatres of the Second World War the India-Burma-China campaign, as originally conceived, was to be no mere appendix to the main Allied war plans. There was to be an offensive on a grand scale to clear the Japanese from the eastern provinces of China, carried out by Chinese armies equipped with American weapons and trained by an American mission. At the same time a concentric attack by the British and the Chinese, supported by American air power, was to be launched against the Japanese conquerors of Burma. This whole strategy had been settled by the President of the United States, Franklin D. Roosevelt, and the Prime Minister of Great Britain, Winston Churchill, at a conference at Quebec in August, 1943, and supported by their military advisers. As far as Wingate's Special Force, to give it its official title, was concerned, no objections raised by the more orthodox British generals were allowed to interfere with its creation and no resources within reason were denied to it.

Few campaigns have started with such high hopes or with troops in such high hopes or with troops in such high spirits: indeed, among the British Chindits there were symptoms of almost religious fervour inspired by their messianic leader, who was one of the oddest generals ever to wear British uniform. The Marauders were more earthy and cynical, but they made a brilliant contribution to Stilwell's enveloping tactics and after their opening move General Tanaka was only to thankful to extricate his troops from a trap of which the Marauders were the steel spring. His tenacious, aggressive defence appeared for a moment to be shattered and the way thus to be open for the nervous Chinese generals to risk an advance. Soon the Chindits were in strength a hundred miles to the south of Tanaka's positions, defying all Japanese attempts to evict them and rampaging at will in an area about the size of Wales or Massachusetts.

Then the complexion of the battle changed. War is not a game of chess and the opening position, that looked so promising on the board, degenerated into a brutal struggle to the death; death being due as much to disease as to fire power and not a little to military incompetence. In no other theatre of war outside Russia were Allied soldiers driven so hard. They responded with endurance and courage on a heroic scale, but these are assets on which the good general does not demand an unlimited overdraft.

After Wingate had been killed in an air accident, on March 24th, 1944, the whole Chindit force, in accordance with the sound principle of unity of command, was placed directly under General Stilwell. Within an inch of success, but frustrated by the tenacity of the Japanese defence and the maddening inactivity of his own Chinese troops, he called on them to go on attacking as long as there was a man left to bear arms. By July the original Marauders had virtually ceased to exist. The wrecks of the Chindit brigades, having fought their way up to the Chinese, were flown out, looking more like survivors from a Japanese prisoner-of-war camp than victorious soldiers. Stilwell had had his success, but some unpleasant facts began slowly to emerge. Convalescent Marauders had been herded into trucks from hospital to provide reinforcements in spite of anguished protests from American doctors. Two British battalion commanders had the painful duty of reporting that the remnants of their men could no longer be relied upon to obey orders to attack. There were some ugly rumours that British soldiers had been held to their task by public flogging. Of one group of Gurkha Rifles 1,350 strong, only twenty-five men were physically able to bear arms. One Chindit brigadier found that he had 300 effectives left out of 3,000 after his final battle and, determined to save his brigade from total destruction, risked court-martial by shutting down his radios and marching out. What had started as a triumph ended as a scandal.

In the pitiless balance sheets of warfare, the price paid for Stilwell's victory was not excessive: Tarawa, Iwojima, the German airborne assault on Crete cost many more in killed and wounded, and in comparison with the holocaust of the Russian front the affair ranks as a skirmish. The irony lies in the fact that the whole enterprise was a waste of human effort and human sacrifice.

Even before it was launched some American strategists had perceived that the China policy was based on a profound misunderstanding of the corrupt and incompetent régime of Chiang Kai-shek, who was ready enough to suck on the seemingly inexhaustible udder of American wealth and determined to do nothing in return in the way of attacking the Japanese. Those among the British who desired the real aim of THURSDAY to be the restoration of Burma to Imperial rule were equally deceived. It was true that the Burmese people hoped ardently to be liberated, but from the British, not the Japanese. No sooner was the war over than their leaders chose to leave both the old Empire and the newer-style Commonwealth. The re-conquest of

Burma proved to be not worth the bones of a single rifleman, black, white or brown. The final defeat of Japan was ensured by battles fought thousands of miles away to the east, in the Pacific.

Much has been written about that strange campaign from different angles: sometimes the writers seem to be talking about different sets of events. The art of public relations, the art of the political cover-up, the art of special pleading have all been brought into play; and the Marauders and Chindits, Wingate who created both forces, and Stilwell who used the weapon, have all become to some extent mythologised. There is good reason to view those events again with the advantage of perspective conferred by the passage of thirty years. The military lessons are simple enough. What fascinates now is the human predicament. It was Foch who, writing on the 'principles of war', quoted the saying of Jomini that 'far from being an exact science, war is a dreadful and impassioned drama.' The truth of that saying has seldom been more awesomely demonstrated than by Burma in 1944.

The process of history that brought the Japanese into conflict with the most powerful nation on earth lies outside the scope of this book. What has to be explained is how the Japanese army came to be occupying a remote territory thousands of miles from their homeland. Their attack on Singapore was understandable. It kicked away the prop underpinning British naval power in South-East Asia and secured their own western flank. But why was it necessary to advance into Burma? For although this ensured the final isolation of China it overstretched Japan's resources – from the Aleutian Islands to the Chindwin River – and her forces were clearly exposed to a powerful counter-stroke.

It is hard not to conclude that the Japanese at that time were suffering from nothing less than failure of their collective powers of reasoning: they were the victims of their own myth. Rationally speaking, their leaders should have sat down, calculated the profit and losses, and thought out how best they could take long-term advantage of a Western world torn by war. They did nothing of the sort. Indeed, they had not even thought out their aim in the apparently endless war in which they had become enmeshed since 1932 in mainland China. They had found the colonial powers, the Dutch, the French, the British, morally and physically unprepared, and easy victims. They had some cloudy notion of a Japanese Asian empire, but had not defined its boundaries, and their string of cheap victories developed its own momentum. The Japanese only stopped in South-East Asia when they came hard up against the geographical barriers of forest and mountain in Burma and when their perimeter was too long and too distant to be effectively manned if it became extended further.

The British in India, although shaken by the Japanese successes in

Malaya, had continued to hope that sheer distance, combined with lack of roads and railways, might deter the Japanese from any further advance once they had captured Singapore, and believed that, in any case, they could at least hold Burma. In this they were disappointed. In December, 1941, the Japanese, with supreme self-confidence, defied all conventional logistics by invading Burma from their bases in Thailand and drove the British back to India.

If British confidence had been shaken by the fall of Singapore the outcome of the Burma campaign of 1942 was such that the damage to both military and public morale in India could not be repaired by propaganda or excuses for lack of military preparation. The Japanese invaders had consisted only of two divisions of infantry whose equipment and training might have been regarded as up to date in 1917. Their fighting spirit, however, was terrific. They attacked with tremendous élan, always seeking for the soft spot, and they were supported by an efficient air force trained to support the army. They met and routed six Allied divisions – two British-Indian and four Chinese – though in fairness it must be added that some tough opposition was put up by units of this hastily-assembled and only partly-trained force. The British did rather better than they had in Malaya. Still, in May 1942, they saw that the position was hopeless and, with the remnants of two Chinese divisions who could not push past the encircling Japanese to the frontier of their own country, withdrew to India. The Japanese then settled down to occupy Burma, leaving only a tiny pocket of the country in the far north-east under the British flag, which was kept flying precariously at the remote Imperial outpost of 'Fort Hertz', or Putao.

For the British the Burma campaign of 1942 was a disgrace which rankled for years afterwards. A barometer of the national feeling was the emphasis placed in subsequent literature on the heroic aspects of the fighting retreat, and the lack of it placed on the fact that the troops and the staff involved in it had not been properly trained to fight the Japanese or, indeed, anyone else. In the wider context of the war, however, it was of no great importance except for the interruption of aid to China, and that concerned the Americans more than the British, who had a low opinion of the fighting quality of Chinese soldiers. Elsewhere, the course of the war was turning in favour of the Allies. That same year the little battle of Alamein and the great battle of Stalingrad were bad omens for Germany, and in 1943 the Americans and British cleared the Axis out of Africa and Italy and out of the war, after their landings in Sicily and Italy, while the Americans drove the Japanese from Guadalcanal and began to deploy their Pacific strategy. By the end of the year Imperial Japan was already doomed.

The Japanese in Burma did not at first have the resources to invade India, and they believed, like the British, that the jungles west of the Chindwin River were impassable. They therefore contented themselves with repelling a courageous but half-baked British counter-offensive in the Arakan. This only served to depress British morale further. The British general staff in Delhi thenceforward concentrated on the defence of India and saw no future in an offensive strategy, at least for a year or more. Such a spiritless and passive attitude however did not suit Churchill, who always urged offensive action on his generals, and was deeply sensitive about the integrity of the Empire and Commonwealth. Also, he had his own good political reasons for demonstrating to the Americans, who now dominated the conduct of the war, that the British were as eager to fight the enemy as they were.

The strategy of the United States planners, which Churchill was determined to support by offensive action on the part of the large and idle masses of troops in India, was based on the fact that the Japanese had been embroiled in mainland China for the past ten years and dared not abandon it. A modernised, vigorously-directed Chinese Army (the Americans, characteristically, were planning to create as a first contingent no fewer than sixty divisions) should therefore be used to draw off a substantial part of the Japanese Army from the crucial sectors where the Americans were engaged. Then, if the Japanese could be cleared from the eastern seaboard of China, air bases could be established, from which the powerful American bomber forces could attack Japan. The man sent to direct this great operation needed to be in the first flight of American generals; and American generals are very good.

'Vinegar Joe' Stilwell, on whom the choice fell, was then fifty-eight years old, able and ambitious. In the doldrums of service in the small, peacetime army of the United States, he had made himself into a Chinese interpreter and later, after much eastern service, had become the United States officer with the greatest knowledge of Chinese affairs. No American was apparently better fitted to fill a post requiring diplomatic as much as military ability, and when Chiang Kai-shek, the autocratic ruler of China, had been persuaded to accept a senior United States officer as his chief of staff and military adviser, Stilwell was chosen. It was a post of immense responsibility, as it involved the correct application of American aid. It was also beset with formidable difficulties, for Stilwell and his team of officers had, as an initial task to create a modernised army in the face of the resistance of the Chinese senior officers to any form of change – to say nothing of their resentment at being instructed by foreigners. Stilwell was a man of uncommon ability, but he saw himself, or yearned to be, a commander of troops in the field. With some excuse, for he alone of the many American officers in his mission had the gift of being able to tease, coax, bully or shame the Chinese generals into sustained offensive action, he persuaded Chiang Kai-shek to allow him to command the Chinese divisions sent in 1942 to assist the British in the defence of Burma.

The débâcle that followed reinforced the contempt and dislike Stilwell felt for the British, dating from his experiences in the First World War, and his belief that the Chinese really could fight when given leadership. One of his divisions had, for a short period, offered a stout defence to the Japanese. When he returned to India his future plans had already taken a firm shape in his mind and his future behaviour followed an undeviating line. He was to train his own Chinese army, an élite, quite different from the one inside China's borders, and lead it himself once it was ready for the field.

All Stilwell's hopes, ambitions and emotions were focused on that campaign, whose object, it must be said, was fully in line with his mission, but whose outcome for him was deeply personal. In 1942, when he was safely back in Delhi after an adventurous journey, he dealt scornfully with the outpourings of the British public relations machine, which was busy applying a gloss of heroism and self-justification to the defeat in Burma. Speaking to a group of journalists he said: 'I claim we got a hell of a beating. We got run out of Burma and it was as humiliating as hell. I think we ought to find out what caused it, go back and retake it.'

These words were both revealing and prophetic. In a year's time his little First Chinese Army was ready to advance from India into northern Burma and he commanded it himself. Nothing was to dislodge him for long from his austere field headquarters until he had broken the obstinate Japanese defence line in the north. Here was born the legend of 'Vinegar Joe' Stilwell, the all-American folk hero with his rough tongue, his contempt for British dudes, his homely Yankee manner, wearing a dirty uniform without badges or medal ribbons, living in a rough jungle shack made of branches and eating a private's rations. It was sedulously fostered by Stilwell himself, but without his urge to command and his single-mindedness there would have been no campaign in Burma in 1944.

But if there might have been no campaign without Stilwell, without Wingate it would certainly have been bogged down in the swamps and forest-clad mountains that bar the way into Burma, where the Japanese, if unhampered by his Chindits, could have fought an indefinitely long delaying action. Both men were complex characters and in many ways, despite a twenty-year difference in age (Stilwell was born in 1883, Wingate in 1903), they were curiously similar. Like

Stilwell, Wingate masked himself with a *persona*, emphasising his scorn for the outward trappings of command and for drawing-room soldiers. He grew a beard, dressed like a tramp, and had an abrasive tongue which did not spare generals. His outbursts, like Stilwell's in Delhi, could be revealing, but in his own way. One day, in 1943, deep in Japanese-occupied territory and leading a long column of the raiders who were the model for the Chindit force of 1944, he called a conference of all officers. They left their units uncommanded reluctantly and even apprehensively, for the whole operation was extremely dangerous and they might meet a Japanese ambush at any moment. They wondered if there was a crisis, or if Wingate had decided on some drastic change of plan. Nothing else could justify so unusual a gathering. Wingate addressed them at length on the subject of the British evacuation from Dunkirk. His theme was that it had been built up into an heroic event, almost a victory, and that this was typical of the British weakness for making excuses for their defeats. It was not an heroic event, he told his officers. It was a disgrace.[1]

Wingate was a natural orator. His piercing eyes, seemingly fixed on each of his listeners, his harsh, metallic voice, his clear and vibrant style with its evangelical Old Testament flavour and biblical turns of phrase, never failed to grip his audience. On this occasion the officers were silent and deeply attentive; perhaps not without feelings of guilt. Wingate reached his peroration and then dismissed them to return to their posts. He had said nothing whatever about the operation in hand. It was a queer incident, they all thought once the spell was broken, but then, they all understood that their leader was 'mad', in the sense used in the British army about any odd or original character, and they thought none the worse of him for that.

Wingate's harangue delivered to a circle of squatting officers in that remote forest glade provides a valuable clue to his whole psychological make-up, but the point here is that it revealed that he was at heart a romantic and a patriot: 'Patriot', in fact, was the form of address he used when speaking to the Burmese-born officers in his ranks. ('Come here, patriot!') Like Stilwell he felt humiliated by the defeat in Burma and his driving urge was to go back and plant the Union Jack on the banks of the Irrawaddy or, more precisely, in his own phrase, 'to give you all Burma north of the twenty-fourth parallel of latitude'.

Wingate's military career had so far been a switchback of success and misfortune. Before the war he had conceived and personally led some counter-insurgency operations against the Arab guerrillas fighting the British mandatory government in Palestine and was duly decorated with a DSO. He was then relieved of his appointment because of his passionate and indiscreet support for the Zionist cause.

However, while in Palestine he had attracted the attention of the future Field Marshal Earl Wavell, whose mind was always open to imaginative and unorthodox solutions to military problems. When some vigorous lobbying by himself and his friends in high places extracted Wingate from a dead-end job in the Home Forces in Britain Wavell, then Commander-in-Chief in the Middle East, accepted him as an expert in guerrilla operations. Guerrilla and counter-insurgence are two sides of the same coin, and Wavell perceived that this game-keeper might make a good poacher. He sent him to stir up the Abyssinians against the Italians. Wingate scored a resounding success, but once more ruined his prospects by his folly. At once fiery and cantankerous, he quarrelled with everyone from his immediate chief, General Sir William Platt, downwards, and again stepped outside his military brief to play a political rôle. Once again he was fired and his guerrilla organisation, 'Gideon Force', was disbanded. In a deep depression, aggravated by physical exhaustion and malaria, he cut his throat, but fortunately his life was saved by devoted nursing and his mind by the advice of a distinguished psychiatrist on the staff of the army medical services in Cairo. He was demoted and sent home.[2]

A major once more, his career seemed wrecked and the army was full of the powerful enemies his own ungoverned tongue had raised against him. But yet again his friends saved him and yet again Wavell, by 1942 the Commander-in-Chief in India, sent for him and gave him employment suitable for his talents. This time he ordered Wingate to study the prospects of organising guerrilla activity against the Japanese forces occupying Burma. Wingate's adventures in 1943 are themselves sufficient for a full-length book: indeed, books have been written by individuals about their own experiences in his first operation. It will suffice here to map out the events which led to the great operation THURSDAY of 1944.

The first landmark is operation LONGCLOTH. Backed by Wavell, Wingate once more used his bizarre but effective training methods. He took some perfectly ordinary, and in some cases third-rate, British and Gurkha troops, with a smattering of Burma Rifles to act as guides, linguists and scouts, and welded them into a force of seven 'columns' which acted in effect as artificial guerrilla bands. Officially the 77th Infantry Brigade, they formed the original 'Chindits': the name is a corruption of the Burmese word for the winged stone lions who are the guardians of Buddhist temples. With his nondescript troops, he infiltrated deep into Burma, fought some minor actions, was nearly trapped, then ordered a general dispersal and return to India, losing 883 men out of 3,000 in the process. He himself confessed later to a friend that he saw the result as a failure and was at first wholly downcast and resigned to his third dismissal.[3] He was saved by two qualities essential in a military commander: luck, and his own refusal ever to admit defeat.

As a purely military enterprise LONGCLOTH was indeed open to criticism, but it had two quite unpredictable results. It revealed to the Japanese high command that the apparently impassable terrain of India's eastern frontier was in fact ideal for the tactics of deep infiltration, which the Japanese understood very well. This led a year later to the Japanese offensives called Ha-Go and U-Go and their crushing and decisive defeat by General Slim. The immediate effect in India was also of great consequence. The public relations machine, engaged in the hopeless task of trying to counter a flow of the most dismal news, saw the heaven-sent chance of exploiting a success story, and it went into action at full power to break the news that for three months a novel raiding force had been deep in Burma harrying the Japanese. All the evocative images dear to journalists were there to exploit: 'commandoes', 'Gurkhas', and above all the mysterious Wingate with a whiff about him of an earlier hero, Lawrence of Arabia. One of the more striking exaggerations in this brilliant publicity exercise caught the attention of Winston Churchill himself: Wingate became 'the Clive of Burma'.

The hero himself was quite unmoved by the ballyhoo. He was as vigorous a writer of English as he was an orator and he concentrated all his passion and energy into writing a report on his exploit. Wingate's mental processes were not analytic or intellectual. He could discard unwanted facts or invent new ones as they hindered or furthered his plans. He was imaginative and creative and now he argued that his guerrilla tactics could be amplified into a strategy for defeating the Japanese. The paper found its way to England and on to the desk of the Secretary of State for India, Leo Amery, another friend and patron of Wingate from the days of his pro-Zionist attachment. The crucial turning point in Wingate's career was, however, when Winston Churchill sent for him to come to England so that he could interview him.

Churchill was due to go to the summit conference called 'Quadrant' in Quebec where the plans for future Allied strategy were to be discussed, and in his impulsive way he took Wingate with him. Wingate, a junior officer who had never commanded a force in full-scale operations and who was not merely a maverick but an insignificant maverick constantly in disgrace with the military establishment, rose magnificently to the occasion. Brilliant he undoubtedly was, but he was quite untrained in staff duties and unfamiliar with the process, half political, half military, of planning for war on the highest level. Yet he managed to convince, in succession, the Prime Minister and Minister of Defence (Churchill), the British chiefs of staff, the United States chiefs of staff and finally President Franklin D. Roosevelt himself that he could, using his system of 'Long-Range Penetration', make a powerful contribution to Allied strategy in South-East Asia. At Quebec he passed a severe test with honours, and he was rewarded with promotion to the rank of major-general and by being given the necessary resources to put his ideas into practice.

Another of Churchill's inspirations was also accepted by the Americans. It was agreed that Admiral Lord Louis Mountbatten should be appointed Supreme Allied Commander, South-East Asia. Without him the whole Chindit enterprise might have foundered. Stilwell may have grappled with British defeatism, but it was the young Admiral Mountbatten, the 'Glamour Boy', as Stilwell called him, who cured it. Old-fashioned army rough-riders, if baffled by a reluctant or 'nappy' horse, used to clap a hot baked potato fresh from the oven under the root of the obstinate animal's tail. This guaranteed the desired forward impulsion and it learned not to 'refuse' again. Mountbatten, a polo-player of repute, may or may not have heard of this cruel practice, but he proceeded, metaphorically, to apply the hot potato treatment to the British command in India, not sparing the most senior officers. At the same time he identified two whose spirits rose with the difficulties and dangers of the path ahead and who were men after his own heart. One was Air Marshal Sir John Baldwin, an ex-Hussar turned flier, who was to have much to do with the air side of Operation THURSDAY. The other was Lieutenant-General J. W. Slim, who had commanded the defeated British corps in Burma, but who had against all expectation extricated it as a formed body with even a few of its guns. He, too, outwardly solid and unemotional, felt deeply and bitterly about the British defeat and he, too, was determined to return victorious to Burma. The third man, Wingate, Mountbatten had already met at Quebec.

Mountbatten began with high hopes, but he found that in spite of all the brave words at Quebec, South-East Asia had the lowest priority for weapons and military supplies of any theatre. As an inevitable result plans to implement the decisions of Quebec were altered, cut down in scope, abandoned and followed by fresh plans that suffered the same process. There was another conference, in Cairo, where it became clear that Chiang Kai-shek was reluctant to commit even his new American-trained divisions without impossible safeguards.

The plans for a major British offensive were postponed in favour of a scaled-down operation, and at one stage in the hectic months of preparation the Supreme Commander put forward a plan to abandon the land offensive in favour of a naval and amphibious strategy swinging far to the south and east in the direction of Sumatra and Singapore. It was vetoed by the Americans. Mountbatten was to discover that at the same time as his official delegation was arguing the case for this plan in Washington, his own subordinate and deputy commander, Stilwell, had sent his own emissary to plead successfully against it.

Wingate also had his troubles. By the beginning of 1944 his soaring imagination had conceived a plan far in advance or excess of a rôle in support of Stilwell. He began to think of flying in whole divisions to secure the territory he was confident his 'guerrillas would liberate. This was firmly resisted, on top of which there were those on the staff who would have been glad to see the whole Chindit plan abandoned. In those circles Wingate was known as 'Robin Hood' or, more derisively, 'Tarzan'. Wingate fought hard to keep his strategic concept from being damaged, using every trick he knew; impassioned memoranda, complaints made direct to Churchill, tantrums and offers to resign – all were brought in to play.

The period between the Quebec conference in August 1943 and the launching of the campaign in Burma in 1944 which we can call 'THURSDAY' (after the code-name used for the initial airborne invasion) was one of intense activity and, at the top level of command, of apparent confusion. To disentangle the full story of the plans and counter-plans is certainly a long and tedious process, but one fact stands out clearly. The task of creating the Chinese army in India and the Special Force was pushed forward with great vigour and efficiency and by the end of 1943 both were forged and fully tempered. It was the two generals concerned, Stilwell and Wingate, who supplied the drive and who set their stamp ineradicably on both the weapons and the course of events that followed. But to understand the story, it is first necessary to look behind the *persona* each man had so carefully assumed.

2

The Two Generals

STILWELL AND WINGATE were both born under the sign of Pisces, and each possessed the artistic sensitivity, the powers of imagination, the dreaminess or vagueness, the intellect, and the passion for secrecy and deviousness this accident of birth is supposed to confer. Each was the product of a family tightly knit by affection and valued its bonds; Stilwell went as far as to include his son and his son-in-law in his staff and both men liked to keep a surrogate family of a few trusted friends near them. Those included in this private circle could see a willingness to confide, a warmth of affection and even a sly humour in their general. This was his private face. The public face was very different: ruthless, remorseless, utterly abrasive in human relationships; and both men, once they had fixed their eyes on a goal, were determined to reach it over every obstacle, human or physical, that lay in their path.

Outwardly Stilwell was an orthodox soldier whose career, already nearing its summit when he elected to take direct command in the field, had followed an orthodox pattern, filling successfully all the testing appointments given to a promising officer in peace. He began, like many of his peers, by enduring the rigours of the United States Military Academy. The British Royal Military Academy at Woolwich, where engineer and artillery officers were trained, had a reputation for toughness, but it was anaemic compared with the hazing, the strict discipline and the academic grind at West Point. The intention was to reduce American youths, however rugged or individualistic, to an unquestioning conformity of thought and behaviour, absolute obedience and devotion to the three-word slogan of 'Duty, Honour, Country'. Wingate, when subjected to a similar régime at Woolwich, proved sullen and rebellious and only graduated with difficulty; not so much from lack of ability as from a stubborn refusal to conform. By contrast the young Stilwell was determined to meet and survive the sadistic treatment handed out to the 'plebes' in their first academic year and eventually began to enjoy himself. At West Point it was a great advantage to be an athlete. Stilwell, slight but wiry, became an excellent all-rounder; a long-distance runner, oarsman, basketball player and footballer. Like many American officers, his tactical vocabulary was to be borrowed from American football, a stylised form of warfare, Stilwell passed out high in the order of merit, was commissioned into the infantry, served in the Philippines, paid a visit to Hong Kong and China which made a lasting impression on him, married early and happily and began to climb the military ladder. The first feather in his cap was his selection to return, when still a junior officer, to West Point to serve as an instructor; an appointment demanding both ability and the highest integrity.

When the United States entered the First World War Stilwell served on the staff in the intelligence branch and so was denied combat experience at the formative level of a platoon or company commander. When at last, in the Second World War, he came to command an army in the field he had no guide but theory. His courage was equal to any of the shocks or hazards of battle but, as the events of 1944 were to make painfully clear, he never had that essential empathy, the 'feel' of troops, which is the greatest gift a leader can have. He thought that American GIs and British privates could be driven uncomplaining to their deaths like the wretched Chinese, whose acquaintance he had made in the inter-war years and who, in his crabbed way, he admired, if only as military automatons.

Stilwell's involvement with China began in 1919, when the future seemed to hold out nothing to an officer in the United States infantry except the boredom and stagnation of life in some prairie garrison and so, his imagination having been captured by the Orient years before, he applied for a Chinese language course, which required residence in that country. After qualifying, Stilwell returned to China to serve there with a regiment, and also as military attaché at the United States Legation in Peking. Like Wingate, who with the same motives had become a linguist in Arabic and had contrived to escape from the boredom of service in England to the Sudan Defence Force, Stilwell wasted little time in the social life of the army but travelled widely and used his knowledge of the language to study not only the Chinese military system but also Chinese history and culture as a whole.

For historical reasons the Americans have always had a peculiar sympathy for the Chinese and a special relationship with China; something never achieved by the British, who underestimated the resilience of the Chinese in their long and seemingly inconclusive war with the Japanese, and in consequence thought that the Japanese, being unable to achieve a quick· victory over the Chinese, were inferior troops. They were accordingly painfully surprised when they first met the battle-hardened Japanese and Korean troops in Burma and Malaya. Stilwell, always deeply cynical, even about the Chinese, had a correct appreciation both of the Chinese political situation and of the value of the Chinese military potential. But his countrymen, romantic and overgenerous, greatly overestimated the extent to which American aid and weapons and American know-how could reanimate Chiang Kai-shek's wretched armies, where corrupt and timid generals commanded half-armed and ragged soldiers.

China, therefore, was the obvious destination of Stilwell in peace or war, but the crucial point in his career was reached when he was appointed head of the tactical instruction wing in the Infantry School at Fort Benning. Stilwell was without first-hand experience of war, but his knowledge of military history led him to understand the part played by what Clausewitz calls 'friction' in the chancy business of combat (or what, in the vulgar language, is called 'Murphy's Law', and states that what can go wrong, probably will). He was thus deeply suspicious of the formal doctrinal solutions and the 'standard operational procedures', as they came to be called later, to which United States Army officers used to cling as Fundamentalists do to Holy Writ. Like Verdy du Vernois at Nachod, Stilwell said, in effect: 'To hell with history and principles! What is the problem?' He preferred to teach tactics in the open on real ground, with only so much of a setting as a company commander might expect to have in real action, than in the classroom or lecture hall. His methods closely resembled those of Wingate, who used to make officers under instruction run all the time, to create the necessary sense of urgency and force them to think when exhausted. His imagination and insight made up for lack of combat experience. Stilwell, like Wingate, was in fact that uncommon military type, the gifted natural trainer of men. Also like Wingate, he had a rough tongue, failed to suffer fools gladly, and poured streams of the bitterest sarcasm on those who proffered foolish solutions or asked silly questions to curry favour, or questions which revealed careless thinking. It was at the Infantry School that Stilwell first acquired the nickname 'Vinegar Joe'. It was affectionate. His students admired him, as they often do an eccentric or a disciplinarian, provided they are sure that he has a real knowledge of his subject.

It was not only his students who admired him. The Commandant of the School was George Marshall, the future chief-of-staff of the army, an unerring judge of men, who at that time reported on Stilwell as an officer capable of reaching the highest posts in the army. In due course Stilwell was one of his selections for promotion to lieutenant-general in the event of the war Marshall so clearly foresaw; among the others were Eisenhower, Bradley and Patton. His original intention had been to appoint Stilwell to plan and command the projected Allied operation in North Africa, but this post went to

Eisenhower. The support of China and the creation of a modern Chinese army, trained and equipped by the United States and capable of playing a major part in the war against Japan, had become an essential part of Allied strategy in Asia, and there was no general of Stilwell's calibre who had an equal knowledge of China and the Chinese. His appointment as chief-of-staff to Chiang Kai-shek, with other high diplomatic and military responsibilities towards his own country, was almost inevitable. Stilwell thus had to abandon his ardent hope of leading the troops of his own country into battle and he never ceased to complain about everything and everybody in his revealing diary. But 'Duty, Honour, Country' held him in line, and he was never to swerve from his mission.

Unfortunately the acidulous qualities, so amusing in a major, proved to be disastrous in a general who was his country's military representative with the Chinese on the one hand, and the British on the other. As Stilwell grew older his tongue became more barbed, his judgments harsher and his manners, bad at the best of times, abominable. Like Wingate, he was verbally aggressive, and could never forego the pleasure of being rude, especially to some unfortunate prevented by military discipline from answering back. To Colonel H. T. Alexander, when that officer was chief of staff of Wingate's Special Force in 1944, he said that 'he knew the British were useless as soldiers but now he knew that they were also yellow' – this of the Chindits. To Mountbatten he burst out with a remark that he thought would please him:

> 'Gee, Admiral. I like working with you! You are the only Limey I have met who wants to fight!' 'Having got him right on this point,' recalls Lord Mountbatten, 'and having quoted General [Sir Harold] Alexander as being really brave and a great fighter, he staggered me by saying, "General Alexander was a coward. He retreated all the way and never stood and fought". I pointed out that Stilwell had also retreated all the way and that nobody so far had called him a coward.'[1]

This shut Stilwell up, and he took no further liberties with the Supreme Allied Commander. Like many verbal bullies he was vulnerable to a sharp riposte.

The trouble with Stilwell was that in spite of a life free from misfortune or hardship, the security of strict but happy upbringing, the comfort of his own marriage and the blessings of children, not to mention success in his career (for he was to be promoted full general in 1944), he suffered inexplicably from a painful and crippling disease: the *odium humani generis*. Apart from a few intimates or cronies and his family, Stilwell despised the human race. He was without compassion, up to a point no bad thing in a general who has to order men to their deaths to achieve a given goal, but Stilwell had too many hates for a well-adjusted man. Allowing for his carefully constructed *persona* of an ordinary, rough American free from affectation and frills and with a vocabulary to suit, there is something revealing about the use in the privacy of his diary of the terms 'frogs', 'limeys', 'niggers', 'coons', 'wops', 'googs', 'huns', and 'chinks' for foreigners. To these outcasts he added other despised categories, such as all those who by his own arbitrary standards he considered effete: the rich, the snobs, cavalry officers and even those who carried swagger-canes, like the British, for whom he had a dislike amounting to a neurosis.[2] Goebbels could hardly have felt more intensely about the Jews than Stilwell felt about the 'limeys'.

As Stilwell's diary reveals, he was also deeply pessimistic. He derived a perverse pleasure from bad news. He obtained actual satis-faction from the disaster in Burma, regardless of the sufferings of the wretched Burmese, as he contemplated the fall of the British Empire, 'with its pants down', and his conviction of an impending British defeat during the opening phases of the Battle of Kohima-Imphal was not followed by any pleasure in Slim's great victory. Nothing illustrates these contrasting facets of a complex character better than Stilwell's behaviour during his last weeks in Burma in 1942. Early in April, the military situation having collapsed about his ears and with his troops in hopeless flight and his Chinese chief-of-staff about to bail out, Stilwell was already brooding on the problem of how to create a new model Chinese army, and putting his thoughts into action. The wrecks of two good Chinese divisions, the 22nd and the 38th, were making for India. Why not, he thought, use them as the nucleus of a new force, and train them in India, away from Chinese interference, where he could counter Chinese indolence and Chinese corruption? There was the stream of cargo aircraft flying 'over the Hump' to China and returning empty. They could be used for bringing recruits to India to fill out the two divisions and create extra artillery and armoured units. He sent one of his staff officers to China to persuade Chiang Kai-shek to agree and another to India to look for a suitable training base.

Having set these plans in train Stilwell was faced with an acute personal dilemma. On May 1st all hope of resistance in Burma was abandoned and all that remained for him was to leave before there was any risk of his falling into the hands of the Japanese. Any assistance to his retreating divisions could be better organised from India, but over and above this it was his absolute duty to preserve his unique qualifications for the mission entrusted to him by his government. There was a great deal for him to do, both politically and militarily, in Delhi and Chunking, and all of it urgent. No one could question his courage if he left. But Stilwell felt that he was not in Burma simply as an adviser or a chief-of-staff or an observer: he was a commander of troops, albeit still without the formal authority of the *chop*, or seal of office, physically issued to him later by Chiang Kai-shek to authenticate all orders as coming from the Chinese head of state. Were he to make an early escape he would, in Chinese eyes, be no better than their own cynical and venal generals, whereas by staying he would gain immensely in authority over them when he again took command of a Chinese army in the field. His course of action in this period of disaster reveals a man of high stature, able to analyse a situation in the confusion of defeat and with the moral and physical courage to follow its conclusions. Where Wingate was intuitive and emotional, Stilwell was clear-headed and remorselessly logical.

Stilwell's decisions were impeccable, but his method of implementing them characteristically perverse. He had discarded, if he had ever adopted, the businesslike staff system as taught at Leavenworth. His was a sort of locker-room, bull-session system of command, with himself as team captain, or, as he was a far older man than most of his staff, the grizzled and respected team trainer. He disliked precise orders – 'Aw, you know what I want: you go get it for me', was his style – and he enjoyed having the 'boys' compete for his approval and teasing them by favouring or confiding first in one and then another. He disliked any organised hierarchy or chain of command or staff responsibility and was always secretive about his intentions. Stilwell continued to linger in his headquarters in Burma, unperturbed by the frequent Japanese air raids, playing solitaire and giving no orders or even a hint of his plans to his staff who daily became more jumpy. Its more senior members bluntly advised 'the Old Man' to pack up and leave, and were silently ignored; the more junior saw no prospect ahead of them except the inside of a Japanese prisoner-of-war cage. Then, at the eleventh hour, a United States Army Air Force transport appeared flying low over the headquarters, a sight which so moved one officer that he broke quaveringly into the hymn 'God bless America'.

Stilwell chose this moment to reveal his plans. The bulk of his staff was to emplane and leave for India forthwith. He himself and a few chosen assistants were to try to reach the town of Myitkyina* in the far north either by rail or road, where he would make one final effort to coordinate the withdrawal of his retreating divisions and then, with luck, a plane might be able to land there and snatch him out.

*Pronounced Mitchinar.

34

Characteristically Stilwell teasingly offered his faithful aide, Lieutenant-Colonel F. Doorn, the choice of flying out or staying with him, enjoying his indignant refusal and affirmation of loyalty.

Throughout this period Stilwell displayed absolute calm. Satisfaction at the fate of the British was not tempered by any shred of pity for the luckless Burmese people, caught up in a war that was not their own and the victims not only of the Japanese Air Force but of the Chinese soldiery. He and Doorn watched with complete detachment Chinese troops, men under Stilwell's command, murder some helpless Burmese priests. On another occasion, obeying heaven knows what deeply-rooted destructive impulse, Stilwell incited his aide to set fire to an abandoned British police station.[3]

Stilwell's project to move his small headquarters to Myitkyina failed. Both the railway and road were cut, and the looting, raping, murdering Chinese, followed by the curses of the wretched Burmese, found their way out on their own. Two divisions reached China's western border and crossed the Salween into China. The 38th Division commanded by the best of the Chinese generals, Sun Li-jen, marched west into Manipur and reached Imphal in fair order. Supported by the immortal British 7th Armoured Brigade, Sun had fought nobly to relieve the British 1st Burma Division when it was encircled. The 22nd fared rather worse, going north up the remote, roadless, disease-haunted Hukawng Valley. Both divisions were to see that valley again, fighting their way south, in 1944.

Stilwell, putting aside for a moment the gnawing worries of high command, gathered his staff and a mixed bag of refugees around him and made off to the west along another route that was to become of significance in 1944; from Indaw to Homalin on the Chindwin River and then over the mountains to Ukhrul and Imphal. He was forced to abandon his transport and radio equipment at the Uyu River, and then went on by raft and on foot, encouraging his little band of men and women by his own example – a man of fifty-eight, yellow with jaundice, plodding ahead of them along a stiff and steep jungle trail. It was a brave effort, and it was also a public relations coup of the first order. For all his affectation of avoiding pomp, medals, a general's insignia of rank or even a tidy uniform, Stilwell, like Wingate, had a highly developed sense of the uses of publicity as a military weapon. It is no injustice to a creditable feat of endurance to say that his famous march out of Burma was the shortest, most highly publicised, most over-rated and most photographed anabasis in military history. This is hardly surprising, as the party was accompanied by two professional newsmen, Lieutenant Fred Eldridge, who was to be the editor of Stilwell's own army newspaper, *CBI Round-Up,* and his public relations officer, and the war correspondent of *Time* magazine.

(One hundred and twenty miles is a long walk in the tropics for untrained men, but the photographs reveal that no one was carrying a pack or a weapon, and Doorn's account reveals that the party was accompanied by Indian servants and cooks.)

Once in Delhi, Stilwell began the preparations which were to lead to his justly celebrated campaign to capture Myitkyina in 1944, and at the same time started the long and acrimonious battle he was to wage against the British authorities, the Chinese and eventually the British troops under his own command. His sheer bile often defeated his own ends. But, when relations were at their worst, what Marshall wrote to Mountbatten, in January 1944, is a just appreciation.

> You will find, if you get below the surface, that he wants merely to get things done without delays and will ignore considerations of his own personal prestige or position as long as drive and imagination are being given to plans, preparations and operations.
> ... I have found him ... irritated by and intolerant of slow motion, excessive caution and cut and dried procedure. On the other hand, he will provide tremendous energy, courage and unlimited ingenuity and imagination to any aggressive proposals or operations. His mind is far more alert than almost any of our generals and his training and understanding are of an unusually high level. Impatience with conservatism and slow motion is his weakness – but a damned good one in this emergency.[4]

That was a just estimate. Every word of it could also have been written of Orde Wingate.

History has been kind to Stilwell. His victories over immense political and logistical difficulties, to say nothing of the Japanese, are justly remembered and his faults, and they were many and severe, forgotten. His deliberately assumed image of a pawky, patriotic, aggressive, no-nonsense Yankee struggling with dandified and effette British aristocrats still appeals to Americans. The British also have their favourite stereotype, not Montgomery, as might be thought, or even Slim, but General Sir Harold Alexander; brave, unassuming, handsome, affable, able, aristocratic and a diplomatist as much as a soldier. Wingate can be fitted into no such simple stereotype.

It is perhaps significant that the official British history, which reveals that many British commanders lacked professional competence, has treated all of them, except Wingate, charitably and objectively; all had to make a lot of bricks with little straw too quickly. Wingate alone, who never lost a battle or a campaign when he was alive, and whom Churchill described as 'a man of genius who might have been a man of destiny', has been very roughly handled in the volume dealing with the war against Japan. He has been damned for his character rather than his competence.

Wingate was one of those non-conformists and 'mavericks', like Fuller or Hobart, who occasionally appear in the ranks of the highly authoritarian British Army (Mitchell or Patton might be cited as their American counterparts). He had been the least promising of cadets at the Royal Military Academy. As a subaltern he showed sparks of the character that was later to astonish the army, but he was unpopular, being rather dreamy, dirty, badly turned out, silent and sullen. He often rebuffed a friendly approach with silence or a snubbing reply. He was in fact dejected and unhappy, and the reasons are not far to seek. He had been brought up by two deeply religious parents according to the strict and gloomy precepts of the Plymouth Brethren. Colonel and Mrs. Wingate, both of strong character and exceptional ability, undertook the primary education of their gifted children themselves, placing great emphasis on religious studies. They were made to work hard and learn whole chapters of the Authorised Version of the Bible by heart. This helped to form Wingate's remarkable literary style, but it is notable that his writing too often resembles a pastiche of the bloodier passages of the Old Testament: there seems to have been nothing in the Wingate version of the Christianity of love, forgiveness or redemption. The unfortunate little boy grew up with a strong consciousness of his sinfulness in the eyes of a jealous God and of inferiority compared with his brothers and sisters. Social intercourse with other children was discouraged for fear of moral contamination, and the young Wingate, who went as a day scholar to Charterhouse, playing no games having little fun and praying in the school chapel in his spare time, lacked a great deal of the essential childhood experience of learning to live with anyone outside his own closely-knit family circle and any practice in forming friendships. Although in the children's games he was always the leader, he had no military ambition, and he seems to have agreed to compete for a vacancy at the Royal Military Academy in a mood of resignation, because he had no better prospect. He was eventually commissioned into the Royal Artillery, having had to spend an extra term there, and as a young officer was remarkable for nothing except a passion for fox-hunting, for which much was excused in the Royal Artillery of those days.

As he grew older normality began to creep in; he made friends, found that he could relax, especially with women, acquired a girl-friend, cautiously tried a little social life, discovered that there were those who actually liked him and who found, in turn, an attractive personality behind the barrier, and he began to enjoy himself. Then, like many British officers, he sought something more exciting than

37

garrison life in England, so he studied Arabic well enough to become an interpreter eventually and joined the Sudan Defence Force. Somehow the hobbles on his enquiring mind were loosened, and by then he was reading widely and voraciously, and studying his profession. As a soldier he was entirely self-taught. However, there were dark shadows in the gradually maturing personality.

Wingate began to develop exaggerated symptoms of aggression and suspicion of the motives of others, and at the same time suffered from fits of deep depression, alternating slowly with bursts of vigorous mental activity. The legacy of a too strict religious upbringing was his belief in his black moods that God, because of his sins, had abandoned him. 'I have seen him,' said one of his closest friends, 'writhing on his bed in agony, praying, and could do nothing to help him'.[5] It seems that Wingate believed that God had some great mission for him, and when he was sent to Palestine as an intelligence officer, he suddenly perceived this to be to help God's Chosen People, the Jews, persecuted, as he thought, by Arabs and the British security forces alike.

Wingate became a passionate Zionist. This is perhaps the key to his whole behaviour. Even before he had ever seen Palestine he had a feeling that he was born to be great, a day-dream perhaps, but great men are those who realise their day-dreams. What he required was an assurance that he was doing God's work, and once he had seen this to be extablishing the Jews in their homeland his doubts were set at rest. The romantic fancies of the backward cadet who one day would show his persecutors his true abilities were reconciled with his divine mission. By becoming a 'great captain', a latter-day Marlborough, he would acquire the authority and status to further the cause of Israel, if necessary with his sword.

Wingate's sanity has been questioned, and the suggestion indignantly refuted by his surviving disciples. Here it is necessary to make two obvious statements. The first is that to suffer from a psychiatric illness is not morally culpable: it is the fate of many, especially those under the stress of war, who are its casualties just as much as if hit by a bullet. Such illnesses are susceptible to treatment as much as any other illness: Wingate was in fact cured when he had broken down and attempted suicide after the fatigues of his Abyssinian campaign. Mental illnesses can have purely physical or chemical causes. In Egypt it is possible, but by no means certain, that a contributory factor was Wingate's improper self-administered use of the anti-malarial drug Atebrin, or Mepacrine. Some strains of typhoid fever are known sometimes to cause temporary mental disturbance and Wingate without doubt returned to intensive work too soon after his severe attack in October-November, 1943.

Secondly, there are characteristic patterns of behaviour in all 'normal' people, to which psychological labels can be given. It is only when these traits are exaggerated through some physical cause or mental anxiety that they become painful to the sufferer or a danger to his associates or affect his judgment. Wingate's distrust of people was deep-seated and paranoid, and when exaggerated led to his unfortunate relations with so many of the officers in key positions in command and on the staff in India. Often violently rude and aggressive without provocation, he found his prophecies of non-cooperation becoming self-fulfilling. He was imperious, refusing to defer or submit to anyone, which gave him strength as a commander, but its other aspect was that he could never take advice: in a discussion with experts, for instance, on tropical hygiene and medicine, or diet. 'He had to *win*', as one officer has put it.[6] If triggered off, on a platform, at a conference or at the dinner table, he was prone to prolonged bursts of loquacity, defying any interruption, which can be a symptom of hysteria. The slow swing of moods characteristic of many men of action could vary in Wingate from his fits of depression, 'my old trouble', as he called it, to furious activity and inventiveness. He was in fact a 'manic-depressive', or to use the less perjorative term, a *cyclothyme*. But he was not 'mad' in the sense that he could not distinguish between the real and the imaginary. His hypermanic phases were purposeful, his torrents of words were not gibberish but contained a flow of ideas which held his listeners riveted, and his aggression was directed towards specific, rational goals.

No incident in his career is more revealing of his character than his assault on the headquarters of the Indian Army in mid-1942. Wingate returned to India before the final retreat from Burma, charged by Wavell to see what could be done in the guerrilla line in the new circumstances, and he became a familiar if puzzling sight in the corridors of General Headquarters, mooning about with armfuls of books, long-haired, untidily dressed, humming to himself and absorbing every scrap of information he could find about Burma. While much of what he read was irrelevant (once, when the United States Air Force Colonel Cochran asked him some practical question about Burma, Wingate, always loquacious when his interest was aroused, replied with a lecture on Buddhism), it was his way to let his mind lie fallow, feed it and then, after a period of apparent lethargy, allow it to burst into intense action.

One day in 1942 he walked into the office of Lieutenant-Colonel C. A. R. Nevill of the Directorate of Staff Duties. Wingate at this time was a full colonel, but unknown and without a post. Without any polite greetings or preliminaries, for his manners, like Stilwell's varied only between the abrupt and the atrocious, he ordered Nevill's secretary to type out, forthwith, the long manuscript he handed her. This was the plan to form the 77th Brigade, the original 'Chindits', whom he was to lead into Burma the next year. Much to the annoyance of the staff hierarchy, who had not merely the right but the duty to comment on plans involving the allocation of men and weapons, Wingate took this direct to Wavell, the Commander-in-Chief, who, to their even greater annoyance, sent it down to them with one of his laconic notes telling them to translate the idea into action.

In the British Army, once a plan has been agreed on, the business of realising it is the responsibility of the Director of Staff Duties, whose branch lies at the heart of the staff system. He coordinates the work of all the other branches and issues the final detailed instructions: drawing up the 'establishment', or table of organisation and equipment which is the authority for the unit's existence and for issue of stores and weapons of all kinds. In India at that time there was an acute shortage of everything, so the Director of Staff Duties, General S. Woodburn Kirby, only too aware of his Commander-in-Chief's personal interest, and hearing that Wingate's demands were likely to be inordinate, decided to take the chair himself at the opening staff meeting in the hope of arriving at a practical and modest solution. He was disappointed. It was not that Wingate merely proved immoderate in his requests and obdurate in his arguments: he treated General Kirby in front of his own staff and the other staff and service representatives present, as if he were the inefficient manager of a rather unsatisfactory multiple store. He simply submitted a shopping list of his requirements and demanded that all should be provided at once, regardless of availability or the prior claims of other units.

For instance, in England Wingate had seen a collar stud with a tiny magnetic compass set in its base for use by clandestine operators behind the enemy lines or by escaped prisoners-of-war. He asked for 3,000. 'But there are none in India.' 'In that case,' said Wingate, 'Send an "operation immediate" signal to England for them to be sent out at once.' 'But soldiers do not wear collars and ties and studs in tropical jungles . . .' Wingate retorted that he was perfectly aware of the fact. As soon as the studs arrived orders were to be given to the ordnance service to convert them to *fly-buttons*; and so this appalling exhibition of irreverence and indiscipline went on, to the horror of all the senior officers present.[7] When Wingate returned in September from the Quadrant conference to renew the attack there was another Director of Staff Duties in the chair, but General Kirby was later to be the chief author of Volume III of *The War Against Japan*, the official British history, and he took his revenge.

But not everyone was horrified by Wingate's behaviour. Some of the younger and more forceful officers were both amused and elated. The inefficiency and sloth of the Indian military bureaucracy has only been exceeded in history by that of the old Austrian Empire, and in the view of its livelier critics nothing but Wingate's frontal assault could have achieved any results whatsoever. Even in 1944, by which time new men were in the key posts and Mountbatten had administered a few galvanic shocks, it still remained creaky and elephantine. The shoulder-flash of the headquarters was the red and black of the General Staff with the Star of India superimposed: 'India sinking from a stormy sky into a sea of ink,' as a cynical young officer once described it.

One of the staff officers present at these meetings was a young lieutenant-colonel of the Black Watch, Bernard Fergusson, in the department of plans. He requested permission to drop to the rank of major, leave the staff and join Wingate's force. This was one of Wingate's great gifts: to attract a wide variety of talent and character to serve under his strange banner, promising them in his best Jeremiah manner nothing but starvation, death and wounds, with no hope but to be left to the mercies of the Japanese if they fell out of the line of march.

Wingate's hypnotic power of leadership remains unquestioned. Where he was out of his depth and temperamentally unable to adjust was in the sphere of high command, where he was to meet men as able, as autocratic and as abrasive as he. In Abyssinia, where conditions were primitive, communications unreliable, logistics rudimentary and based on camels, the forces he had to handle tiny and his subordinates mavericks like himself, Wingate's system of command was well suited to the circumstances. He was free with his fist and his boot, clouting a man in the ranks, kicking an interpreter, knocking an officer down for faltering in the presence of the enemy and punching one of his battalion commanders in the face during a discussion about the correct course of action.[8] But the men of Gideon Force were not the sort likely to invoke the relevant sections of the Army Act or the King's Regulations, for which they had little use themselves. What is suitable in a leader of guerrillas, however, is totally unacceptable in a major-general commanding the equivalent of an army corps of regular soldiers. Nor had men like Mountbatten, Slim or Baldwin any time for the furious quarrels and altercations in which the long-suffering General Sir William Platt had to intervene in Africa.

One group which above all aroused Wingate's paranoid dislike was the 'staff',[9] inconsistently, since he himself, back in 1936, had complained bitterly at the injustice of not being selected for the Staff College and in consequence had been appointed, although without staff training, to a post on the intelligence staff in Palestine, thus setting his foot on the first rung of the ladder to fame. He bullied his own staff unmercifully, and as a result many of them were terrified of him and disliked him. Curiously it never occurred to him, the supreme exponent of talking to the troops, to let his staff into his mind until prompted by his own chief of staff, who himself was too often the public victim of Wingate's rough tongue. When Major Mead, a friend of Wingate from the days of peace, arrived in 1944 as a volunteer for the Chindits, Brigadier Derek Tulloch, the chief of staff, sent him up to join Wingate at his forward headquarters in Imphal: 'Orde says he wants someone up there who isn't afraid of him. Most of the staff are scared stiff, and while I can't say I altogether blame them, he finds it a bit trying.' Mead, a shrewd and sympathetic observer, saw no bully but a tired and overworked man, who discharged his desk-work promptly and effectively, and still had time for his favourite pastime of a long, strenuous walk, talking the while. Because of their old acquaintance, he had already been admitted behind Wingate's prickly defences. In the course of a candid conversation Wingate revealed to his younger friend how he recovered from the tragedy of LONGCLOTH. 'Everything is propaganda,' he said.[10]

It is clear enough what he meant by this. Having once decided, after deep brooding, that a certain policy or a certain course of action was the correct one, he focused all his formidable powers of persuasion on the task of ensuring that it was adopted. His report on LONGCLOTH was a dazzling piece of work, with no fewer than sixteen appendices explaining every aspect of his new and radical strategy. He had no more scruples about exaggerating his successes and minimising or supressing his failures than a politician in similar circumstances. Wingate was a political animal; untaught, but with an instinctive feeling for the art. It was this that had enabled him to bypass all channels, outwit Delhi and ensure that his paper was read in London by Churchill.

Very different from his welcome to Mead was the treatment Wingate inflicted on Lieutenant-Colonel Piggott, his GSO 1 (Operations), a senior and responsible officer filling a key post, and selected by Wingate himself. Wingate, in one of the tantrums which suddenly afflicted him, took it into his head, quite mistakenly, that Piggott had not made the necessary arrangements for transport to meet them both at an airfield at which they were about to land, and disgracefully assaulted him and threw him out of the aircraft as it taxied to its dispersal. Piggott, to his eternal honour, kept this fact to himself for over thirty years.[11]

Wingate's mistrust of his staff went occasionally to absurd extremes. It will be understood that air support, like artillery support, is run on the principle that within broad priorities and the availability of aircraft, the authority for calling for fire must rest with the commander in direct contact with the enemy, and the sole responsibility of the staff is to work the agreed army/air force staff procedures so as to achieve the fastest possible response time. In March 1944 the first mission in real action, as opposed to training, was called for by Brigadier Calvert, who was so delighted by the results that as soon as the battle was over he sent a generous congratulatory signal, which was displayed on the notice board in Special Force Headquarters. There it was seen by Wingate when, as it happened, the GSO 2 (Air Operations) was standing near. As the officer in question (the then Major David Tyacke) recalls, Wingate 'in his characteristic way put his little beard up and glared at the notice board' and seeing the staff officer concerned was present angrily demanded, 'By whose order was this strike made?' Tyacke, seeing the storm signals set at danger, tried to explain the 'drill', or agreed 'standard operating procedure', to be cut off with another furious *'By whose order?'* He was only released after a severe dressing down, with orders never to presume in this way again but refer each and every strike to Wingate himself. This had a ridiculous sequel. The next call was in the middle of the night, for the following day's programme, and Tyacke woke up Wingate in his pitch-dark hut and read the signal out by the light of an electric torch. Without opening his eyes Wingate agreed. 'Had you failed to inform me,' he said solemnly, 'you would have been disobeying my orders.' No corps commander could run an operation on such lines and the rule was quietly dropped.[12]

An insistence on being informed in advance about every decision and a tendency to meddle with detail was combined with a secrecy or furtiveness about informing parallel or higher headquarters, stemming from Wingate's deep-seated fear that everyone everywhere was in league to frustrate him. He also, with more reason, feared that plans might reach the Japanese intelligence network. Copies of his operation orders were not always circulated to Slim's staff at Fourteenth Army, under whose command Wingate had been placed, and he was apt to take action unilaterally, without informing even his own team: for instance, he had one serious dispute with Colonel Cochran, commanding the USAAF No. 1 Air Commando, after he had allowed the Royal Air Force to base fighters at the Chindit stronghold of 'Broadway' behind the Japanese lines without consulting Cochran, his own air adviser and commander. The RAF had not been slow to reap the accruing publicity, which stung the intensely publicity-conscious American. He annoyed Air Marshal Baldwin by not concerting the move of Special Force headquarters with him. He rebuked one of his staff on one occasion for not doctoring an intelligence report: the copy going upwards, Wingate explained, should always exaggerate Japanese strength, to underline Chindit dangers and achievements, but that going down should minimise it, so that the Chindits would be encouraged.[13] One way and the other Wingate tried his colleagues and superiors to such a degree that Slim and Giffard, who had the onerous but thankless task of Army Group Commander, ceased to trust him,[14] and even the tolerant Mountbatten's patience with him was at last exhausted.

These are harsh criticisms, but Wingate's flaws as a commander cannot be glossed over. It must also be said that they were dwarfed by the scale of his achievements. He certainly cheated shamelessly in the haggling and in-fighting of military politics, but his goals were noble ones. The root of the matter was in him. He perceived that the only way to make war was to take the battle to the enemy, and that training was as much a matter of winning over the minds of the soldiers as it was about the technicalities of combat. He was a daring innovator, and when it came to warfare had a clear and logical mind.

Four times, on an ascending scale, beginning in a small way in Palestine, he had been given an unusual and intractable problem to study. Each time he had come up with the correct solution. Each time he refused to remain at his desk but, in the face of many practical difficulties and much obstruction, first created the instrument necessary to realise his plan and then took command of it in the field. His invention of the 'Night Squads' in Palestine was a seminal event in the theory of counter-insurgency. The operations of Gideon Force were masterpieces in the art of insurgency. LONGCLOTH, for all its lack of material results, was a *tour de force*: Wingate showed that the impossible was possible. When he was killed at the beginning of his fourth and last campaign the prospects were bright. He was an outstanding man, capable of flashes of genius and the fact that he made serious errors and had continually to wage an intense inner struggle with himself does not diminish his stature.

3

Preparations

THE WAY THE two generals set about creating their new model armies offers an interesting contrast in national attitudes. The heart of the British system was morale and motivation based on the social dynamics of the human group, the 'Regiment'. The Americans believed in the dynamics of the production line.

Wingate was fortunate in that he was able to form the new Chindit force from well-trained battalions of high morale, mainly from the all-British 70th Division commanded by Major-General Symes. Stilwell had no such good fortune. Few Americans, with actual experience of the Chinese, and no British, believed that they were good for anything. Stilwell's success was due, apart from his faith in the Chinese, basically to the pre-eminent national skill in management which was manifested in the United States armed forces. The British were methodical, but they were also intuitive and allowed scope for flexibility and variation in methods so as not to damp initiative. The Americans were analytic. They approached warfare as they approached any other large enterprise; breaking it down to its essentials, cutting out what was superfluous, defining tasks and roles and training each man as if he was about to take an individual part in some complicated industrial process. Indeed, the American system for basic training resembled a conveyor-belt, with soldiers instead of motor-cars coming off the end. Only in this way could the United States have expanded its little peacetime army to the millions of men required for a world war. By British standards the end-product was somewhat soulless, but it produced a standardised army of identically trained men in identically organised regiments and divisions, all interchangeable and into which reinforcements could fit in without fuss or re-indoctrination.

In Special Force, by contrast, there were many traumas within the exclusive regiments when 'outsiders' were introduced into their ranks as reinforcements, and when Wingate insisted on nominating veterans from his old 77th Brigade to command appointments. Stilwell was thinking on an American, that is, a really large scale. In China proper he aimed to produce no fewer than sixty divisions. His own personal

45

ORDER OF BATTLE
SPECIAL FORCE, or the 3rd INDIAN INFANTRY DIVISION

Command and Staff

Commander	(1) Major-General O. C. Wingate
	(2) Major-General W. D. A. Lentaigne
Deputy Commander	(1) Major-General G. W. Symes
	(2) Brigadier D. Tulloch
Brigadier (General Staff)	(1) Brigadier D. Tulloch
	(2) Brigadier H. T. Alexander
Headquarters	*Rear HQ* at Gwalior, Central India (BLUE)
	Main HQ first at Imphal and then at Sylhet, Assam (RED)
	Launching HQ at Lalaghat (UNITY)
	Tactical or forward HQ, Shaduzup, Burma (AMITY)
Air Force	
No. 1 Air Commando	United States Army Air Force (a)
	Colonels P. Cochran and J. R. Alison, USAAF
Royal Artillery	'R', 'S' and 'U' tps 160th Field Regt. 'W', 'X', 'Y' and 'Z' tps 69th Light Anti-Aircraft Regt. (b)

Brigades

Each brigade had a rear HQ sited near an airfield and responsible for all supply in the field. It also had a headquarter column in the field, with a column number, omitted here.

5307th Composite Unit (Provisional), US Army (GALAHAD) (c)
(1) Brigadier-General Frank D. Merrill   (2) Colonel Charles N. Hunter (d) 1st, 2nd and 3rd Battalions, organised in columns on Chindit lines.

3rd (West African) Brigade (THUNDER)
   (1) Brigadier A. H. Gillmore   (2) Brigadier A. H. G. Ricketts
   6th Bn Nigeria Regt: Nos. 66 and 39 Columns. (e)
   7th Bn Nigeria Regt: Nos. 29 and 35 Columns
   12th Bn Nigeria Regt: Nos. 12 and 43 Columns

14th Brigade (JAVELIN) Brigadier T. Brodie.
   2nd Bn The Black Watch: Nos. 42 and 73 Columns
   1st Bedfordshire and Hertfordshire Regt: Nos. 16 and 61 Columns
   2nd Bn York and Lancaster Regt: Nos. 65 and 84 Columns
   7th Bn The Leicestershire Regt: Nos. 47 and 74 Columns

16th Brigade (ENTERPRISE) Brigadier B. E. Fergusson.
   2nd Bn The Queens Regt: Nos. 21 and 22 Columns
   2nd Bn The Leicestershire Regt: Nos. 17 and 71 Columns
   51/69 Royal Artillery: Nos. 51 and 69 Columns (f)
   45th Reconnaissance Regt: Nos. 45 and 54 Columns (f)

23rd Brigade (g)

77th Brigade (EMPHASIS) Brigadier M. Calvert.
  3rd Bn 6th Gurkha Rifles: Nos. 36 and 63 Columns
  1st Bn The King's Regt: Nos. 81 and 82 Columns
  1st Bn The Lancashire Fusiliers: Nos. 20 and 50 Columns
  1st Bn South Staffordshire Regt: Nos. 38 and 80 Columns
  3rd Bn 9th Gurkha Rifles: Nos. 57 and 93 Columns (h)

111th Brigade (PROFOUND) (1) Brigadier W. D. A. Lentaigne
                          (2) Lieut-Colonel J. Masters
  1st Bn The Cameronians: Nos. 26 and 90 Columns
  2nd Bn The King's Own Royal Regt: Nos. 41 and 46 Columns
  3rd Bn 4th Gurkha Rifles: No. 30 Column
  3rd Bn Gurkha Rifles: (after May 16th)

Morris Force Brigadier J. R. Morris.
  4th Bn 9th Gurkha Rifles: Nos. 49 and 94 Columns
  3rd/4th Gurkha Rifles: No. 40 Column (k)

Dah Force   Lieut-Colonel D. C. Herring
              Kachin Levies

Bladet   (Blain's Detachment). Gliderborne commando engineers (l)

Notes

(a) Exclusively in support but not under command Special Force. It provided strike and casualty evacuation, but the burden of supply had to be carried by Eastern Air Command as a whole. It ceased to exist on May 1st, 1944.
(b) A British 'troop' was the equivalent of a 'battery' in other armies' nomenclature. The troops listed here were specially selected non-mobile units designed to defend the 'strong-holds' and 'blocks'. Weapons were 25-pdr field-guns and 40 mm Bofors and 0.5 in Hispano LAA guns.
(c) Each brigade was given a code-name. GALAHAD became the accepted name of this unit, owing to its clumsy title. 'Merrill's Marauders' was the coinage of a journalist and not used by Stilwell or the men of the unit.
(d) Colonel Hunter was *de facto* in command throughout.
(e) Except in the case of the Gurkhas units, the column numbers were coined either from the old numbers of the infantry line or from the line number of the column commander's former regiment.
(f) Both these were infantry columns made up from Royal Artillery or Reconnaissance Regiment personnel.
(g) The 23rd Brigade was removed from the order of battle and distinguished itself raiding the communications of the Japanese west of the Chindwin.
(h) Originally the garrison of Broadway. 77th Brigade also had Morris Force, 7th Nigeria, 12th Nigeria No. 74 Column and 45th Recce under command at various times.
(k) No. 40 Column's attachment was unplanned.
(l) The idea was to glide in, perform the mission and then be 'snatched' into the air again. All the gliders crashed on the first mission. The detachment later manned the flame-throwers at the battle of Mogaung, incurring severe casualties.

instrument was more modest, an 'army' in Chinese terminology, or in Western parlance a 'corps', of two American-type infantry divisions with a number of extra armoured artillery and other specialist units.

This, together with staff officers and other specialists for the main armies inside China, were trained on American lines and by American methods at the huge training camp and depot Stilwell and his staff had set up, not without a lot of haggling with the British which did nothing to improve Stilwell's opinion of the 'limeys', from Wavell down, at Ramgarh, 200 miles west of Calcutta. There a strong and numerous team of United States Army officers were assembled and got down to work with customary American efficiency and drive. The British attitude, at first sceptical, turned to admiration. Even Wavell went to inspect it, and approved, although his famous taciturnity gave no hint of his feelings and disconcerted his American hosts. The principal obstacle the American instructors had to face was the attitude of the Chinese officers. Contempt for 'foreigners' is a Chinese national trait, and the Chinese officers had a full measure of both national and military arrogance which made it impossible for them to accept that the Americans knew better than they did. There was also the national concept of 'face', which prevented them from submitting to the same sort of training as was being given to their men and made any constructive criticism of performance or monitoring of progress at first impossible for them to accept. The senior commanders were corrupt to a man, and it was with dismay and chagrin that they learnt that the United States authorities had empowered only American officers to pay the troops, and that in conformity with the usual practice the money was to be disbursed into the hands of the individual soldiers and not handed over in bulk to the commanders of divisions and regiments so that they could embezzle it.

As for Chinese generals' ideas on the conduct of operations, theoretically they were supposed to be guided by the indirect strategy of Sun-Tzu rather than the more brutal methods of the West, deriving from Clausewitz. But in practice the truth was that armies and divisions were the assets on which the wealth and status of their commanders depended, and they had no intention of squandering them on anything so rash as offensive action: fighting battles was not part of their philosophy. ('When the enemy advances we retreat', may have been Mao Tse-tung's tactical slogan, but the Chinese armies had been practising it against the Japanese invaders for years.) They had no sense of time, which apart from wrecking carefully constructed training schedules, made it impossible to synchronise any operational plan of action. If the achievement of Stilwell and the American officers and non-commissioned officers had been only to re-educate such intractable and unpromising material it would have been outstanding. The Chinese were by no means fully converted and it took Stilwell's personal presence in the field to induce them to take the offensive, and time and again their dilatory tactics robbed him of a quick victory; but he taught them how to fight, and fight eventually they did.

The real strength of the Chinese armies, as Stilwell had without any sentiment discerned, lay in the durability of the rank and file, the *pings*, derived from the patience, frugality, hardiness and infinite endurance of the Chinese peasantry from whom the bulk of them were recruited. They were vilely treated. One batch of recruits despatched over the mountain ranges of the 'hump' in unheated aircraft were found to have been economically stripped of their uniforms, as the Americans were to issue them with new ones, and some had died of cold during the journey. They had no medical services to look after them, let alone any form of welfare. They were robbed of their rations and pay by their officers, subjected to a brutal and demoralising discipline, beaten, sometimes to death, for venal offences without any trial, and under-equipped. In many units there were not enough weapons to go round, and the rearward ranks were told to arm themselves in battle from the fallen. Yet these were the soldiers, badly led, often defeated, endlessly marching backwards and forwards, who for twelve long years had frustrated the martial Japanese. Stilwell fervently believed that with the correct treatment he could make real soldiers out of the wretched *pings*.

In Ramgarh they were properly paid, clothed and decently fed for the first time in their lives, medically examined, treated for their endemic dysentry, malaria and skin ulcers and taught some rudimentary sanitary measures. 'And in return,' said one of them in astonishment, 'all the Americans want us to do is to fight!' When they had put on some weight and were physically fit, basic training began. This, according to the American system, was done *en masse* on a system of progressive instruction. Long queues of troops passed through echelons of specialist instructors each teaching one phase of a weapon from introduction through operational use to maintenance and tactical employment. Squads a hundred strong would go down on the firing points of the ranges together; the instructors, helped by interpreters, or using sign language if they had none, ran up and down the line coaching them. There were courses for the riflemen, light and heavy machine-gunners, mortar and grenade crews; there was instruction in the use of telephones, radios, rocket launchers and anti-tank guns. Field artillery courses of only six weeks produced batteries of the useful little 75 mm pack howitzer and the standard US 105 mm and 155 mm howitzers. They were unequal to any refined artillery techniques, but the crews could point their pieces in the right direction and the officers were capable of rudimentary fire direction. The individuals so trained were grouped into squads (British 'sections') and platoons, at which level supervised collective training ceased. Manoeuvres and exercises on the grand scale were in any case incomprehensible to the Chinese commanders who, Stilwell believed, could work out their major tactics for themselves Not that he intended to allow them much latitude. Stilwell's staff made all the plans in detail and exercised control through United States liaison officers positioned at every headquarters and connected to him by a separate radio network. They could not command but they could advise, and their reports were a check on the often erroneous or fictitious Chinese ones.

The final product was the First Chinese Army, whose major units were the reconstructed 22nd and 38th Chinese Infantry Divisions. Organised along American lines, each division consisted of three regiments of infantry, artillery, engineers, signals, and supply services. There were additional combat troops in the shape of artillery battalions and a group of light tank battalions, commanded by a United States officer, Colonel Rothwell Brown (the only non-Chinese commander, all the others being engaged in staff or liaison duties). The whole was known as the Chinese Army in India (CAI) and its headquarters, from which Stilwell exercised command, was known as Chih Hui Pu. The theatre was called the China-Burma-India (CBI), which he also commanded. A large force of United States Engineers, headed by the appropriately named Brigadier-General Pick, was assembled near Ledo ready to drive a road and pipe-line down the Hukawng and Mogaung Valleys to Myitkyina and onwards to connect with the old 'Burma road' in the wake of the advance of the First Chinese Army.

A clear and logical organisational chart was drawn up by Stilwell's staff to define command and administrative channels. But this was soon disregarded by Stilwell, who had an anarchic mistrust of staff structures, and in whose opinion all the staff did was to hold conferences ('walla-wallas', in the language of his private diary) or produce 'poop' (useless paper: in English, 'bumf'). In practice, therefore, Headquarters, First Chinese Army was never activated, nor was that title much used. Stilwell directed operations from Chih Hui Pu, and later, when he moved into the field to take personal command, he invented yet another entity, the Northern Combat Area Command (NCAC), as will be explained later. This added one more facet to his Protean military personality and thoroughly fogged the lines of command so that they could be what he meant them to be at any time in his two-fronted war against the British on one side and his master Chiang Kai-shek on the other. 'Slippery' Joe might have been more appropriate than 'Vinegar' Joe, but it must be said in fairness that his cunning was directed against those among the British who said that he couldn't do what he had set out to do, or against Chiang Kai-shek, who was determined that he shouldn't. Defying them both and pouring out his bile in his diary, Stilwell created his new model Chinese army and ordered the leading regiment of the 38th Division to advance into the Hukawng Valley in October, 1943.

*   *   *

Stilwell, an American officer, had the great advantage of working from a fixed military doctrine covering strategy and tactics. He also had the services of a body of officers who had no doubts about what they were teaching and how they were to teach it. In Special Force things were very different. Wingate had to reduce guerrilla tactics to a system and then, partly from his experience and partly from his enormously inventive imagination, produce 'drills', or 'standard operating procedures' for marching in jungle, blowing up bridges, bivouacing, crossing rivers, crossing open spaces, receiving a supply drop from the air, laying an ambush, attacking a village, taking evasive action in jungle and, in extreme danger, dispersing into small parties to re-assemble in an area some distance away. He wrote or drafted all the more important instructions himself. At the same time his thoughts began to move more and more to alternating guerrilla tactics with conventional attack and defence.

He called his strategy 'deep penetration' ('long-range penetration', LRP, was a later variation) and in his basic training instruction, *General Rules for the Forces of Deep Penetration*, states:

> To sum up, therefore Deep Penetration means the operation of regular columns of high calibre in the heart of the enemy's war machine, engaging targets he is unable adequately to protect, and thus compelling him to alter his plans, thus causing a situation of which our *own main forces are able to take advantage* (Author's italics).[1]

Chindit tactics were essentially *evasive*. In another of Wingate's training instructions he defines 'mobility' as 'the power a column possesses to move away from an enemy in such a way and into such country that the enemy will be unable or afraid to follow it', and he goes into great detail as to how pursuit should be discouraged by the setting of booby traps by the rearguard on the tracks of the column, and so forth. Colonel Graves-Morris in his account makes it clear that he considered his rôle was to engage in 'tip-and-run' tactics, emerging from the jungle to blow up a dump or ambush an enemy convoy and slipping away again into the jungle.

Wingate's original plan, so powerfully argued in the paper seen by Churchill, was to repeat his LONGCLOTH manoeuvre of 1943 and skilfully infiltrate his brigades on foot through the Japanese lines, using the cover of the jungle and deception plans to disguise the point of penetration. He had flatly turned down the offer of parachute troops, then training in India. The reason he gave was that they could not reach his own exacting standards in the time available. This is inconsistent with his acceptance of units not even trained as infantry, such as the armoured reconnaissance regiment and the artillery from the 70th Division. The real reasons are more likely to have been his mistrust of Indian troops, as opposed to Gurkhas, and his jealousy of a *corps d'élite* whose loyalty might be to the Airborne Corps, already ferociously exclusive, rather than to the Chindits.

Tulloch reveals that Wingate had a 'hoodoo', or irrational aversion, to all parachute troops. He was, however, to be rapidly converted to the use of gliders by Cochran and Alison of No. 1 Air Commando. Having convincingly argued the merits of infiltration into Burma on foot, in a new training note he wrote: 'Gliders would avoid stumbling their way through the mailed fist of the enemy [*sic*] which involves them in innumerable hazards before their work has begun and renders them immeasurably less capable of doing it when [the operational area] is reached.'[2] This is not the best example of Wingate's style. But it is a good example of the rapidity with which he could execute a *volte face*.

The provision of the strike aircraft of No. 1 Air Commando, USAAF, for his exclusive use also led Wingate to a fresh line of thought. Its fire-power was a substitute for heavy artillery. The moment he perceived this, Wingate saw that in deep penetration strategy there was no need to wait for the 'main force' to exploit the situation he had created: he could do this himself, using the combination of air strikes and Chindit columns. In the later stages of the campaign, after Wingate's death, the Chindits complained that they were being used as ordinary infantry and not in their proper rôle. The fact is that Wingate's doctrine was ambiguous or, perhaps it is fairer to say, developing. His last training instructions describe the methods to be used when assaulting a strong position, and his THURSDAY plan hinged on the formal defence of a fortified position by Calvert, as we shall see. Nevertheless, the brigades had been at first too vigorously schooled in evasive tactics and the idea persisted. Too often a 'column', getting wind of the presence of the Japanese, would melt into the jungle instead of considering offensive action, and this was found to be a weakness.[3] This was not Wingate's idea at all. He defined 'evasion' as the Chindit interpretation of the principle of mobility. It was aggressive, in that its purpose was to draw a pursuing force into the jungle where it could be ambushed, or to elude it altogether, re-emerge at a different point, sting the enemy where least he expected it, and vanish once more.

The trouble was that the new Chindits were being trained according to the tactics designed for LONGCLOTH, a purely raiding expedition, while Wingate's doctrine was evolving towards more positive and aggressive action. This was never sufficiently impressed on the units because Wingate was not in control during the formative period, owing to an attack of typhoid fever which put him out of action for over a month. The exception was the 77th Brigade, but Calvert was not just an aggressive commander but a tactical innovator himself.

The basis of Wingate's tactical system was the column. Essentially it consisted of a strong rifle company of four platoons, a heavy-weapons platoon, a commando platoon skilled in demolitions and setting booby traps, and a reconnaissance platoon with a section of Burma Rifles, led by a British officer of that regiment, and riflemen recruited from the Kachin and Karen tribes. The conventional battalion organisation was abandoned and each battalion was divided into two independent columns, so a brigade consisted of eight such columns and a headquarters. Calvert, the leading Chindit tactician, favoured the aggressive and offensive policy. He used the column organisation to 'march divided but fight united', as the old military maxim has it. In practice brigades did not move on a wide front so as to deceive the enemy, as originally intended, but in an immensely long single file through the jungle.

In the early part of the campaign there were some twenty-four columns operating, rising later to thirty-two. Command and control was to be remote and by radio from a headquarters in India, from which Wingate would manoeuvre his guerrilla bands very much as an air force commander directs his fighter planes from a ground headquarters. Supply was to be by air, parachuted or free-fall loads being dropped at a point indicated by the column concerned.

The basic weapon of the column was the marching infantryman, armed variously with rifles and light machine-guns (Brens), two good, old-fashioned Vickers .303 water-cooled sustained-fire machine-guns and two 3-inch mortars per column, and a few flame-throwers, a weapon Wingate was very taken with but appears to have been of little use and an embarrassing load to carry, and some PIAT hand-held anti-tank weapons firing a finned bomb with a shaped charge. The heavy weapons and radios were carried on the mules, but the infantryman carried seventy pounds on his back; fifty pounds of equipment, including weapons, clothing, a full water bottle and ammunition, with another eighteen pounds of rations immediately after a supply drop, which was gradually eaten down to zero. To complete the load there was sometimes a *chagal*, or canvas water container, with a quart of water in it and a spare bandolier of ammunition. The whole weighed even more after crossing a river or in monsoon rain since the webbing packs absorbed water. This was the monstrous load every Chindit from brigadier to private had to carry, throwing it off only to fight or to snatch a few hours of uneasy sleep on the ground; to resume it groaning, each morning. The straps cut ever deeper into the back as the day wore on, and it gradually eroded the endurance and numbed the power of thought of men who, as the campaign continued, were gradually dying of malnutrition and disease. This must be kept in mind when reading the account of each march, each combat and each decision taken by a commander. As one officer put it, all his courage and resolution was eventually focused down to the mental effort required 'to put one foot in front of another'.[4]

The infantryman was the Chindit weapon, and the transport by which he lived was the mule. 'Deep Penetration' tactics based on air supply had freed the columns from the navel string of a land line of communication, but instead had inflicted on what should have been a highly mobile guerrilla band a slow, vulnerable hampering train of seventy pack-mules. At the heart of the system were the ten mules needed to carry the heavy radio, its batteries, petrol and charging plants required to maintain contact with air base. Five days would see the meagre rations exhausted, and all the ammunition could be shot away in a single action lasting half an hour. Mules, like men, if working hard require their calories in the shape of four pounds of grain and six of *bhoosa* (a sort of fodder). They are hardy, but they are *mulish*, and can be diabolical, especially if asked to swim a river, and they must have ample supplies of clean drinking water, about which they are fastidious. If the mules were killed, or the muleteers ineffective, or there was no water, or the radios were damaged, or transmission was blocked by static, or no petrol was dropped for the portable generators used to recharge the batteries for the radios, the column, with no means of obtaining supplies or orders, and with empty bellies and empty ammunition pouches, ceased to be a fighting force. Mules, water and radio were the vital links in the Chindit biological chain. Mules tended to bray, a grave disadvantage in semi-clandestine operations in jungle where secrecy and surprise were all-important, so the cruel step was taken of severing their vocal chords by surgery. The best muleteers were the Punjabi Mussulmans of the Indian Army, but Wingate objected to the employment of any Indian soldiers. Those arrogant soldiers, the Gurkhas, thought that driving mules was beneath their dignity, while the British treated them too much as pets.

The conversion of the regular, conventional battalions into Chindits was completed in the astonishingly short space of twenty weeks. The drive and inspiration came from Wingate and this feat alone entitles him to an honoured place in the ranks of British military commanders. Nevertheless, credit must be given to the British staff which, by 1944, was at a high pitch of efficiency.

The rôle of the staff in India has been the subject of a great deal of myth-making and distortion. The 'staff' was one of Wingate's stereotype bogies, a sentiment unfortunately shared by his own chief-of-staff, Tulloch. It is true that Wingate fully expected, and met, both lethargy and obstruction from the Indian military bureaucracy, which indeed had had for a century no other approach to any problem. All the same, the staff itself was being revitalised and reorganised as the flow of efficient officers, most of them civilians, emerged from intensive short war courses held at the staff colleges. Slim's victories in the 1944 and 1945 campaigns, with their acute logistic difficulties, are proof of its efficiency. On his arrival in India Mountbatten took his own steps to galvanise the high commanders of Indian formations into action, and one of the things he did was to order rapid action by all staff fronts to help Special Force. He did not hesitate to bring to heel the Royal Air Force – always, in their own view, a law unto themselves – when there was an attempt to interfere with the provision of aircraft for the Chindit training programme.[5]

Inevitably there was friction; there always is in preparing any big operation. To overcome it an emollient approach works better than a rough one. To yield a little is good tactics, as scoring off an opponent only tends to establish him as an enemy. Unfortunately Wingate was incapable of seeing that the shock tactics which had served him so well in 1942 were now out of place and it was doubly unfortunate that his chief-of-staff, Tulloch, a shy man with an abrupt manner, too often chose to follow Wingate's lead and to bang the table when a little finesse might have been better. The backlash from the staffs at Delhi, the Fourteenth Army and Eastern Air Command, was to be felt later. During that hectic period the army and the air staffs were to do wonders, especially on the administrative side, where a mistake can ruin the best operational plans and the work is drudgery, attracting neither glamour nor thanks.

Wingate and Tulloch were fortunate in inheriting the efficient headquarter staff of the 70th Infantry Division, which, suitably reinforced, became the staff of Headquarters, Special Force. The officers continued, understandably, to feel that their allegiance was to their old divisional commander, Major-General G. W. Symes – in their view unfairly demoted to become Wingate's second-in-command – rather than to the new Brigadier, General Staff, Tulloch. When, however, they saw that Symes loyally supported Wingate and the Chindit idea they followed his example. A report prepared inside Headquarters, Special Force records that the work of the staff, whose good effect was felt right down to the combat ranks, was one of the factors on which the high morale of the Chindits was based.[6]

Over the years there has been much talk among Chindits of the resistance by the blimps of the regular army to Wingate's ideas. This reproach could never have been levelled at Symes. Wingate was extremely fortunate in his deputy, to which post Symes had been appointed from the beginning, before Wingate's arrival, for he was an outstanding officer who had been especially selected to command an outstanding all-regular division in war. To his acute disappointment, instead of being used in action the division was left to moulder in a vacuum, becoming ever more bored with the endless repetition of conventional training for a whole weary year in Southern India: the 'sloth-belt', in the pre-war soldier's contemptuous phrase. Symes immediately perceived that the Chindit idea made sense and welcomed the prospect of action. He was soon hard at work preparing the division for the new rôle when Wingate arrived back in India in September. In his messianic way Wingate at their first meeting demanded to know if Symes had 'faith in his methods'. Symes bluntly replied, 'If I hadn't I wouldn't be meeting you today.'[7]

He took Wingate's measure accurately: 'fanatical, ruthless, supremely self-confident, a master of duplicity, arrogant, argumentative, untidy, unorthodox . . . the magnitude of his plan in conception and in detail was amazing . . . he was essentially a "doer" and was satisfied that he could do anything better than anyone else . . . He knew everyone [in his force], had their confidence and demanded implicit faith from his subordinates. He lacked administrative and organisational knowledge, and knowing it, had an inferiority complex on the matter. [He displayed] impatience and ill-temper when he construed any quetion as an obstruction to his ideas . . . He appeared deliberately to make enemies . . . Looking back, it was amazing that he got the help he did. A different approach would have got willing cooperation, for he could be extremely charming and captivating if he wanted to be; he revelled in talk and argument and was difficult to combat.'

Symes, endorsing the grand aim, like an honest workman set his professional skill to remedy the deficiencies. He found that he could agree with the clever Neville Marks, and they put the administration on a sound footing, but Tulloch he weighed in the balance and found wanting. He also spent much time in smoothing ruffled feathers in the various headquarters where even the most sensible and cooperative of officers were left seething with indignation after every contact with Wingate.

Symes concentrated on administration, as neither Wingate nor Tulloch had experience of organising and equipping a force on so large a scale, and when Wingate was prostrated by typhoid fever he assumed temporary command and supervised the higher training as well, leaving Tulloch to attend to the operational side and the politics of the enterprise. He was always perfectly direct with Wingate, and pressed him, as soon as he saw how his ideas were shaping, to clarify his ideas about the Chindit rôle, especially the distinction between pure guerrilla work and conventional fighting, and what his policy was about campaigning in the monsoon. Wingate avoided answering both these key questions: he always preferred to let his ideas grow and not to disclose his plans until the latest possible moment. He came to respect Symes's honesty and military capacity, but his confidant was Tulloch.

Derek Tulloch had been selected by Wingate on the basis of friendship. They had been in the same 'term' (class) at the Royal Military Academy, and their friendship had been cemented by a common passion for the horse and fox-hunting. His nominal appointment was 'brigadier, general staff', with responsibility for operations, plans and intelligence, but he became in effect the chief-of-staff of Special Force. He was fundamentally what the British call a 'regimental' and the Americans a 'line' officer, with no ambition to serve on the staff; in fact, he had only attended a short war course in staff duties and that only under protest. He himself would have been the first to admit that he lacked the intellect or sophistication to operate successfully in the higher altitudes of the command and staff hierarchy. What he brought to the appointment to which he had been so suddenly and surprisingly elevated after he had responded to a summons from Wingate, equally suddenly and mysteriously appearing in the guise of a major-general, was unquestioning loyalty, integrity and a modicum of common sense. Wingate might have selected a cleverer man, but no other officer could endure his moods and tolerate his idiosyncracies.[8]

Of the other leading members of the staff, Neville Marks, an Indian Army officer, proved a brilliant brigadier in charge of administration. H. T. Alexander, as colonel in charge of training (and later chief of staff), Lieutenant-Colonel Piggott, Lieutenant-Colonel Ormiston, Lieutenant-Colonel Kyte, all on the general staff side, were exceptionally able officers, as were many of the majors beavering away on the 'grade two' level where the work is done.

Wingate had trained the original 77th Chindit Brigade personally in every aspect of its work but even without his illness, it would have been quite impossible to do this for a force the size of a small army corps. He poured out training instructions, of which many were drafted by Alexander, and as often as he could he would descend in a cloud of sometimes wrathful and sometimes inspiring oratory, leaving the troops blasted and dazed with the realisation of their own incompetence. But the hard slog of progressive training in every aspect of Chindit tactics had to be left to the brigadiers and commanding officers of battalions and columns. There he was fortunate, for his brigadiers were able men even by the exacting standards of wartime selection.

Outstanding, and nearest to Wingate in his views on war – he might have been Elisha to his Elija – was a young major in the Royal Engineers who had fallen first under his spell and his banner in Burma in 1942. Major Michael Calvert's talent for irregular warfare had already been recognised and he was at that time commandant of an establishment called the 'Bush Warfare School', in reality a clandestine outfit concerned with training guerrillas and commandoes for work behind the enemy lines. On Wavell's orders Wingate, to give him rank and status, was ordered to take over command. Calvert's momentary disappointment at being supplanted was forgotten in the first impact of the new colonel's personality. They took an instant liking to each other. Calvert, like Wingate, was a natural rebel, a maverick, and full of original ideas on irregular warfare, and Wingate flattered him in the truest way a senior officer can flatter and win the loyalty of a junior: by treating him as a mental equal and listening to his ideas on tactics and the failings of the British Army.

Calvert was physically very strong, a long-distance runner and a bruising rather than a skilful boxer. His own view of the army and his intolerance of authority and of accepted ideas had not been improved by his experiences in another military debacle, that of Norway in 1940. He had a mordant, if sometimes schoolboy, sense of humour and a great zest for combat. One of his staff remarked later on that he had not been taught at Camberley that it was part of his duties to carry a satchel full of grenades in case his brigadier ran out of ammunition. But physical courage and panache were not Calvert's sole qualifications for command. An engineer officer in those days had first to 'pass out' (graduate) high in a competitive field from the Royal Military Academy, Woolwich, and then, while serving, spend no more than two years at Cambridge where, if he was to continue in a corps which has always provided a high proportion of the intellect in the British Army, he had to obtain honours in the difficult Mechanical Science Tripos. Calvert's cheerful and irreverent exterior concealed a thoughtful and well-educated soldier. There was no arrogant or domineering element in his character. His manner was quiet. His method of giving orders was gentle and even hesitant. He was dreamy: 'Sometimes when receiving reports you felt he wasn't listening to you' said one subordinate. But his competence, his habit of leading from the front and his empathy won the complete devotion of the 77th Brigade.

After Wingate's departure Calvert formed the instructors and pupils of the Bush Warfare School into an irregular unit remarkable even by the standards of an era famous for irregular units, reinforcing it by men he pressed or kidnapped from convalescent depots, parties of reinforcements looking for some unit to join, prisoners released from detention and even, it is said, a posse of military policemen, who could be better employed, Calvert felt, in fighting than in enforcing correct dress and saluting and deterring private soldiers from sampling the dubious joys of brothels and opium dens. This outfit Calvert led in some dashing and sometimes costly forays. Militarily these were, perhaps, futile. But in terms of morale they were worth much fine gold in those dark and defeatist days when the Japanese were regarded with superstitious awe as invulnerable.

Calvert himself gained much valuable experience in leadership in battle. After he had seen the remains of his little force back to safety in India he returned to twist the Japanese tail for as long as he dared. He finally escaped from Burma in company with some Indian refugees disguised as an Oriya woman. Back in India he had sought out Wingate, to become in due course his most gifted lieutenant and loyal disciple. He stood out among the leaders who proved themselves in the searing ordeal of the LONGCLOTH operation and was promoted rapidly from major to brigadier to be entrusted with the task of re-creating the 77th Brigade.

Calvert's unyielding loyalty to his chief obscures his own gift of tactical innovation. Where Wingate was guided by flashes of inspiration Calvert was thorough and practical. He trained his brigade to switch rapidly from guerrilla tactics to the toughest type of conventional infantry fighting, and from defending an entrenched camp against full-scale attack to an 'encounter' battle and finally to the attack on a fortified city. His columns entered Burma militarily and mentally prepared for anything the dreaded Japanese might throw against them.

Brigadier B. E. Fergusson, like Calvert, had shown his mettle as a column commander in 1943 and been promoted to brigadier in command of the 16th Brigade, but there the resemblance ended. He volunteered to join Wingate after a glittering early career: Eton, Sandhurst, the Black Watch, *aide de camp* to Wavell, the prized appointment of instructor of cadets at Sandhurst; then, finally, experience while still young to staff duties on the highest level. Apart from training his own brigade he did valuable work first as second-in-command of the 111th Brigade, the next to be formed after the revived 77th; then at large among the jealous or suspicious battalions of the 70th Division in preaching Wingate's tactical doctrine and reconciling them to the Chindit idea. 'I'm sorry to keep ramming our experiences down your throats,' he would say disarmingly, 'but there's every reason why you should learn by our mistakes.'[9] He was a natural diplomatist. His brigade was to infiltrate on foot into Burma, not fly, and the route lay through Stilwell's operational area, something that had to be negotiated with delicacy. Stilwell sent a message to Brigadier-General Boatner (later to be regarded by the Chindits, very unfairly, as no less a bane than his Anglophobe master) which read: 'See if you can help this guy: he looks like a dude, but he may be a soldier.' His relationship with Wingate was uneasy. Later he was to refer to him as a 'paladin', but he was too clear-eyed and sophisticated for hero-worship and took his measure accurately. The two men quarrelled, over rations for the field (the casualties during LONGCLOTH were due to malnutrition as much as any other factor), and over encouraging the loyal tribes such as the Karens and Kachins to rally to the British and then abandoning them, to such a point that Wingate demanded Fergusson's resignation. Matters were smoothed over and Fergusson was entrusted with the most gruelling and important mission in Wingate's plan.

Wavell when still Commander-in-Chief in India had ordered another long-range penetration brigade to be formed and that an outstanding officer should be appointed to command and train it. W. D. A. Lentaigne of the 4th Gurkha Rifles was chosen. 'Joe' Lentaigne was an able and orthodox staff officer who had commanded a battalion of his regiment in the Burma campaign and proved himself a fighting commander of dash and courage, always attacking, and leading bayonet charges himself on occasion. Wingate never really approved of him. Born in 1899, Lentaigne was over forty, in fact forty-five, when he returned to Burma in command of the 111th Brigade, and Wingate was suspicious of any nominees but his own; even if they were made by his patron the Commander-in-Chief. Calvert was an unorthodox maverick whose pondering on military problems led him unerringly and correctly to orthodox solutions. Lentaigne was a deeply orthodox product of that most professional of corps, the Gurkha Rifles, and the Staff College, who was forced into unorthodoxy against all his instinct and training. Looking round for a capable lieutenant who understood Gurkhas, of which there were two battalions in his brigade, he selected his young friend from his own regiment, Jack Masters, as his 'brigade-major' – the executive, principal staff officer, a chief-of-staff in miniature, and confidant to a brigadier commanding a brigade. The other brigadiers were appointed by Wingate, relieving the existing holders. Brodie, a quiet, rather reserved infantryman, went to the 14th Brigade. Perowne, a Royal Engineer, went to the 23rd, but he and his brigade were removed from Special Force to take part in the great Imphal-Kohima battle and so had no share in the Chindit saga. When, after a tussle over extra battalions to garrison his jungle 'strongholds', Wingate was given the 3rd West African Brigade he removed the commander on grounds of age and appointed A. G. Gillmore.

Finally there were the various commanders of the American brigade, known officially as the 5307 Composite Unit (Provisional), more conveniently as 'Galahad', its code-name (always used by Stilwell) and later and popularly as 'Merrill's Marauders' – the pardonable coinage of a journalist who could hardly set the American public's imagination alight however he presented its exploits under so statistical and precise a title: it was 'composite' because its volunteers were drawn from all arms, and 'provisional' because it was temporary, being planned for a ninety-day campaign, like the Air Commando. It arrived in India under the command of Colonel Charles B. Hunter, United States Infantry, who initially organised and trained it. Stilwell appointed Frank D. Merrill to command in the rank of Brigadier-General, but Merrill only assumed command in January to be relieved by Hunter in April, when he was evacuated after a severe heart-attack. Galahad was removed from Wingate's to Stilwell's command, but they were trained as Chindits and the fortunes of the two forces were to be closely interlocked.

When battalions were divided into columns the commanding officer took over one and his second-in-command the other. For the most part the column commanders were drawn from their own regiments, but Wingate, to the irritation of some of the battalions, was apt to introduce his favourite veterans of LONGCLOTH. Lockett went to the 7th Leicesters. Walter Scott, a wartime soldier, commanded the regular battalion of his own regiment, the King's. Herring, another civilian soldier from the Burma Rifles, led a raiding group called Dah Force. Sergeant-Major Blain, a Highlander, was promoted major to command 'Bladet', (Blain's Detachment), a glider-borne demolition squad.

As for the battalions themselves, their names were like a drum-roll of British military history, their courage resting on a bedrock of tradition and the ingrained belief in each that it was unique, apart and an élite. They continued their specialist training under the piercing eye and scalding criticisms of their extraordinary new general, whom a badly sited machine-gun or a faulty radio-set could throw into paroxysms of wrath, but it was not simply this which induced the stolid British to follow him. Slim likened Wingate in his exalted mood to an Old Testament prophet. It is a just comparison. Wingate in the grip of his daemon could terrify, and he could crush his audiences with a sense of their own incompetence or idleness, but he could also exalt and inspire. This was the power that enabled him to weld together and inspire his polyglot force, Gurkhas, British, West Africans and half a dozen tribes, a few Burmese and even some Hong Kong Chinese into a single entity, with complete faith in their commander and their mission. He went from unit to unit, exhorting them in turn. Carfrae, a captain, twenty-eight years old, only saw him once, but the impression was uneffaceable. Wingate was already legendary, and all the officers of the 7th Battalion, the Nigeria Regiment, awaited his first visit to their training camp with interest. There appeared, walking alone out of the jungle, a short, hatless apparition with long hair and a short beard, the red tabs of a general and the ribbon of the Distinguished Service Order visible on a filthy drill shirt. The colonel of the battalion went to meet him and asked him if he would like to be introduced to the officers. Wingate looked at his own feet and mumbled something inaudible. Then he raised his head and started to speak. It was, as always, an unforgettable experience.[10] Wingate had none of the jaunty optimism, or jokes, or metaphors drawn from cricket and football. The enterprise they were engaged in was a dangerous one. Victory would only be gained by sacrifices. He had obtained the best weapons and the best of everything for the Chindits and it was now their duty to look after them properly and use them well.

Another young officer recorded:

This exercise was followed by a large-scale conference presided over by Wingate. It was the first time I heard him lecturing and it was an experience not to be missed. He was the worst-dressed officer I have ever seen. The most remarkable thing about him were his eyes and his voice, which were as sharp as steel and with both of which he seemed to stab anyone to whom he was talking. He was a man in whose presence anyone from lieutenant-general to private felt uncomfortable and aware of his shortcomings. He spared no one in his criticisms and never used soft words to the victims; he had absolute mental and moral courage allied with a complete lack of pity, so that he said what he liked, to whom he liked and where he liked . . . During this long conference I never heard Wingate use the expressions 'it seems to me', 'it is probable that' or 'in my opinion'. With him it was always 'the Japanese reaction will be', 'the result will be', 'such and such a thing cannot happen', always with complete confidence in his predictions and his reasoning. There was something awe-inspiring in his certainty and his dogmatism, yet something which inspired the fullest confidence, so that one went away saying, 'with him in command we cannot fail'.[11]

And another, having described how a chance meeting with a gruff and taciturn Wingate had been so disappointing after all they had heard about him:

> The moment Wingate got up to speak he had us. His eloquence was of a strange brand, requiring a large audience, yet spoken in a thin, rasping voice. He did not search for words, for they were already formed in his lips; he knew exactly what he wanted to say and was convinced that he alone could say it. It was this complete confidence that impressed us most, as he spoke to us of the 'form of warfare I have perfected', and outlined the measureless possibilities of long-range penetration columns.

A subaltern of the King's Own, newly the commander of a reconnaissance platoon, together with his men, thought Wingate's theories rather far-fetched until Wingate discussed the use of such platoons on one of the elaborate map-models he used for training, when everything became clear and he too fell under the spell.[12] (Wingate had a passion for maps and insisted on his staff papering the floors with half-inch cover of the whole of his operation. The fact that the grid-lines began to diverge and widening gaps to appear he put down to the inefficiency of his staff. It took some time to make him understand that it was one of the ineluctable consequences of spherical trigonometry.)[13]

Wingate was an actor and a demagogue, and it is a common enough hazard of such occupations to fall sometimes into bathos. He did not get across to Colonel Hunter or his tough Americans in the American contingent. Hunter 'held the parade' as he puts it, and after Wingate was out of earshot addressed his command to the effect that the United States Army did not require to learn anything from a British general. (In the event, Galahad owed a great deal to Wingate's training methods.) 'Your bones will whiten in Burma, but your fame will live for evermore,' he said to the irreverent Cameronians in the 111th Brigade, who had been inoculated by many a Calvinist sermon and to whom Wingate's pastiche biblical style was not as strange as it was to the a-religious British, and they reacted with their usual Glaswegian cynicism.[14] On another occasion Wingate, fixing a front-rank man with his eye, exclaimed: 'You are going to die in Burma!' to which the discomfiting reply, 'Then I'm not bloody well going there!' caused a ripple of laughter.[15] But running all through the British diaries, narratives and recollections of that period there is a constant *leit-motiv*: absolute confidence in Wingate, the man and his methods.

Not under command, but indissolubly attached to the Force during its brief existence, was the No. 1 Air Commando, United States Army Air Force, whose existence, as already explained, made Chindit tactics possible. The Commando was a unique affair, the individual inspiration of General Arnold, Chief of the United States Army Air Force. He was an officer notably uninhibited by the more formal procedures obtaining in the Royal Air Force and the United States Air Force. Wingate had originally asked only for a force of light planes capable of short take-off and landing in hastily constructed jungle strips to evacuate his wounded, but General Arnold was an early enthusiast for airborne warfare, and he generously provided something much more radical and imaginative. He sent for two young fighter pilots, Colonels Cochran and Alison, and outlined his ideas, saying: 'Wingate marched into Burma the first time. I want him to fly in and fly out.' He then gave them a short written order which was a charter to commandeer, carte blanche, the men and aircraft they needed.

The men they picked, many from training establishments, were all experts in their various skills, and many of the pilots could fly two or three types of the aircraft in the unit. The troop transport element consisted of a hundred CG-4A (WACO) gliders, the light plane force of a hundred, mainly L-5s with a few L-1s, the latter being an even more versatile STOL aircraft than the L-5, and a strike force of thirty of the incredibly robust P-51A (Mustang) fighter/ground attack aircraft and twenty B-25H (Mitchell) fast medium bombers. Twenty C-47 (Dakotas), and twelve UC-64 (Norseman) constituted the troop transport, supply and general transport wing, and there were half a dozen prototype Sikorsky helicopters, the first ever to see operational use. Altogether initially there were 288 aircraft manned with 600 of all ranks to provide crews and servicing, a ratio of 1:2 where normally it might be 1:5 or 1:10. A little air photography was attempted using hand-held cameras in Mitchells at low altitude, the processing being done by men borrowed from a USAAF unit in Eastern Air Command. The Commando was not self-sufficient. Designed for only a ninety-day mission, it had no administrative or repair backing other than first-line, and it required reinforcements to meet the full supply demands of Special Force and tugs for the glider air lift. By January the Air Commando was taking part in joint training, which included the precise landing by night of eighteen gliders carrying a detachment of the Black Watch, with Mountbatten among the spectators, and 'DAS', or direct air support, for which they showed remarkable enthusiasm. The secret of their success, the Chindits claimed, was that they were soldiers – the United States *Army* Air Force – and saw their chief duty to be to help their comrades fighting on the ground – as opposed to the Royal Air Force who saw themselves as an independent arm with strategic rather than tactical goals. The Chindit air control system, invented by Robert Thompson, a colonial civil servant and wartime air force officer, also a veteran of LONGCLOTH and one of Wingate's chosen band of followers, was simple and effective. Air force radio-communications, manned by the Royal Air Force, would be built into the Special Force command radio-network, and RAF officers so equipped would march with the columns. When DAS was called for they could, using their special communications and their knowledge as pilots, 'talk down' the supporting aircraft so that they were able to bring their tremendous fire-power to bear on the Japanese even when they were locked in combat with the columns. The Chindits learnt to trust their accuracy implicitly.

The accession of No. 1 Air Commando transformed the Chindits. Without it Special Force could have been no more than a raiding force relying on occasional help from the RAF and with an air instead of a land supply route. Arnold's initiative had converted it into a single, unified airborne weapon ready to Wingate's hand. There was no division or jealousy in command: harmony between air and ground was complete. Cochran said perceptively that after being initially puzzled by Wingate's manner he was suddenly converted to the Chindit idea when he grasped that Wingate was proposing to manoeuvre his columns by radio from a distance, exactly as fighter pilots are controlled. He used to refer to Wingate as 'The Man'. Alison made it his personal duty to fly Wingate on his trips into Burma in one of the fast Mitchell B-25 bombers, ensuring his safety in air space haunted by Japanese fighters.

By February, the whole force was ready for action. The only question now was, what was this action to be?

4

The Generals Make Their Plans

THE LONG CHAIN of military reasoning which brought about the North Burma campaign began with the determination of the Americans to realise the vast military potential of China and bring it into the war against Japan. This, they believed, could be done in two stages. For the past decade the Japanese Army had been locked in bloody but futile campaigns in Eastern China. It won all its battles, in a narrow sense, but there was always another Chinese army to be defeated. If the Chinese could only be modernised and effectively led they could, the Americans believed, absorb the effort of many Japanese divisions and so prevent their redeployment against the United States in the Western Pacific. If this holding operation could then be converted into an offensive, the eastern seaboard of China could be cleared and bases established there from which American air-power could be brought to bear at close range upon Japan itself.

For this, it was essential to reopen to China the land line of communications severed in 1942 when the British-Indian and Chinese divisions in Burma were defeated by the Japanese and went reeling back in hopeless disorder. For the moment, all that remained was an expensive and dangerous air route from India to China 'over the Hump' – the mountain mass whose peaks, swept by storms and turbulence of great ferocity, rose to altitudes of 20,000 feet. A more southerly and safe route was barred by Japanese interceptor aircraft based on the North Burmese town of Myitkyina. To reopen a new Burma Road to replace the old one running from Rangoon to Lung-Ling in Yunnan it was first necessary for the Japanese to be cleared out of North Burma: a task made doubly difficult by the logistic problems of maintaining a modern army in a country consisting largely of mountains clad in dense tropical forest and devoid of communications, and the tenacity of the Japanese as fighters. The Japanese Army was in fact better suited than any highly mechanised Western one for war in Burma, for it was a simple rifle-and-bayonet affair with only light field artillery, prepared to go anywhere on foot. It was more like an army of 1917 than of 1944 pattern, but it had one important asset in the shape of a highly efficient and modern air force. The problem of how to defeat it and open the road to China was one of the subjects discussed at the fateful Quebec conference of August 1943 (Quadrant), where Wingate made so remarkable an impact when he explained his strategic solution. All that was, or could be, agreed at such a high-level conference was an intention and a general idea. The whole complicated business of realising them required hundreds of man-hours of staff work, matching goals with logistics and resources, assessing the priorities of the plans for other theatres and, in this specific instance, the attitude of an unpredictable ally, Generalissimo Chiang Kai-shek, the ruler of China.

What was agreed in outline as desirable – it was hardly a 'plan' in the strict military sense of the term – was a triple offensive into Northern Burma to be mounted as soon as possible in the dry season of 1944. General Stilwell was to attack southwards with his new First Chinese Army from the extreme north-east corner of India. A retrained and reorganised British-Indian Army was to attack eastwards from Assam into north-central Burma across the mighty Chindwin River, while another corps advanced in Arakan. (This force had no name or commander at that moment, but it was to become the Fourteenth Army and its commander was to be Lieutenant-General J. W. Slim.) The third thrust was to be made by another of the new American-trained Chinese groups of armies in Yunnan westwards across the Salween River and into Burma.

Wingate's proposed contribution to this scheme of operations was essentially very simple. He had, he explained, perfected a system of warfare using regular troops but based on guerrilla tactics, specially designed to operate in the rugged Burmese terrain and for raiding deep behind the enemy lines. The Japanese in Burma would be fighting on three fronts with their vulnerable supply lines radiating from the centre like the spokes of a wheel. Given the resources, Wingate explained, he could put one of his brigades astride each of them and ensure that they were cut. Bereft of food, ammunition and reinforcement by this enemy in its guts (to use Wingate's favourite simile), the Japanese defence must inevitably collapse. It was an altogether too facile theory, but all who saw Wingate's performance at the Quebec conference were deeply impressed. He was, as has been said, an emotional man, something of a demagogue and an actor, and apt to be carried away by his own enthusiasm. Nothing could have been more restrained than his behaviour, both on the liner *Queen Mary* during the voyage across the Atlantic and at the conference itself. The voyage was a preliminary discipline, as he was ordered to explain his ideas and submit to questioning by both the British Chiefs of Staff Committee and Joint Planning Staff and by Churchill himself, who was a formidable interrogator. He had had no staff training or staff experience, and therefore no formal instruction in the nice art of preparing formal military papers and making staff presentations. He was generously helped by the planning staff, but in all important matters he worked out his own approach and style from first principles. When he came to the supreme test, of facing the hard and critical audience of the combined United States and British chiefs-of-staff, his attack was free of rhetoric and biblical quotations. It was clear, logical and factual, while at the same time conveying his tremendous self-confidence. It secured more than mere approval from the Americans, who instinctively warmed towards a soldier with offensive, positive ideas. Wingate at this stage still planned to infiltrate his columns into Burma on foot, between the Japanese outposts. It was the Americans who changed the whole concept of long-range penetration by providing the resources to introduce them by air. They also decided to contribute the 3,000 volunteers from the United States Army who were to become famous as 'Galahad' and 'Merrill's Marauders'.

Wingate's next presentation was more daunting but less difficult, as Churchill had already become Wingate's patron and supporter. It was in private, to Churchill and Roosevelt alone, with Admiral Lord Mountbatten, the Supreme Allied Commander designate in the new South-East Asia Command, in attendance. Mountbatten, although Wingate was to try his patience sorely, was also to prove his whole-hearted supporter. The two great men were not content with listening to a tactical exposition, but probed Wingate with questions on topics ranging far outside his own particular operation, all of which he answered with impressive understanding. At the end Churchill said: 'Brigadier Wingate, we owe you our thanks. You have expounded a large and complex subject with examplary lucidity.' Wingate replied superbly: 'Such is my invariable practice, sir.'[1]

If ever a man had risen to an occasion it was Wingate, and his reward was a considerable personal victory over his enemies in India, real and imaginary. When the British chiefs-of-staff informed the commander-in-chief in Delhi of the decisions taken at Quebec and the man-power requirements to be met to make Wingate's operational rôle possible there was great consternation. To maintain three brigades inside Burma would require a total of six, so as to make reliefs possible every three months; it being Wingate's opinion, based on his previous experience, that ninety days was as long as a unit could retain its efficiency when fighting without rest or relief behind the enemy lines. In addition there would be a considerable bill for supporting and ancillary troops extending right back to the training base in Gwalior in India and the logistic base, as well as inroads on the limited resources of the Royal Air Force. There seemed no way out of meeting the demands of the chiefs-of-staff except by breaking up the all-British 70th Infantry Division with its high proportion of regular battalions, veterans of Crete and Tobruk. To the staff in India it seemed intolerable that this fine division, an essential part of the army reserve for the forthcoming battles with the Japanese, was to be handed over to a man they regarded as a charlatan. A furious bombardment and counter-bombardment took place between the chiefs-of-staff and the staff in Delhi, with top-secret signals for missiles. Wingate himself had the satisfaction of drafting the answers from the chiefs-of-staff, who had no intention of backing down or modifying decisions taken jointly with their American colleagues.

The effect of all this on Wingate was profound. As has been said, at an early point in his military career he had become convinced that he was a man of destiny, sent by the Almighty to play some great part in the world. He believed that he had failed twice, if not three times, and that these failures to complete his God-given missions in Palestine, in Abyssinia and in Burma in 1943 were due partly to his own sinfulness and partly to a conspiracy within the British Army staff to frustrate him. Only eighteen months earlier he had crashed to the rank of major and was recovering from the after-effects of a mental break-down and attempted suicide. And only twelve weeks earlier he had feared that the casualties of LONGCLOTH would prevent his further employment.[2] Now at Quebec the Lord had at last rewarded him. He had put words in his mouth to speak before the councils of the mighty and held up his arms in debate. As for the ungodly who had thwarted him in India, he had triumphed over them, but what was sweetest in his mouth was the Prime Minister's last instruction. If Wingate's plans were obstructed, Churchill told him, he was empowered to communicate with him direct. All this was heady stuff, and Wingate became intoxicated.

There can be no doubt that Wingate was a man of powerful if undisciplined intellect, great creative imagination, courage and the utmost determination. He had a natural political instinct and knew how to solicit the support of the men at the top. He was, however, in some ways politically quite unsophisticated. He did not understand how the different centres of power balanced each other in the armed forces just as in other sorts of politics, or the need continually to seek friends at all levels and to coax and cajole as well as bulldoze his way to his objectives. Later he seemed to imagine that he had *carte blanche* to pursue any objective he pleased: a position he only left momen-tarily when he demanded that there must be no variation from the plans he believed to have been irrevocably laid down at Quebec. He did not understand the extensive and complicated process of staff planning, or grasp how in months or even weeks the premises on which the outline plan had been based could change for political or military reasons.

Those changes which took place can be briefly outlined. The staff of headquarters South-East Asia Command (SEAC) got to work and produced no fewer than fourteen detailed plans or sub-plans, some being modifications of the earlier versions, made to meet a lack of resources. Very sensibly they looked first for options which avoided a hard, slow slog through the jungle and made full use of the superior mobility of the Allies in the air and at sea. The basic concentric attack, CHAMPION, remained. But there was, for instance, an amphibious descent on the Andaman Islands (BUCCANEER), or on Rangoon (DRACULA); and a landing by two airborne divisions inside Burma (TOREADOR). There was also CULVERIN, a much more ambitious and far-ranging strategy to by-pass Burma altogether and lever the Japanese out by invading Sumatra and cutting them off from their main base. Another airborne plan was to follow up Wingate's Chindit force by air landing an ordinary Indian infantry division, the 26th, in the area around Indaw. This was TARZAN.*

TARZAN was to remain an obsession of Wingate. It had caught his fancy because it enlarged his own operation to something much more decisive and ambitious than a mere raid on a grand scale. He could never understand the fact that a plan had no real existence until the necessary resources had been allotted and it had been finally approved. Here was the rub. All these plans required ships, landing craft and aircraft, especially transport aircraft, of which the United States held a virtual monopoly. The Pacific and the invasion of North-West Europe across the Channel (OVERLORD) had priority, so the SEAC plans had to be scaled down or discarded altogether. There may have been enough aircraft to fly in the 26th Division, but never enough to maintain it solely by air supply as well as maintaining, the large Chindit force. TARZAN was never a runner, although before the Japanese offensive of March changed the whole face of operations the prospect of reinforcing Wingate was held out to him as a sop.

The political consequence of this scaling down was that Chiang Kai-shek reneged on his agreements. He had, as gradually became clear, no intention of ever committing his own armies from inside China as spearheads, and he seized on the cancellations to hold back the Salween offensive. The Chinese effort was therefore reduced to nothing. The British offensive was scaled down to a cautious step-by-step advance by the XV Corps in Arakan, and another across the Chindwin by the IV Corps. The trans-Chindwin offensive, (CAPITAL)

*A sly joke by the planners in allusion to their nickname for Wingate.

was delayed by acute logistic problems and in that sector in any case Slim was veering round to the opinion that he would do better to fight a defensive battle on ground of his own choosing west of the Chindwin. Japanese intentions could not be left out of the equation, and there were strong intelligence indicators that they were preparing for a major thrust into India.

Whether the Japanese high command really hoped to invade India, or believed that the Indian peoples would rise in rebellion against the British, and whether their offensive was in fact a 'march on Delhi', or simply a spoiling attack against their most dangerous opponent is a matter for debate. Wingate's successful infiltration into Burma in LONGCLOTH in 1943 had certainly shown the Japanese that the jungles astride the Chindwin were no obstacle to properly organised infantry, confirming their own experience in Malaya in 1941 and in Burma in 1942. What the Japanese did was to launch two offensives at a month's interval. The first, 'Ha-Go', was a powerful counter-attack in Arakan in February 1944, aimed at drawing in the Fourteenth Army's reserves. In March followed the main offensive, 'U-Go', by the Japanese Fifteenth Army under General Mutaguchi against the IC Corps of the Fourteenth Army. Both offensives were utterly crushed. Had they not been, the least damage done would have been the disruption of the ground supply routes to the American air bases and the flights over the 'Hump', and the abortion of Stilwell's offensive. The whole Stilwell-Chindit operation (ALBACORE and THURSDAY), it must be understood, was fought to the thunderous accompaniment off-stage of the great and decisive battle of Imphal-Kohima. At the end of 1943, that event had not yet occurred. But what was already perfectly apparent was that all hopes of a decisive victory in the theatre in 1944 had vanished. The TARZAN concept had been shelved; and besides the Fourteenth Army's limited operations there remained only Stilwell's plan in its original form and, linked to it, Wingate and Special Force in their supportive rôle agreed at Quadrant. These two operations – by Stilwell and his own Chinese Army and by the Chindits – must therefore be seen as being conducted by two wings of the same army whose fortunes interlocked.

There can be no doubt that the dominant wing was the New First Chinese Army and the dominant personality was that of Joseph Warren Stilwell. Without his steely determination there would have been no Burma campaign of 1944 at all. The fact that the Limeys had abandoned any idea of a far-ranging offensive neither surprised nor upset him. They were (he felt) always droning on about logistic difficulties (a blank spot in Stilwell's own mental armoury), and in any case he did not believe that they could fight. In the early stages of his planning he did not place much faith in the Chindits or consider that their intervention would be of any great advantage to him, although at his one meeting with Wingate (January 3rd, 1944) the Chindit leader gained his respect. He was essentially an American general indoctrinated with American ideas, who believed that the shortest route to his objective was the best. He had referred to long-range penetration as 'shadow boxing'.

Stilwell had been given a number of missions of the highest importance but clearly the core of American strategy was aid to China and the essential link in this was the new Burma road (or the Ledo road as it came to be called and later the 'Stilwell Highway'.) He believed in offensive action as the first principle of war and that such action must not be delayed. What ever else was going by the board in South-East Asia, he determined, he would persist in the northern offensive – the mission given him by his own chief-of-staff, General George Marshall. With considerable diplomacy he persuaded Chiang Kai-shek to free the First Chinese Army still training at Ramgarh for his projected offensive and – vital to his control of it – confer on him the powers of full command authenticated by the seal or 'chop'. He began his advance into Burma in October 1943.

His plan of operations, code-named ALBACORE, was characteristically simple. Clearly the vital objective was Myitkyina, and to it there was only one possible route, either as the axis of an advance or for the road. This ran from Ledo over the mountain range barring the way from India to Northern Burma and then southwards up the Hukawng Valley to a watershed and down the Mogaung Valley to a town called Kamaing, thence to the town of Mogaung and so along the railway from Mogaung to Myitkyina. Myitkyina was therefore indubitably his goal: all other considerations were subordinate. The mountains confined Stilwell's line of advance to a single axis along the valleys, but he was determined on better tactics than a series of frontal attacks. He intended either to manouevre the Japanese out of their positions, or cut them off where they stood and destroy them, preferably the latter.

Stilwell's opponent was Lieutenant-General Shinichi Tanaka commanding the élite Japanese 18th 'Chrysanthemum' Division. Tanaka was a skilled defensive general and Stilwell knew that his resistance would be dogged, and so it proved from the beginning. Stilwell was a simple but effective tactician. His scheme of manoeuvre was to make a series of frontal thrusts combined with encircling movements round one or other of Tanaka's flanks with the aim of cutting the road behind him and so forcing him to withdraw, stage by stage, from one defensive position to another. This policy Stilwell pursued unswervingly until his vanguard reached the outskirts of Myitkyina in May 1944. Stilwell had one particular difficulty, however. He could not persuade his Chinese officers to press home these outflanking attacks. They feared that they might be cut off in turn, and in any case it conformed more with Chinese ideas of strategy to allow a dangerous enemy an escape route. Indeed, it was one of Stilwell's most intractable problems to persuade the Chinese to fight at all, and his success in this was one of his most remarkable achievements. He yearned, however, for some American combat troops whom he could trust to obey their orders. None could be spared to him from the United States, and he felt it wrong that Wingate had been given an American regiment. He demanded that the 5307th Provisional Unit (Galahad) should be transferred to his operational command. (It was already under his command for administrative purposes and for personnel matters such as command appointments.)

There are two versions of how he obtained Galahad. According to Brigadier Tulloch, it was settled amicably between the two men. Another version is that it was arranged behind Wingate's back, and that when a Colonel Brink, who briefly commanded Galahad, and Colonel Hunter heard the news through United States Army Staff channels, they intercepted Wingate, who was touring the training areas, and immediately informed him. Wingate exploded. 'You can tell General Stilwell,' he said, 'that he can stick his Americans up his arse.' He then quickly recovered himself and apologised.[3] It is significant that he immediately accepted the situation instead of, as he did on most other occasions, making the most violent protests. He knew that the whole Chindit operation, and his own ambitious and far-reaching plans, depended to a great extent on American goodwill and cooperation. Or, possibly, he may have mistakenly formed the opinion that Galahad was an inferior unit.

Wingate's own approach to operational planning was in sharp contrast to Stilwell's direct simplicity. It is always hammered into British as well as American officers that the first step in planning is to define the object, or aim, and then the intention, or mission. Wingate's real intention, expressed in his order of the day for THURSDAY, seems to have been to use his own patent method of warfare for the grandest of goals. He declared the first to be the liberation of Burma: next the defeat, no less, of all Japanese in South-East Asia, for which he suggested using a vast force of twenty-five Chindit brigades (or 100 battalions, or 95,000 bayonets.)[4] For the operation he was about to launch he had three separate operational plans in mind. The first was to enable him to fulfil his legitimate rôle of assisting Stilwell in ALBACORE. It was to be called THURSDAY, although this strictly speaking referred only to the air-borne entry of two brigades into Japanese-occupied Burma.

Wingate still hankered after TARZAN. With six brigades of Special

Force, already with its ancillary units the equivalent of a small army corps, and three brigades of the 26th Division he would be in possession of a force powerful enough to attempt his goal of liberating Burma. He therefore demanded that the 26th Indian Division be transferred to him in advance of the launching of THURSDAY, so that he could suitably train and indoctrinate it, but he was abruptly refused. This had brought on one of the tantrums which so marred his performance as a military commander. He complained to Mountbatten that 'British generals' did not have their heart in his enterprise, that it was therefore doomed to ignominious failure. He threatened to resign and wildly recommended that the Chindit force be broken up. It says a lot for Mountbatten's tolerance that he did not immediately dismiss his brilliant and ungovernable subordinate, but soothed him down, while rebuking him for treating friends as enemies and creating resistance where none existed before.

Wingate may have been placated but he was never defeated. He so planned his THURSDAY deployment that it was weighted towards the old TARZAN plan. If he could capture the Indaw airfields and control a significantly large area around them then he would once more demand the 26th Division to be flown in to secure it. 'Look,' he could announce (firing off signals to Churchill the while), 'at the prize I have secured for you: the key to victory and the first part of the Empire to be liberated from the Japanese! Is this to be thrown away for want of a division sitting unused and idle in India?' And so on.

The briefing he gave Brigadier Fergusson just before he led the 16th Brigade into Burma is strong evidence of this. He told Fergusson that his mission was to secure the Indaw airfields, and that he would be relieved there by a division flown in from India, while at the same time the triple concentric thrust (CHAMPION), by that date in reality modified almost out of existence, would take place. Fergusson continued to believe this until after the war was over.[5] This had a sequel which might have made any commander other than Wingate blush.

Wingate was accompanied on this occasion by his GSOI (Operations), Lieutenant-Colonel Francis Piggott, and it was at the end of the return flight that the lamentable assault on this senior member of his staff took place, as already described. The next day Colonel Piggott asked for a private interview with Wingate. He had too much dignity to refer to that incident: he had a more serious complaint. 'My knees were shaking slightly,' he recalled, but he stated politely enough, though extremely bluntly, that he could not understand the information Wingate had given Fergusson. If it was accurate, then Wingate had been concealing facts of the utmost importance from a member of his staff who was fully entitled to know them; indeed, he could not do his work effectively if he was kept in ignorance of the very fundamentals of the plans. Either way it was a matter of trust, and he felt justified in asking to be relieved. There was no explosion of wrath, nor did Wingate give a direct reply: as another officer recalled, if caught out Wingate 'would smile so sweetly' and abandon the topic. He treated Piggott's complaint as if it arose purely from incompatibility of temperament, and accepted the request with grace saying, 'Yes, perhaps our faces don't fit', and was most solicitous in offering to find Colonel Piggott another post commensurate with his undoubted ability.[6]

This secret intention to increase the whole scope of his operation did not run counter to his task of assisting Stilwell, but he was also lured towards a totally different objective. In his private conversations with Brigadier Tulloch, Wingate used to refer to his legitimate rôle as 'Plan A'. He also had a 'Plan B'.[7] Wingate was aware of the possibility of a Japanese offensive and saw this as offering an alternative path to the resounding success he so ardently desired. He would abandon his legitimate mission altogether, or leave only minimum forces to carry it on, while with his reserve brigades he turned against the rear of the Japanese Fifteenth Army as it attacked Slim. Nor was even this final, for there was yet another consideration in Wingate's mind. Strictly speaking three of his brigades were intended for use as reliefs, but if he implemented Plan B he intended to introduce them into Burma without delay because he feared, not altogether without reason, that if the Fourteenth Army was hard pressed, his reserve brigades might be taken away from him to be used as conventional reinforcements. (As indeed the 23rd Brigade was.)

During the preparatory period Wingate's tactical ideas had been evolving and he conceived the idea of fortified bases sited in remote jungle, each with a C-47 airstrip and defended by its own garrison of infantry and artillery. Each base would serve as port of entry for reinforcements, a refuge and rest area for his columns, and a collecting point for casualties. For this he demanded extra troops and there were further altercations during which he once more asserted that his mission as laid down at Quebec was being made impossible, while recommending again that Special Force should be broken up and that he should be allowed to resign. He won a partial victory. Instead of having to use his Chindits for the garrisons of his strongholds he was allotted the 3rd/9th Gurkha Rifles, and he was allowed to draw on the battalions of the 3rd West African Brigade, officially part of his reserve. At last, by January 1944, Wingate was able to settle down to some concrete planning on the basis of a directive given him jointly by Slim and Stratemeyer, the commander

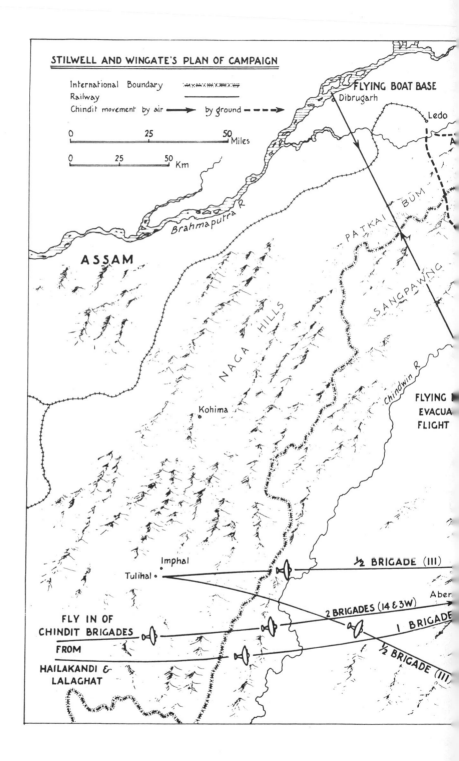

STILWELL AND WINGATE'S PLAN OF CAMPAIGN

International Boundary
Railway
Chindit movement by air ——→ by ground ---→

0   25   50 Miles

0   25   50 Km

FLYING BOAT BASE
Dibrugarh
Ledo

ASSAM

Brahmaputra R.

PATKAI

BUM

SANGPAWNG

NAGA HILLS

Chindwin R.

Kohima

FLYING
EVACUA
FLIGHT

Imphal
Tulihal

½ BRIGADE (III)

Aber

2 BRIGADES (14 & 3W)

FLY IN OF
CHINDIT BRIGADES
FROM

I BRIGADE

HAILAKANDI &
LALAGHAT

½ BRIGADE (III)

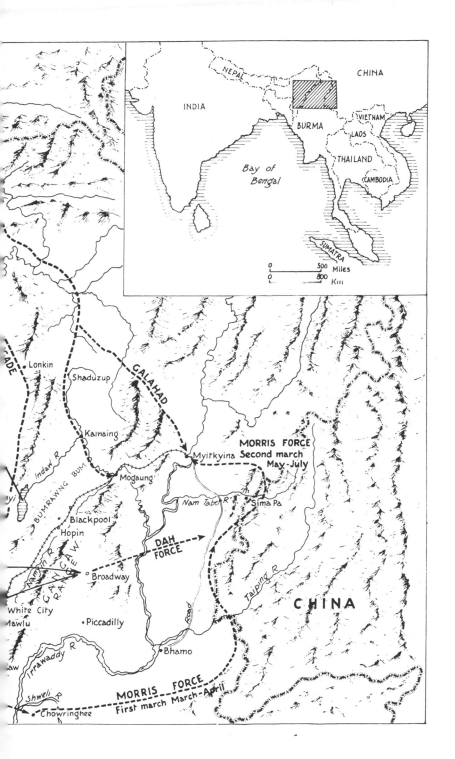

CHINA

NEPAL

INDIA

BURMA

VIETNAM

LAOS

THAILAND

CAMBODIA

Bay of
Bengal

SUMATRA

0   500   Miles
0   800   Km

Lonkin

Shaduzup

GALAHAD

Kamaing

Indaw R

Mogaung

BUMRAWNG BUM

Myitkyina

MORRIS FORCE
Second march
May-July

Nam Tabet R

Sima Pa

Blackpool

Hopin

DAH
FORCE

Broadway

Namyin R

CRANGAW

White City

Mawlu

Piccadilly

Bhamo

Road

Taiping R

CHINA

Irrawaddy R

Shweli R

MORRIS FORCE
First march March-April

Chowringhee

of Eastern Air Command, who was responsible for the very large air transport operation involved in THURSDAY; an odd conjunction between an army commander and a theatre commander-in-chief. It was an unusual chain of command, tailored to fit Stilwell's prejudices. The overall ground forces' commander in the theatre was the British General Giffard, commanding 11th Army Group. Stilwell in his capacity as a ground forces' commander in SEAC would logically have come under him, but he had taken a violent dislike to Giffard, and Mountbatten rightly refused to confuse his own responsibilities by becoming directly involved in the control of a corps-sized operation, for his headquarters was only concerned with policy and planning on the highest level and was not in any case geared for day-to-day operational control. Stilwell, however, had considerable respect for Slim and volunteered to accept orders from him. (This was a ridiculous anomaly because Slim was younger and junior in rank, and Stilwell in another capacity was deputy to Mountbatten, and if Mountbatten had been *hors de combat* for any reason Slim would have been commanding his own acting supreme commander!) As Wingate's legitimate rôle was subordinate and ancillary to Stilwell's, and as Stilwell had a strong objection to having Wingate under command, Wingate was placed under Slim as well. Slim in any case was better fitted than anyone except Mountbatten to keep Wingate in order. For this reason it fell to Slim to issue Special Force with its directive jointly with the American Major-General George E. Stratemeyer, US Army Air Force, for Eastern Air Command. They defined his mission as:

To block the flow of supplies and reinforcements northwards to the Japanese 18th Division facing Stilwell and draw in the Japanese reserves against himself.

To create a situation favourable for a Chinese advance across the Salween.

To inflict the maximum confusion, damage and loss on the Japanese in Northern Burma.

Of these three tasks the second was almost as important as the first, for if the twelve Chinese divisions stationed east of the Salween on the old Burma road, opposed by only a single Japanese division in observation, could be encouraged to attack, the whole complexion of the battle in the north would be changed. Bearing this in mind, how Wingate disposed of his resources is significant. He selected three targets: the Bhamo-Myitkyina road, the railway, and Indaw.
Wingate's plan of deployment to meet these requirements is easy to

understand provided that his 'indirectness' is borne in mind. All the columns were to be landed at some point remote from their objectives and were then to steal secretly on to them under cover of the jungle.

The 16th Brigade (Fergusson) was to enter Burma on foot in February starting from Ledo, make for Indaw on the railway, and secure the two airfields. On the way it was to assist Stilwell by detaching two columns to seize and hold Lonkin, a Japanese outpost guarding Tanaka's left flank.

The 111th Brigade (Lentaigne) was to be landed in the jungles east of the railway at PICCADILLY, make for the area south of Indaw and in Chindit fashion, using ambushes, road blocks and demolitions on the railway, prevent any interference to Fergusson's movements by Japanese coming up from the south. The glider-borne demolition squad, 'Bladet', was to assist in blowing up some railway bridges.

The 77th Brigade (Calvert) was to be landed east of the railway at BROADWAY, march to a pre-selected point on the railway and there establish a fortress block on the railway itself.

The 4th/9th Gurkha Rifles ('Morris Force') was to be landed at CHOWRINGHEE east of the Irrawaddy River and make its way to the mountains flanking the road from Bhamo to Myitkyina and mount raids from a base there.

Dah Force* (Lieutenant-Colonel D. C. Herring) was in fact a military mission whose task was to organise bands of guerrillas from the warlike Kachin tribesmen, who lived in the jungles astride the Bhamo road, and supplement the operations of Morris Force. It was to be landed by glider in a jungle clearing east of the Irrawaddy, code-named TEMPLECOMBE.

Calvert was ordered to develop BROADWAY† as a stronghold and allotted the 3rd/9th Gurkha Rifles to garrison it. In addition he was to detach the two columns of the King's Regiment from his brigade for extra protection in view of its importance.

Similarly Fergusson was to establish a stronghold, ABERDEEN, as soon as he arrived in the area of Indaw, and be allotted the 6th Battalion, the Nigeria Regiment.

There are certain aspects of the THURSDAY plan which are worth noting and must be borne in mind when following the events of March and April. There was the conflict between evasive, guerrilla-type tactics and the deliberate challenge to a stand-up fight as offered to the Japanese at Calvert's blocking position and at Indaw.

* A *dah* is a long, slightly curved, single-edged sword, as typical of the Burmese as the *kukri* is of the Gurkhas.

† Piccadilly was the original choice for development into a stronghold but, as will be told, it was never used as a landing ground.

The legitimate part of Wingate's Plan A clearly related to the two main arteries supplying Tanaka: the railway and the Bhamo-Myitkyina road. Wingate allotted three battalions to the railway and only one to the road. The second of the tasks given to Wingate was to create a situation favourable enough to encourage the Chinese Expeditionary Force in Yunnan to advance, and for this a whole brigade on the Bhamo road would not have been too much. In any case a single battalion could not effectively close the road, even, as it proved, when an extra column was added to it.

The force allotted to the Indaw operation was six battalions, or seven if the Nigerian battalion for the Aberdeen stronghold is included. The balance of forces was simply not consistent with the tasks given to Wingate, but if Wingate's private objectives are regarded as equally legitimate (or practicable) then his choice of Indaw was correct. From a central position he could revive TARZAN, bring in the rest of his force, follow 'Plan A' or 'Plan B' or strike in any direction occurring to his ever-fertile imagination.

THURSDAY, because of the time taken to prepare it and the need for a full moon to coincide with final readiness, was not launched until the first week in March. In the meantime ALBACORE had gathered momentum. Two of the Chinese divisions trained in India at Ramgarh and a group of light tanks manned by Chinese were committed, and Stilwell, relegating all his other responsibilities to second place, took personal command in the field himself. No one else, he knew, could effectively command the Chinese. He also had in his hand the ideal instrument for the encircling movements through the jungles which were his tactical hallmark. In February Galahad went into action with truly American élan, and gave him his first major success.

5

Galahad Goes to War

WINGATE AND THE Chindits may have regretted the departure of Galahad from their company, but in general headquarters in Delhi there were deep sighs of relief. The British, or at any rate the English, prefer their soldiers to be not only well-disciplined, which is a purely military virtue, but also docile and well-behaved. In their view a good regiment was one that could be dumped into some God-forsaken tract of the Empire and be content with cricket and football and a little discreet drinking and whoring on Saturday nights. The United States Army felt much the same, and in fact its disciplinary code was stricter and more harshly applied than the British, but Galahad was a maverick unit, far from home and the bright lights of garrison towns, whose members, shipped out to incomprehensible British India, felt cheated at not being immediately engaged in the 'hazardous mission' for which they had volunteered. Instead, they found themselves in a tented camp without the most elementary amenities (a sad failure on the part of their hosts), eating scanty British soldiers' rations, and for some time trying to train without any equipment. Many of the Galahads were a wild lot, and they reacted accordingly.

They kept the military police busy, the neighbouring natives in a state of terror, and their guardhouses full. Christmas 1943 was celebrated by a *feu-de-joie* of small arms and ball ammunition discharged skywards – or mostly skywards – by half the soldiers in the camp, which nothing the officers or non-coms could do would stop. A British officer asked over by his American friend for a 'quiet Christmas' enquired mildly what Americans did when they held a noisy one. But this was the mildest of Galahad behaviour. One large party, feeling in need of rest and recreation, flagged down the Bombay express mail train on the track where it passed near their camp and disappeared for a spell of unofficial leave. Galahad's exit from India was as noisy as its sojourn. On the long, boring journey from Gwalior to Ledo the officers in one train were startled to hear the sound of shots. Some of the men were amusing themselves with rifle practice from the carriage windows, using as targets cows, water-buffaloes and even the peasants working in the fields. Galahad, without the supporting structure of the United States Army and not amenable to the British, could at any time become a political embarrassment. No British officer foresaw that what appeared in his eyes to be a disorderly mob of armed hooligans would shortly write a glorious chapter in the history of the United States infantry.

Some American officers might have been equally doubtful. Galahad had been badly handled by the American command and staff over one question vital to the successful creation of a new unit. Such a group is made up of eager, or inquisitive, or suspicious individuals with no common bonds and disorientated as a whole. It urgently requires to be inspired and assured of the importance of its mission. Galahad needed insignia, a recognised leader, a sense of mission and consciousness of its own identity: in short, a soul. ('Soul' is not a word used by modern military sociologists, who prefer less emotional terms, but that is what a fighting unit needs, because it is dealing with the basic stuff of man's existence on a primitive level; the comradeship of the group, combat, survival, and death.) Galahad had started as 3,000 unscreened volunteers lumped together under the label 'Casual Detachment 1688' who, after a sea voyage of forty-two days, were dumped without equipment in a tented camp without any amenities in the middle of Asia. From then on their only common feeling as a group was that they were abandoned and neglected by their country and left to pull Stilwell's chestnuts from the fire by breaking a trail for the Chinese. Even their title was degrading and absurd. Yells of contempt and rage sounded through its ranks when the men heard that their battle title was to be the '5307 Composite Unit (Provisional)'. They were given no distinguishing badge, shoulder patch or flag. Wingate visited them, and even the Limey admiral, Mountbatten, the Supreme Allied Commander, but not Stilwell. The first essential for a new unit is an identifiable leader, who helps the unit to identify itself. By an odd arrangement, by no means compatible with normal United States Army practice, Stilwell sent two full colonels in succession to supervise training while the draft conducting officer, Colonel Hunter, looked after discipline. Not until New Year's Day, 1944, was the position regularised, when Stilwell appointed one of his favourites, Frank D. Merrill, as Brigadier-General in Command, with Hunter as his deputy.

The 5307th to an outward or a British eye might well have looked unpromising, but in fact its 3,000 volunteers were a sample of American society, rich in talents and skills of every kind and ready to be turned to good military use by a leader who knew how. One of the most daring patrol leaders was a regular officer, the other a man waiting for the war to be over so that he could be ordained as a minister of religion. They were infinitely adaptable. The radio sections were self-taught and built up from scratch, and when some light artillery was parachuted into the jungle men were found to create a serviceable battery in twenty-four hours. The Americans are the most mechanically conscious of all peoples, but when, shortly before Galahad was called forward for operations, herds of mules and ponies arrived, 700 potential drivers, or 'mule skinners', were discovered in the ranks. The man who proved to be the deadliest marksman was a Sioux Indian. The mainstay of the intelligence and reconnaissance platoons was a group of American-born, or *Nisei*, Japanese. All that was required with such material was to give it a military shape, and then breathe some soul into it. No doubt Colonels Brink and Cranston, who sojourned briefly with Galahad as training Officers, made a contribution to its military skill, as did the genial Merrill for the short time he was in command, but the man who converted Galahad into a fighting unit was Charles N. Hunter.

Hunter had been serving as a weapons instructor in the United States Army Infantry School at Fort Benning when he volunteered for 'hazardous duty' of an unspecified nature. By virtue of being the senior officer on the USS *Lurline*, which brought 'Casual Detachment 1688' across the Pacific and the Indian Ocean to Bombay, he became unofficially the unit's first commandant, and he wasted no time in organising it in three battalions and appointing officers to command them. It was he who trained it, for no one was better qualified. It was not for nothing that he had been a weapons instructor, and Galahad's musketry was to prove formidable. He was to be the effective commander in the field from its first clash with the enemy until the bitter end in August 1944, when disease, wounds and death had claimed all but a handful of the original Galahads. By his own confession he was the least inspiring of men, but soldiers respect and trust above all a leader who knows his own mind and understands their craft.

Colonel Hunter has painted, perhaps unconsciously, a candid portrait of himself in his memoir of Galahad. He represented a type common in the American, German and Japanese armies but at that time rare or non-existent in the British: the complete professional soldier, tough, capable, a little narrow-minded perhaps, authoritarian, and completely bound by the doctrine and the regulations laid down by the United States Army for the guidance of its officers. Characteristically, he began his book with a lengthy quotation from the Field Service Regulations. Those were the days before the military self-confidence of the United States had been dented by Vietnam, and he believed, as a loyal American soldier should, that his country was the source of everything that was good, that the army of the United States was the best in the world, that the infantry was the queen of the battlefield, and therefore, *a fortiori*, that the United States infantry was the perfect example of a combat arm.

These qualities were softened by education (not many regular American officers could quote Montaigne), humanity and a dry sense of humour. A strict disciplinarian, he would never have tolerated the brutal and illegal punishments inflicted on erring British Chindits. He was indignant when officers or men were publicly scolded or 'blown up' in the old style. He flatly refused to follow Wingate's instructions to 'debray' his mules, by cutting their vocal chords, maintaining that the 'only pleasure a jack-ass ever had was in braying'. Unromantic, he could laugh at himself. Later at Myitkyina, when he was riding up and down on his pony ordering the ranks of a Chinese battalion before an attack, he suddenly asked himself (he recalled): 'Is this "Chuck" Hunter, of Oneida, N.Y. or General "Chinese" Gordon?' By nature Hunter was a perfectionist, but in training his men he did his best in the short time available, complaining between his teeth that not enough attention was being given in the schedules to discipline, or to the 'checking, marking and issue of equipment', as per regulations.

He was not an easy man. What was in the regulations was what had to be done. When he indicts Stilwell it is not for his admitted oddities of behaviour but because he departed from regulations: 'There was the army's way, and Stilwell's way,' he comments grimly. When at different times the general commanding the supporting artillery or the Inspector-General of Infantry demanded his presence at headquarters, he mentally thumbed the regulations and informed them that as he, Colonel Hunter, was in command and engaged in combat they must come forward and see him, if they so desired. In the end it was Hunter alone, unsupported by Merrill, who faced up to Stilwell and told him that he had mishandled Galahad. But West Point had left its stamp on Hunter, as it had on his commanding general, and 'Duty, Honour, Country' came first with him too. For him the supreme military virtue was to obey orders, and he commanded, deputised or cooperated as the situation demanded without grumbling or, in the British phrase, 'belly-aching'.

Stilwell, who disliked Hunter and treated him badly, retained him as second-in-command to advise Merrill, rather in the manner of a member of the old German general staff, whose business it was to guide the footsteps of a crown prince or grand duke in the days when the nominal high command was reserved for blood and birth. Merrill was a member of Stilwell's 'family', not by kinship but by the other great password to Stilwell's favour; membership of the group he led out on foot from Burma. At that time he had been a major, acting as United States liaison officer with the British forces. Merrill was a cavalry officer who had been shunted off on the branch line of language studies, in his case Japanese, and while he had some merits as a soldier he sadly lacked knowledge and experience. He had no experience of active operations except as a spectator, and knew little or nothing of the work of infantry. All agree that he was kind, popular, courageous, unsparing of himself and calm in action. He seems to have had too much good sense to exert his authority over his far abler deputy, but unfortunately these qualities were negated by his lack of firmness in command and his subservience to his patron. But that was a weakness of all of Stilwell's staff. He also had a weak heart, which Stilwell knew well, for Merrill had collapsed and nearly died on the march out. He was quite unfitted to lead a ranger-type unit in tropical jungles or stand up to the strain of command. Nevertheless, he was to play his part bravely enough, and to Galahad the arrival of the genial Merrill seemed propitious, coinciding as it did with a flow of much-needed equipment and generous American rations instead of the inedible British variety.

On January 27th Galahad left its training camp and ten days later it arrived at Margharita, the railhead. From there Hunter decided to move by route march and not by truck, to give the battalions a final hardening and the 'mule skinners' a chance to accustom themselves to their recently arrived changes.

For the moment, therefore, all was set fair. The men having completed their long march felt uplifted by a sense of achievement. Stilwell met the senior officers and gave them a short and soldierly address of welcome. There was a new spirit among the Chinese troops, he said, and now that Galahad was here the campaign could start rolling. His orders were verbal, brief and in the Stilwell style. Beginning formally, he broke off, and taking Merrill aside, gave him a broad instruction to attempt a wide encircling movement to the east and cut in behind the Japanese east flank to block their line of retreat. He included a vague instruction that Merrill was not to become too involved – meaning, presumably, that if the Chinese dragged their feet as usual he was not to take on Tanaka single-handed. But his precise intentions were never confirmed in written orders, to Hunter's disgust. He simply said: 'Oh hell, Frank, let's settle this together. You know what I want, so go and get it for me', or something to that effect. Frank did know and Galahad did get it for him.[1]

The salient features of the country over which Stilwell had to advance were, first, the Hukawng Valley, into which drains a whole system of rivers, all tributaries of the mighty Tanai, which flows north-west in a series of loops until it meets the wall of the Paktai

Bum* in the north, where it changes its name to the Chindwin and turns south. These Chinese forward troops were as far south as Tapai Ga, where the rough track, which was all the valley boasted in the way of a through road, crossed the Tanai. Some twenty miles further south the road crossed first the Nambyu River and four miles on the Numpyek, where there was a little village. That was Merrill's objective. If Galahad could make a secret flanking march through the jungles to the east of the valley, which meant crossing twelve sizeable rivers, including the Chindwin-Tanai, it offered an ideal blocking position to trap the Japanese while the Chinese infantry and American-led Chinese-manned tanks attacked down the road towards Maingkwan. That was to be the first phase, and Galahad's first battle-honour was to have the ungainly name of 'Walawbum', the name of the village.

The next phase was to capture the Jambu Bum, the watershed between the Hukawng and the Mogaung Valleys. Tanaka's forward depots were in Kamaing, on which Stilwell had his eye, and what he intended was to repeat his right-handed punch with the Chinese and his left hook with Galahad as opportunity arose. The eastern wall of the valley became higher and more difficult towards the south, but he noted that the Tanai gorge might offer a covered flanking approach usable by a specially trained force like Galahad. From then on Stilwell left his options open. If Kamaing fell, then the way to Myitkyina was open. If his operations bogged down in the monsoon rain, he would be contented with a lodgment in the Mogaung Valley.

The Japanese defences consisted of no more than four battalions spread out astride of the road leading south from Maingkwan, with a string of small isolated posts extended to the flanks. Tanaka had far too few forces to hold anything resembling a continuous line. He had to rely on patrols to cover the gaps, and on Japanese dash and aggressiveness to throw back the Chinese by counter-attacking the attackers. Against this weak force of some six equivalent infantry battalions supported by a few light guns, Stilwell could bring to bear eighteen Chinese battalions with artillery and tanks, and Galahad.

Putting Galahad in the right place was the crux, and it depended on locating Tanaka's most extreme right-hand or easterly position so as to sneak round it without detection. It so happened that there was already operating in this area a clandestine force of Kachin tribesmen led by American officers of the OSS (the Office of Strategic Services,

* Burmese place names are not spelt phonetically, and are difficult to pronounce. *Bum*, pronounced 'boom', indicates any mountain, ridge or elevated ground. *Ga* means a village. *Ky* is pronounced *ch* as in cheese: hence *Myitkyina* is '*Mitchinar*', and Nphum Ga is '*Noom Ga*' (see page 96). Long names, e.g. *Hsamshingyang* are easy if split up into syllables, i.e. 'Sam-shing-yang'.

the American equivalent of the British Special Operations Executive), whose mission it was to provide exact information about the Japanese dispositions, but through some inexplicable neglect this information was not passed to Merrill. For Stilwell to give Merrill his mission and the briefest of instructions was perfectly appropriate in the circumstances, but he also left him in the dark about the Japanese dispositions. However, Merrill made a good plan for his preliminary move. He saw from the map that there was a possible route swinging wide round the Japanese right flank, and he started along it with his main body and his own headquarters, while sending a reconnaissance platoon from each battalion to scout ahead, locate the Japanese and choose a forward assembly area. The 1st Battalion's platoon was to follow the trail until it reached the east bank of the Tanai River. The 2nd and 3rd were to follow in the tracks of the 1st, but to wheel west at predetermined points and probe for the Japanese right flank.

The reconnaissance platoons were the élite of the Chindits and Galahad, and they needed to be. Without the frills, reconnaissance boils down to approaching a concealed and alert enemy in the hope at best of seeing him first or at worst of enticing him to betray his position by presenting a target; the first information of his presence being shots fired at the leading scouts, or 'point'. It is a nerve-racking business in any conditions. In the silence of the jungle, where a foot carelessly placed on a dry teak-leaf can sound like a pistol shot, where the field of view may be no more than five yards, and where a burst of fire can be expected as the patrol rounds every bend in the trail, it is an excruciating test of the nerve of the bravest men. When contact is made the patrol commander is faced with a difficult decision as he goes to ground. Should he now disengage and report, when perhaps all he has bumped is another patrol as overstrung as his own? Or should he attempt to discover the enemy's strength by drawing his fire, and so risk losing men and becoming pinned down?

The commander of the leading reconnaissance platoon was Lieutenant Sam Wilson, a former junior instructor at Benning, who had thrown up his job and also the prospect of joining OSS in favour of accompanying his chief, Hunter, in the 'hazardous mission' that turned out to be Galahad. After many hours' marching Wilson heard bursts of firing behind him, first one and then another; doubtless both the other platoons had bumped the enemy, unless – disagreeable thought! – Japanese patrols had cut in behind on the trail to ambush them. Wilson pushed on and by the evening of his second day's march, on February 25th, had covered thirty miles and was about where he had hoped to be. Away to the north-west he could hear occasional artillery fire marking the line of contact between Tanaka and the Chinese, and he found a jungle hamlet with signs of digging and Japanese occupation, but empty. This, he judged, was a suitable assembly area for Galahad and well behind the Japanese.

Now to send back the news! The long-range Signal Corps type 284 radio was off-saddled from its mule, the aerial erected and the generator cranked, but the evening is always the worst time for static, and as the darkness fell the devilish Burmese variety blotted out every transmission. A despatch rider would have to be sent back, and Wilson on reflection decided that the information was too important to be trusted to anyone but himself. It so happened that Wilson was something of a horseman and also something of a horse-coper. When the herd of untrained mules and ponies was thrust on Galahad in India he had noted in it a black pony with a touch of blood and breeding and had annexed it for his own. Putting his platoon into defensive positions and handing over command to his sergeant, he ordered a mounted private to accompany him and set off back along the trail like Paul Revere himself.

The jungle was fairly open and fortunately there was a good moon, and all went well until Wilson, going at a canter, reached a broad sandy stream bed with an open glade on the far side. The jungle can be an alarming place even to the uninitiated, and though the great felines are amongst the least of its admitted dangers, Wilson cannot be blamed for his terror at what he saw, and heard: two leopards or tigers fighting or, more probably, mating. His póny shared his fear, rearing violently, the girth slipped and Wilson found himself and his saddle underneath the plunging beast with one foot caught in a stirrup. He struggled free and did the sensible thing, yelling at the top of his voice (the risk of attracting Japanese attention quite forgotten) and firing a shot in the air. The disgusted cats decamped in search of some quieter glade uninfested by humans, and Wilson remounted to resume his headlong ride. He found Merrill and his headquarters some eight miles up the trail, and gave his estimate of the situation. Grissom and Weston, of the 2nd and 3rd Battalions had, as he had guessed, hit the Japanese. Weston had been nearly taken in by a favourite Japanese ruse – that of pretending to be Chinese – but he had shot his way out of the trap. (Logan Weston was the catechumen who had postponed taking holy orders so as to fight the Japanese, to be labelled, regrettably, by journalists as the 'fightin' preacher'). After a short rest, Wilson rode back to his platoon, all in one day; a tribute to the fitness of horse and rider.

Merrill wasted no time in setting off with the main body. Five days later he had crossed two large rivers, received that essential preliminary for a Chindit-type operation, a supply drop, made contact with the enemy, brushed him aside, and prepared Galahad, now blooded, for its first battle.

South of Maingmaw the road turns sharply to the east, crosses the Nambyu at the village of Kumyen Ga and, cutting off the triangle between the Nambyu and Nyumpyek Rivers, hits the west bank of the Numpyek and resumes its southerly course. This stretch was commanded by a low rise on the east bank, on which stood Walawbum village. The battlefield was not a true jungle area, but there was a great deal of vegetation, denser along the river banks, with open patches of rice paddy and '*lalang*' grass higher than a man.

Merrill, obeying a modification to his original plan by Stilwell's headquarters, spread his force rather wide. He was told to block the road east of the river at Kumnyen Ga with one battalion, three miles from his main position, which was on the rise overlooking Walawbum. McGee's 2nd Battalion was sent to the forward position, the 3rd, Beach's, to cover Walawbum from the east bank. The 1st, Osborne's, remained as force reserve, to guard the drop zone and light aircraft strip and post a screen of pickets to the north in case any of the Japanese came down on his right flank. The Chinese 113th Regiment of 38th Division were to move on the eastern flank and link up with Galahad, while the Chinese tanks moving inside them also closed up on Galahad's blocking position from the north, and the 22nd Division advanced down the road towards McGee on a broad front. It all

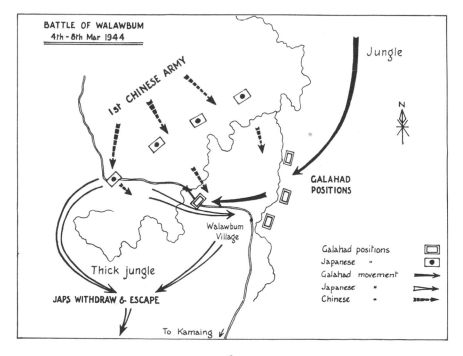

BATTLE OF WALAWBUM
4th - 8th Mar 1944

Jungle

1st CHINESE ARMY

N

GALAHAD
POSITIONS

Walawbum
Village

Thick jungle

Galahad positions
Japanese "
Galahad movement
Japanese "
Chinese "

JAPS WITHDRAW & ESCAPE

To Kamaing

looked pretty in coloured chinagraph pencil on a map, as plans always do until the enemy takes a hand.

Tanaka, reassured by the snail-like advance of the Chinese and made aware by the preliminary skirmishing that Merrill was round his flank, guessed what Stilwell was up to. Being the man he was, he estimated that it would be safe to hold off the Chinese with the minimum of his force while he turned the rest round to savage Galahad. A confused battle followed, a 'soldier's battle' if there ever was one, in which Galahad hung on unsupported and savaged Tanaka. Like all the fighting in jungle, it was a mosaic of isolated platoon and company battles fought at close range and amid great confusion, without any clear idea on either side where anyone was. Beach, reconnoitring his position, ran face to face with a Japanese, who was shot dead by his orderly. Colonel Brown chose a line of advance for his tanks which coincided with the line of withdrawal of a Japanese unit, and led to some interesting situations and a night of close-range skirmishing. The rendez-vous with Brown being so important, Hunter himself with a protective patrol went out to find him, and ran into the Japanese.

The main weight of the attack fell first on the isolated McGee, who took a heavy toll of his assailants, but then, running out of ammunition and unable to be resupplied, he abandoned his block and fell back to the main position. He had held on for thirty-six hours.

A remarkable little action was also fought by Weston, whom Beach had placed on the far side of the Numpyek stream and who was pinned against its bank by a Japanese company. He formed a close perimeter, while one of his *Nisei* Japanese, Henry Gosho, listened for shouted orders and translated them so that Weston could run from side to side countering each move with fire. Under cover of the battalion's 81 mm mortars, worked by a much-admired expert and Pacific veteran, Lieutenant Woomer, known to the troops as 'Woomer the Boomer', Weston crossed to the safe bank. In the lay back party he sent ahead there to cover him was a Sioux chieftain and marksman, Norman Janis. When he saw the snout of the first Japanese machine-gun poking out of the bushes on the far bank, he killed the crew, and six more men later, while the rest of the party accounted for two more machine-guns and their crews. Weston was able to withdraw intact with all his wounded.

It was Beach's battalion that finally halted the Japanese advance. The simple tactical fact was that Galahad could shoot fast and straight, and the terrifying Japanese assault, delivered with suicidal bravery and accompanied by blood-curdling screams of *banzai*, made no impression on the Americans. The devotion of the officer commanding Beach's mule train, who kept him supplied with ammunition from the drop zone, ensured the defeat of the attack. The 56th Regiment left 400 bodies in front of Walawbum, seen and counted later.

It was a notable success, but Stilwell was unable to snap the jaws of his trap together. This was only partly due to the Chinese dragging their feet. At the crisis of the battle, when his grip was needed most to exploit the situation presented to him by Galahad, his staff completely failed him. Stilwell believed that Merrill had redeployed with a view to putting another block on the road further south, whereas in fact, acting on some hint or piece of advice he understood Stilwell had given him, he had pulled the whole of Galahad out of the fight. Merrill perhaps felt as the British Chindits did, that his unit was not designed for a prolonged dog-fight, and he knew that there was no means by which his casualties could be replaced. He therefore interpreted his brief from Stilwell as imposing caution. Radio-communications to him failed, and no effort was made by Stilwell's staff to restore them, or to re-establish contact by other means. The painful truth is that the staff work of Stilwell's headquarters, as its lamentable performance throughout the campaign was to show, was inept. This is all the more surprising as the United States Army staff as a whole is second to none in efficiency, and its officers had done wonders at Ramgarh. Yet once in the field they displayed, as at Walawbum, their proneness to commit the most elementary blunders. They had the vicious habit of planning from a map without looking at the actual terrain, they failed to circulate information, to ensure lateral liaison between units, to issue confirmatory written orders after verbal orders, to visit troops in the field or to keep the 'boss' informed.

Stilwell's headquarters in the field was a mere ten miles from Walawbum, and his staff had no excuse for not restoring radio-communication to Merrill the instant it faltered. Failing that, it was open to any staff officer to jump into a light plane and obtain the information personally. There was no lack of talent. Stilwell's son and son-in-law, both occupied key positions on the staff and although their appointment was regarded by some as indiscreet at the time, both were able men who rose to general officer's rank by their own merits. The trouble probably came from the top. A staff surely reflects its master's foibles, and all knew Stilwell's – his capricious favour-itism, his aversion from any clear-cut line of responsibility, his dislike of paper work or precision of any kind, his secretiveness. Stilwell seems seldom to have disclosed his hopes and intentions, even to his deputy and chief-of-staff General Boatner, whose duty it was to make the staff machine work, but who was too often detached for special missions.

Stilwell's own attitude to visiting was curiously ambivalent. He was famous for his personal prodding of the Chinese commanders in the front line, but he seldom visited his Americans and never the hated 'Limeys' when the Chindits came under his command. His tolerance of the flaccid handling of the Walawbum operation by his favourite Merrill is significant compared with his vitriolic denunciation of the Chindits in similar circumstances. As it turned out, these lapses made little difference to the final outcome of the battle. Tanaka was not to be trapped on the Kamaing road. With great foresight his chief engineer had cut a path through the forests lying to the west and joining the road much further down. He could see the Chinese coming down on top of him in strength, he had lost control of the Walawbum River triangle, and he had been badly mauled by Galahad. He deemed it the moment to slip away by his secret route.

Stilwell started to think about his next move, to the line of the Jambu Bum. Two plans were put forward. Stilwell's staff were in favour of a short hook to make sure of seizing the pass and to give the best chance of a quick link-up with the main force of Chinese. Merrill, sending Hunter, whose plan it probably was, to argue the case, was in favour of a deep thrust aimed at cutting the road between Shaduzup and Kamaing, using the whole of Galahad and a Chinese regiment, the 113th; more force than Tanaka had available to hold the front and counter any flanking, blocking move. This was a good plan and observed the principles of concentration and unity of command. A suitable route led round Tanaka's eastern flank through the dense jungle of the Kumon Bum, along the crest of the ridge which formed the western or left wall of the gorge through which flowed the north-bound Tanai River, to emerge in the Mogaung Valley a few miles north of Kamaing, the site of Tanaka's forward depots.

The final plan was an unfortunate compromise between the two, weak in each area of decision. One task force consisting of Osborne's 1st Battalion in the lead followed by the 113th was to carry out the short hook. Hunter, commanding another task force of the two Galahad battalions, was to follow the Tanai route, aiming to cut the road near Inkangahtawng. The men of Galahad were now at the top of their form, and although like all other soldiers they had not enjoyed being shelled or the sight of dead or, infinitely more unnerving, hideously wounded men, the raw troops had learnt that fear is controllable. Better, they had killed some 800 Japanese for the loss of eight killed and thirty-seven wounded, and proved that man to man Americans could thrash this dreaded enemy. The battalion commanders had proved themselves in combat and the natural leaders had begun to appear in the ranks. The soft stuff was being etched out: the Americans in their frank way recorded ten evacuated, who for psychiatric reasons had broken down in combat. More ominous, however, was a figure of 136 evacuated sick – nineteen with malaria – and it was still the dry season. All the same, Galahad was 2,300 strong. It had three good battalions of some 700 men each, fed, rested, and ready to strike again.

The inner hook went well. Osborne ran into a skilfully handled Japanese screen, but equally skilfully managed to disengage. A bitter little action took place, in which the intrepid Sam Wilson, taking over from a badly shaken rearguard commander, held things together, going forward with a radio to bring down covering fire from the invaluable 81 mm mortars. He broke away in his turn, bringing back all the wounded and a few men 'paralysed with fear'. Osborne then cut his way through the jungle to arrive undetected in the valley, where he brought off a smart coup. His reconnaissance discovered a complete Japanese supply depot and a camp of service corps troops, idling, fishing and washing their clothes, safe, as they believed, and far behind the front. Moving to assembly positions by night, the 1st Battalion attacked at dawn with fire and bayonet, survived the inevitable counter-attacks and were able to hand over in due course to the Chinese 113th Regiment, 'always the last to a fight and the first to a feast', as the saying goes. The line of the Jambu Bum was secured, but the whole Chinese 22nd Division was equally laggard, and once again Tanaka was able to slip away.

There was therefore little love lost between Galahad and the Chinese who, when they did link up, proved incorrigible thieves. Wandering through the Galahad bivouacs they stole anything left unattended, rushing to the area of supply drops intended for other units, running away with everything they could carry, and occasionally threatening anyone who objected with their weapons. They were generally a squalid nuisance. Many were carriers of amoebic dysentry and their habit of defecating wherever they felt inclined did not endear them to the hygiene-conscious Americans. One British officer, when threatened by a Chinese soldier who was looting his supply drop, knocked him down, with excellent results for the future, though for diplomatic reasons Stilwell had ordered complete submission by Americans to Chinese bad behaviour. At his own headquarters a Chinese officer, properly challenged by an American sentry for the pass-word, spat in his face. He, too, was knocked down to teach him manners, but the unfortunate American was imprisoned for striking an officer.

However, on this occasion the 1st Battalion, who had fought thirteen actions on the line of march and the final one to secure the block, viewed the Chinese arrival with pleasure. Osborne gave his men a rest and set off at a leisurely pace to rejoin Galahad. They had not been moving long, however, when Merrill signalled to them to step out. The rest of Galahad was in dire straits.

For, in the meantime, Hunter's operation had turned out to be a sequence of mishaps and misunderstandings. He arrived after a gruelling march punctually in the Mogaung Valley on March 24th. McGee had successfully crossed the Mogaung River, blocked the road and was fighting to evict a small Japanese post from Inkangahtawng village. Hunter was developing his operation undeterred by the news that Osborne's arrival at Shaduzup was delayed, when information reached Merrill of a strong Japanese force arriving from the south. Its strength was exaggerated and so, possibly, were its intentions, which on the basis of a captured map were deduced to be the somewhat ambitious plan to use Hunter's very route following the Tanai gorge to execute his manoeuvre in reverse and surprise and evict the Chinese forces from Shaduzup. The unwisdom of splitting the blocking force was not apparent. With Osborne and the 113th delayed, the Japanese could concentrate on Hunter, but if Hunter was withdrawn out of contact then, when Osborne finally did reach his block, the Japanese could concentrate on him. Hunter, always aggressive, was prepared to stay where he was and even raid Kamaing which he believed to be undefended, but Merrill, to Hunter's disappointment, vetoed this as too rash. Stilwell's staff, over-anxious at the prospect of a counter-attack, ordered Merrill to withdraw and establish a road-block on the line of the Japanese advance. Merrill's orders, whose issue was hampered by communications difficulties, succeeded only in throwing Hunter's task force into disarray. McGee received parts of the message direct instead of *via* Hunter, and obeyed immediately. The first intimation an angry Hunter received of this was when he flew over to McGee's position to find out how he was getting on, only to see below him McGee's battalion carrying its wounded and trekking back in the opposite direction from the enemy. Not pleased, Hunter had now to alter all his well laid plans, abandon his positions and his new airstrip, and evacuate his wounded while arranging that most difficult of exercises, a formal withdrawal in the face of the enemy, with troops who had never practised it. Merrill's broad instructions to Hunter were to go back up his original route and establish a defensive position at Auche with one battalion and place another some miles to the north at Hsamshingyang, where an open valley offered the site for a drop zone and light plane strip.

Hunter, at last in touch with the OSS Kachin detachment, obtained a fix on the reported Japanese force and turned a flight of Mustang fighter bombers on to it. He then gave the necessary orders for units to take a last supply drop, and for Beach and his 3rd Battalion to go through to Hsamshingyang and McGee to Auche. Finally, he posted rear-guards and, in the best tradition, waited personally until the last man was clear. Then he set off on foot to march through the columns to Hsamshingyang where he hoped to meet Merrill, muttering his disapproval to himself at such unprofessional muddling and vacillation. Galahad was now to come face to face with the true visage of war, contorted and horrible.

The Japanese force which had been estimated at three battalions was in fact only part of Tanaka's reserve regiment, the 114th, under Colonel Fusayusa Maruyama. It was a hard-worked, much-travelled unit based on Myitkyina, one of whose battalions had already become involved with the Chindits far in the south and had received a bloody nose at Calvert's stronghold, while the other had detachments out in the upper Irrawaddy Valley sparring with the Fort Herz garrison. Tanaka's units were now all at about half strength, or less. Maruyama had with him only his headquarters and 700 infantry and as many clerks and supply service men as he could scrape up, formed into two weak battalions, with four light guns. Later he was reinforced by some infantry from the 56th Regiment, withdrawing from Walawbum.

Maruyama, though shaken by the attack by the P-51s who had caught them fairly in the open on the trail to Auche, plodded on to meet the Galahad rearguards on the uphill trail through the jungle. They consisted of Logan Weston and his reconnaissance platoon and a rifle platoon commanded by a Lieutenant Smith. This doughty pair, with some eighty men, proceeded with consummate skill to set a series of ambushes, shooting up the heads of Maruyama's column and then breaking neatly away to repeat the process. When they finally disengaged they had not lost a single man, had inflicted sixty casualties, and had reduced Maruyama's pursuit to an anxious, snail-like crawl up the track. This was just as well, because McGee's 2nd Battalion had suddenly lost its nerve.

Morale is a fragile commodity and nothing is more important in its creation than a successful first battle. McGee's men had now fought in two actions, each initially successful, but in each they had been suddenly ordered to withdraw in the face of some unspecified threat whose magnitude grew as rumours spread through the ranks. McGee himself, as his record was to show, was full of courage, but his sense of urgency sowed the seeds of panic. He marched back as far and as fast as he could, with no pause for rest, forcing the men, long without food, to eat their 'K' rations out of the packets on the move. Hunter noted with disapproval, as his steady stride took him past the battalion in its long single-file column, that there was no rear party guarding the tail. The non-commissioned officers were losing their grip, and as the faster men had begun to overtake the slower the squads and platoons were losing their coherence. One man was lying exhausted by the trail, pleading that he couldn't go on. Hunter, unsympathetically, said that in that case 'you're going to be awfully lonesome, soldier', got him on his feet, encouraged him until he had caught up the battalion, and gave him a cigarette.

It was McGee's misfortune that the trail was practically straight and his battalion presented a perfect enfilade target. The Japanese 75 mm gun was a high-velocity weapon whose shell had a nasty habit of arriving without a warning bang or whistle, and Marayuma's battery commander dropped one into action and started to rake the trail firing blind. Some lucky shots fell on the now disorganised column. Only a few men appear to have been wounded, but this was the last straw. The battalion bolted, and nothing McGee could do would stop it. A long, over-extended single file is, in any case, the worst formation over which to exercise any kind of leadership, and the best suited for the transmission of panic as the men behind start to shout and curse and urge those in front to press on. The weaker brethren threw away their weapons and packs, so as to march faster. Some fugitives pushed on until they ran into Galahad headquarters.

Hunter, whose rapid stride had taken him well past McGee's column, had rejoined Merrill in the tiny forest village of Nphum Ga* and was shaved and washed when the leaders of the rout arrived, hysterical and crying that all was lost. Merrill and the staff immediately moved out to stop the battalion and restore some kind of order until McGee with the harder core of the battalion caught up with the fugitives. Merrill ordered McGee to go back to Auche, but that was now out of the question. At Nphum Ga the ridge above the Tanai spreads out into a cirque, whose rim provided good defensive positions, while the bowl below it, where the village stood, gave cover for the signal section, headquarters and mules, and there was also a precious spring of clear water. McGee set up a tiny perimeter, 400 by 200 yards, and ordered everyone to dig in as fast as they could. The 'psychoneurotic' cases, as the Americans called them, were also told to dig, and then, if they couldn't fight, to go away and hide. Some of them recovered under this treatment, and rejoined their comrades. Maruyama caught up with McGee on March 27th and spent that day and the next feeling out his position. By the 29th he had stealthily moved all round it, and McGee was cut off. The siege of Nphum Ga had begun.

What honour the men of the 2nd Battalion had lost they speedily regained in their successful eleven-day defence of this obscure Kachin hamlet. The Japanese fought with their usual ferocity and less than
* Pronounced 'Noom Ga'.

A patrol of Lancashire Fusiliers in the dense, forbidding Japanese-haunted jungle.

Major-General Orde C. Wingate, who founded and led the Chindit Long Range Penetration Groups.

General Joseph W. Stilwell, Commander in the field of the First New Chinese Army.

Major-General G. W. Symes, Deputy-Commander, Special Force.

Major-General W. D. A. Lentaigne, who assumed command of the Chindits after Wingate's death.

Brigadier B. E. Fergusson, Commander, 16th Brigade.

Brigadier Michael Calvert, Commander, 77th Brigade.

Lt-Col. John Masters, Commander, 111th Brigade, after Lentaigne.

Brigadier Abdy Ricketts, Commander, 3rd West African Brigade, after Brigadier Gillmore.

An L5 aeroplane attracts some native admirers on the Naman Strip and, *right*, a pilot just before take-off.

Above, Piccadilly is blocked! Colonel Alison and Lt-Col. Scott hold the air-photo while to their left an RAF officer, Calvert, Wingate and Tulloch take their first look at the bad tidings.

Below, All smiles at Broadway – after the safe arrival of 77th Brigade, (*l-r*) Alison, Calvert, Wingate's ADC, Wingate and Scott.

A Kachin girl accepts a piece of chewing-gum from Galahad Private Wayne C. Martin, US Army.

An aerial view of the terrain around the Mawhun Railway Bridge.

George Allen, RAF, attached 50 Column, with the signals detachment near the White City in April 1944 calling for supplies on the powerful radio equipment, capable of communicating with the base in India.

Four days' rations for a Chindit: biscuits, cheese, meat or 'spam', sugar, salt, chocolate, tea, matches, powdered milk and cigarettes.

Birthday celebrations behind the Japanese lines: RSM Hemmings, 2nd York and Lancaster, presents his CO, Lt-Col. Graves-Morris with a prized bottle of beer.

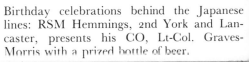

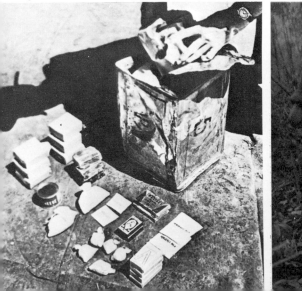

their usual finesse. Maruyama did try at first to contain McGee and push on past him downhill to Hsamshingyang, where he could have paralysed Merrill's base and light aircraft strip, but did not persevere, either because he did not feel strong enough or because his troops lacked battle-craft. He decided to settle the issue by continual pressure and a series of headlong assaults in traditional style on McGee's perimeter which, the more it contracted, the more it concentrated its fire-power.

It is impossible not to admire the Japanese soldiers. Hardy and frugal as they were, they were no more immune to continual privation and disease than their American opponents. As has been well said:

At this time the spirit and morale of the Japanese forces had reached a very low ebb. Their uniforms were so tattered and worn that many were nearly naked, a great number had no shoes, all were suffering from malaria and beri-beri, and most were affected with varous skin diseases. Their daily ration consisted of a handful of rice. Most of the sick could not be treated because of the scarcity of medical supplies, and there were no trucks available to transport the wounded. The average strength of infantry companies dwindled to fewer than thirty men. One company consisted of ten men commanded by a sergeant.[2]

Ammunition was scarce. Tanaka's forward holdings were a bare 150 rounds per weapon of all kinds, and to supply his troops he had only a few trucks and some local animal transport. Any supplies or munitions reaching him had to traverse the rough road from Lasio to Bhamo or be shipped up the Irrawaddy and from then on run the gauntlet of the Chindit raiders on the Bhamo-Myitkyina road, be ferried over across the Irrawaddy and hauled another fifty miles along bad roads from Mogaung to Kamaing. The supply convoys and formed bodies of troops could only move safely by night, as the American Tenth Air Force hunted them remorselessly by day, and once they concentrated to fight, as at Nphum Ga, they were subjected to the accurate fire-power of bomb and machine-gun from the P-51s to within a hundred yards of the perimeter; indeed, the Japanese were only safe from this terrible battering when they were locked in close combat with Galahad.

The result was some close-quarter fighting of the bloodiest and most primitive kind. No quarter was asked or given. A few Galahads whose nerve had broken – something that happens in the best regiments – died under Japanese bayonets crouching numb with fear at the bottom of their fox-holes. The saintly Logan Weston, fighting his way into the position with the relief force, kicked aside a piece of sacking to find two young Japanese soldiers in the same plight underneath it, and shot them both out of hand. So close were the two lines that one Japanese, missing his way in the dark, eased himself into an American fox-hole under the impression it was his own, and was killed by the occupant. The only safe place for a man to relieve himself was in his fox-hole; one American who rashly left his in the dark for the purpose was shot dead by his comrades coming back. McGee had a crawl-trench dug so that he could go the rounds of his forward platoons in safety.

Such indeed was the proximity that the *Nisei* Japanese could hear the Japanese officers giving their orders for yet another attack. On one occasion this made an elaborate ruse possible. McGee drew back from the threatened sector, stiffened the new line with machine-guns, and booby-trapped the empty fox-holes that his platoons had pulled out of. The attackers, bewildered by the unexpected sight of the abandoned objective, hesitated for a moment and were cut down by fire from the new, undetected positions. So they tumbled into the empty fox-holes, with unpleasant results. Then they heard a Japanese voice, in fact that of Galahad Sergeant Roy Matsumoto, calling for another charge, and once more in their fanatical way jumped out and responded. Fifty-four bodies were counted after McGee restored his line. What he could not do was to recapture his vital water-point, overrun by Maruyama at an early stage and grimly held as his only hope of success. By the end of the siege thirst was acute, there was no water to make plaster casts for the wounded, sulpha drugs were swallowed dry and those mules not killed by fire had died from lack of water. The 2nd Battalion was saved by the water containers dropped to them by the air force; indeed the whole defence was only made possible by the accurate dropping of supplies and ammunition into the tiny perimeter. The loads that missed the target helped to sustain the besiegers, so close were the opposing lines.

While McGee fought on, his wounded emulated the Japanese by going back to the firing line after treatment if they could walk and handle a weapon. Hunter, as usual in operational command, directed Beach to fight his way up the hill from Hsamshingyang against the Japanese stops to the north of Nphum Ga. He eagerly awaited the arrival of Osborne and the 800 badly-needed men of the 1st Battalion, who were scrambling desperately towards him across the grain of the ridges on the direct route from Shaduzup. Hunter was also promised a Chinese battalion, but 'one day two capable looking Chinese sergeants appeared, stayed a while and disappeared up the track to the north, but nothing happened'.

What did arrive at Hsamshingyang, carefully crated, and dropped by parachute, was something more valuable than any problematical

Chinese: two little United States 75 mm M 116 pack howitzers, in pieces, complete with a book of instructions. This was Merrill's last useful service to Galahad. On March 28th Hunter, who had gone up to Nphum Ga to look over McGee's dispositions, came back down the Hsamshingyang track to find Merrill prostrate and unconscious. His heart had not proved as strong as his spirit, and there was nothing to be done except fly him out. From then on Hunter assumed the full responsibility for the command of Galahad. Merrill had seen at first hand how bad for morale it was for troops to fight an enemy with artillery without support from their own, and while in hospital had put in an urgent demand for the guns. What the Chindits would have done with such a gift is an open question, but the chances are that the British infantry, with their strong caste rules, would have refused to have anything to do with so technical a weapon as an indirect-fire gun and demanded gunners from the Royal Artillery to come to handle them. Not so that dedicated infantryman Charles N. Hunter. Two crews were rapidly formed, he signalled McGee to find an ex-artilleryman to act as observer in the perimeter, and having assembled his cannon according to the instruction book, remembering to fill the buffer system with oil, he tried firing them with a twenty-five foot length of improvised lanyard from cover, in case either of these dangerous weapons blew up in unaccustomed infantry hands. Having proved them, Hunter decided to shoot in for a base point, and called up the pilot of a passing P-51 to oblige as an air observer.* There was a little initial misunderstanding among the gun-layers over the difference between a 'sensing', i.e. how wide the shell burst was from the target, and a correctional order, which caused them to put everything on the sights backwards. But this was soon ironed out and when Hunter, acting as gun position officer, had dropped a round, fortunately without harm, in the centre of McGee's perimeter, the battery was ready for action. From then on, as Hunter said proudly, the Galahads had a 'crack artillery unit'. In a day or two, he abandoned scientific gunnery for more primitive siege methods and moved the guns up the trail to fire point-blank with great effect at the Japanese bunkers blocking the route to Nphum Ga.

Frequently during the prolonged fighting around Kohima and Imphal distant observers, who ought to have known better, looked at their maps and measured distances and peevishly enquired why it took so long to move a mile down the road to Imphal, or 800 yards to an objective on a crest. They had never fought in tropical jungle against the Japanese or even walked in it. A weary column could

---

* A demonstration of the versatility of the USAAF of those days. The RAF would have demanded a week's notice, and the whole matter would have been referred to the topmost echelon for approval.

often see its bivouac site, or its objective, a mile or so away, to know from hard experience that in such country a mile meant a journey of an hour or more. If the Japanese were in the way, dug into their almost invisible little burrows from which they had to be extracted by grenade or flame, cunningly covered by a criss-cross of narrow arcs of fire so that when the attacker stood triumphant on top of one position he was exposed to the next, it could take days. It was against this sort of defence that Beach's men inched their way upwards towards their beleagured comrades in Nphum Ga. A day's gain of fifty yards was a matter for congratulation. It became a commonplace in the theatre for artillery forward observers working in thick jungle to have to creep up so close to their targets that they were inside the zone of error of their own guns; not seeing the fall of shot but adjusting by ear. Lieutenant Woomer's order in such a situation remains a classic. He was controlling the fire of Beach's mortars and ordered 'Drop 25' (yards), adding, 'If you don't hear from me again, I've overdone it'. The riflemen lying by him would then have had to inch their way forward on their bellies to see if they drew fire, drag up their machine-guns, dig themselves in firmly against counter attack, and then repeat the slow process all over again.

On April 4th Hunter ordered an all-out, concerted effort, which by the 7th had taken the 3rd Battalion to within 500 yards of their final objective. Never one for heroics, but apt to arrive in the forefront of the battle to point out in his critical way some badly sited weapon or the absence of a look-out, he was asked by Beach to address his officers before H-hour. Pausing to collect his thoughts he said: 'We've been attacking up this goddam hill for four days getting two-bitted to death and getting nowhere. Today let's take casualties we have to get the job done. In the end it will cost less. Good luck.'

On April 7th Osborne arrived, his men exhausted and riddled with dysentry and malaria. Hunter selected 250 fit enough to fight and sent one half round to the east to create a diversion, and the other to work round to the west, sit on the track south of the Japanese and cut their supply line. On the 8th they were in position and Beach had closed up. On the 9th, which was Easter Sunday, Beach arranged a recognition signal with McGee to avoid being shot by weary but alert men, and his leading troops stepped gingerly into view of his perimeter. Maruyama had had enough, and leaving his 400 dead rotting and stinking to heaven, he left his camp fires burning and stole away.

The reaction after such a fight, even if victorious, can be intense depression. Hunter, a profound believer in the adage that the devil not only finds work for idle hands but sombre thoughts for them to brood on, briskly set the survivors to work. The battle had cost

McGee fifty-nine killed and 314 wounded, who, together with another sixty-five too ill to recover in the field, were flown out. The dead were buried and the swollen corpses of the 2nd Battalion's mules, mostly killed on their picket lines, burnt. A relief garrison was posted in Nphum Ga and patrols sent out. The men were rested, fed and re-kitted. Then to make sure that they all realised that they were still a unit in the United States Army, Hunter ordered daily close-order parade drill: even the United States Marines would have approved. By way of recreation a mule race meeting was organised complete with bookmakers.

Hunter's own recreation was to consider the next move. Stilwell was to obtain great kudos for the manoeuvre to be known as his 'end run': his secret flank march over the Kumon Bum to seize Myitkyina. Merrill, by then back at Stilwell's headquarters, conveyed the general idea to Hunter, who was not one to sit idle or allow his staff to do so. He set them to working out a plan, consulting his Kachin scouts about routes over the mountain range.[3]

It has been necessary to follow the fortunes of Galahad as far forward as April, because they form a continuous thread from the first clash at Walawbum until Marayuma had recoiled from Nphum Ga. Galahad's success was central to the successful advance of the First Chinese Army, which in turn was central to the whole North Burma enterprise of Stilwell and Wingate. In the meantime, however, Wingate's own great operation, THURSDAY, had begun. Two Chindit brigades had been successfully flown into Burma in the first week in March, two strongholds, or fortified airfields, had been established deep in the jungle, the main railway line supplying Tanaka had been cut, and there had been widespread fighting deep in the Japanese rear. It is now necessary to turn back to the month of March and follow in time the Chindit operations as they developed in March and April.

6

Operation Thursday

D-DAY FOR OPERATION THURSDAY was finally fixed as Sunday, March 5th, as giving the best moon conditions, for all the sorties were to be flown at night, and H-hour as five p.m. Night flying was the course naturally adopted in the hope of evading Japanese aircraft, as the Japanese had no sophisticated early-warning or ground-air control equipment. But had a Japanese bomber ventured over Lalaghat airfield in Assam where the gliders of the No. 1 Air Commando were concentrated on that Sunday it would have found a juicy and vulnerable target. Eighty gliders stood marshalled in pairs in a long file, their nylon tow ropes neatly laid out for attachment and their C-47 tugs standing adjacent. A glance at Hailakandi ten miles to the south or at Tulihal in the Imphal plain might also have revealed unusual activity. All, however, was peace. No Japanese fighters or bombers arrived to disturb the serenity of the afternoon, and the only cover the troops took was from the sun as they sat under the square-tipped wings of their gliders and waited patiently for the orders to emplane.

The Japanese air force had been dealt a staggering blow the day before. To avoid the far superior Allied Eastern Air Command, which combined the forces of the USAAF and the RAF in the theatre, its bulk had been held back in Siam, but it had exposed itself as it deployed forward in preparation to support 'U-Go', the projected onslaught across the Chindwin. Eastern Air Command was working on the Japanese, and on March 4th Cochran flew an offensive reconnaissance in strength to look over Anisakan airfield and caught a large concentration of Japanese aircraft on the ground, destroying twenty-six. Fortune favours the bold. On March 8th, when THURSDAY was in full swing, a P-51 sweep from the Commando was to catch an even larger concentration unalerted on Onbaik and Shwebo airfields, and took a heavy toll. Cochran, back in Assam, was listening to the in-flight radio chatter between the P-51 pilots 300 miles away and ordered twelve B-25s to be bombed up at once to follow up their attack. It was typical of the versatility of the Air Commando pilots that both the commander and deputy commander of the bombers

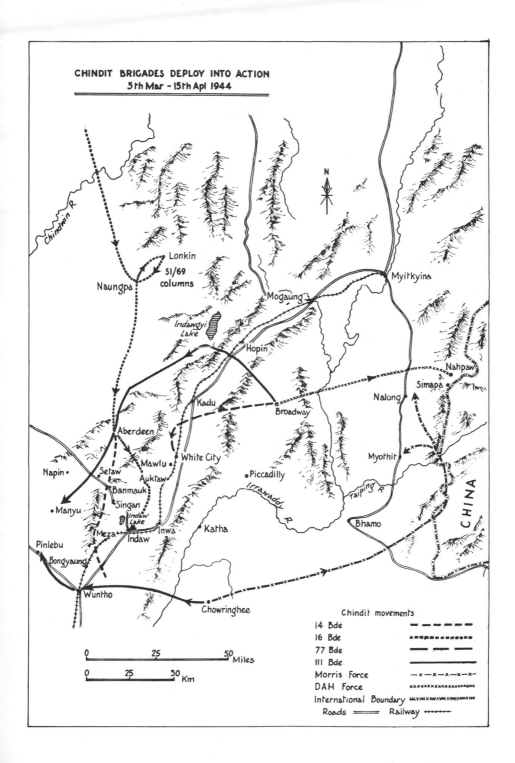

CHINDIT BRIGADES DEPLOY INTO ACTION
5th Mar – 15th Apl 1944

Chindwin R

Lonkin
51/69 columns
Naungpa

Myitkyina

Mogaung

Indawgyi Lake

Hopin

Nahpaw
Simapa
Nalong
Kadu
Broadway

Aberdeen

Myothit
White City
Mawlu
Napin
Setaw
Auktaw
Piccadilly
Banmauk
Irrawaddy R
Taiping R
Singan
Manyu
Indaw Lake
Inwa
Bhamo
Meza
Indaw
Katha
CHINA
Pinlebu
Bongyaung
Wuntho

Chowringhee

0   25   50 Miles

0   25   50 Km

Chindit movements
14 Bde
16 Bde
77 Bde
111 Bde
Morris Force — x — x — x — x —
DAH Force
International Boundary
Roads ══════   Railway ┼┼┼┼┼┼┼

were piloting P-51s in the raid. On their return they changed into their own proper aircraft, 'without pausing for a cup of coffee', and led the B-25s to continue the havoc, to be joined by the Royal Air Force who had been also alerted by Cochran. Over thirty aircraft were destroyed, again on the ground, and many more damaged. Operations were only halted when the dense cloud of smoke from burning aviation fuel blotted out the target.[1]

The full effect of these strokes were not known on D-day, but the progress of the air battle relieved the greatest anxiety gnawing at the minds of the planners of THURSDAY; that the Japanese air force might catch the slow-moving gliders and C-47s in the air or, equally disastrous, on the ground when the troops were deplaning and unloading. There was indeed always the danger of ground action, but the landing zones had been sited in accessible areas, and no one thought it possible that their precise locations could be predicted by Japanese intelligence staff even if they had wind of an airborne operation. This confidence was abruptly shattered at precisely four thirty p.m., half an hour before H-hour. A light plane landed at Lalaghat, and a pilot rushed up to Cochran and thrust a sheaf of photographs of the landing-zones hot from the photo-reconnaissance cell in the Commando. The gliders were destined for three landing zones: Broadway, Piccadilly and Chowringhee. Broadway and Chowringhee were clear, but Piccadilly was blocked, apparently systematically, with tree-trunks.

That this had not been detected before was due to an inexplicable lapse by Special Force Headquarters, but whether through the fault of the staff or of Wingate himself is not known. Wingate was aware that the photo-reconnaissance ability of the Air Commando was limited to the use of hand-held cameras from B-25s, which had to fly low and obviously over a specific target to obtain clear results. He had therefore put a ban on all reconnaissance flights over or near the landing zones from D-day minus seven days. This was an unnecessary precaution and a risky one, because, as his G(Air) staff must have known, or the Royal Air Force could certainly have told him had he asked, the specialist photo-reconnaissance squadrons of the Eastern Air Command flew almost daily sorties over Burma at 15,000–20,000 feet and from this altitude could have maintained a discreet surveillance over the crucial areas without causing the Japanese to smell a rat.[2] The risk was aggravated by Wingate's refusal to use parachute troops in any form. The airborne forces in Europe had, after much experience, developed the use of small 'pathfinder' parties whose rôle was to drop in shortly before the main body of troops was committed in order to carry out a close ground reconnaissance and mark the exact landing zone.[3] In the absence of either parachutists or photography, to launch the leading wave blind was a dangerous gamble and no one saw this more clearly than Cochran.

Cochran's position was an uncertain one. He was virtually responsible to no one but General Arnold, and while his rôle was the exclusive support of Special Force he was not, strictly speaking, under Wingate's command. He was rightly uneasy, but rather than have a dispute he had privately and on his own initiative ordered a B-25 sortie to photograph the landing zones on the morning of D-day. The resulting belated discovery that Piccadilly was blocked, apparently with malice aforethought, was a bombshell, and it exploded in front of a distinguished audience.

Those who had arrived at Lalaghat to see the fly-in launched included the American chief of Eastern Air Command, Lieutenant-General George E. Stratemeyer; Slim, who was Wingate's operational commander in the field; Air Marshal Sir John Baldwin, who together with Slim had issued the operation order for the whole enterprise; and Brigadier-General William D. Old, commanding the joint USAAF-RAF Troop Carrier Command, who was directly responsible for the air side of THURSDAY. Wingate was naturally present, accompanied by Tulloch and Calvert. The awful question posed to this distinguished assembly was, had the Japanese somehow discovered the details of Wingate's plan, and if so, was there a possibility that near the unobstructed landing zones the Japanese were lying in ambush under the cover of the forest?

As it turned out the Japanese were completely surprised by the descent of Special Force that night, and the blocking of Piccadilly was a routine forestry operation – the logs had been laid out to dry after felling in what was a convenient forest glade – but in arriving at the correct course of action everyone concerned was severely tested and each behaved in character.

Wingate exploded into rage before he had taken thought and demanded to know why his orders had been disobeyed. This was followed by another outburst: that the whole operation had been betrayed. Slim, perhaps anxious that the confidence of juniors standing by, some of them American, should not be shaken, took Wingate aside out of earshot, where he calmed him down and focused his mind on the problem. The dangers of carrying on were great, but the damage to the high morale of the waiting troops would be severe if there was a postponement, and D-day had been chosen to give a week of three-quarter to full moon to assist navigation and to miss it would mean a month's delay. To vacillate might ruin the whole prospect of the operation for ever. The answer, Wingate saw, was to divert the sorties scheduled for Piccadilly to Chowringhee, but though his courage was irreproachable, his imagination was also vivid, and the very quality which made him a master of strategem and enabled him often to read his opponent's mind also cursed him with horrible visions of the consequences of a mistake. He was always ready to believe the worst. Quite rightly, he consulted Calvert, whose brigade was the one destined for the post of danger. Calvert was unshaken and unhesitatingly in favour of going in then and there, but he objected to sending half of his brigade into Chowringhee leaving it with the mile-wide Irrawaddy across the route to its objective. He said: 'I am prepared to take the whole of my brigade into Broadway and do without Piccadilly.' According to Calvert, 'Wingate was still not happy', and he and Slim then came and listened to Calvert reiterating his readiness to go on with the operation. Slim 'turned away silently' (and characteristically – he was a remarkably taciturn man!) A few minutes later Slim and Wingate came back again to Calvert and wished him luck. That clinched the matter.

The various accounts of this transaction differ, which is not surprising, as it is a commonplace of historical and legal evidence that perfectly reputable witnesses can give conflicting accounts of the same event. Slim's version caused much resentment among loyal Chindits. Doubtless it reflects his indignation with Wingate, who reminded him sourly, when he announced his decision, that the final responsibility if things went wrong rested upon his, Slim's, shoulders. This was no way to talk to an army commander and yet another example of how Wingate's unbridled tongue could serve him ill. Slim was also annoyed by the effrontery of Wingate's subsequent memorandum, claiming that he had correctly analysed the situation and taken the final decision while Slim remained passive. This makes the evidence of Tulloch and Calvert, both of whom were and are intensely loyal to Wingate, all the more reliable. Slim, as Tulloch admiringly records, was inscrutable and rock-like in his imperturbability; listening and saying little except to give the final affirmative order, which could only be his, and his alone. Baldwin was practical, and went off to arrange a big fighter sweep for the next morning which he felt might be necessary in the new circumstances. Wingate, all nerves, behaved as he had behaved in other crises: throwing a tantrum and then mentally boxing the compass until he had settled on a final course. Calvert, never one to flap, really settled the issue by his show of confidence. One thing, however, is indisputable. The combined thrust of the testimony of recorded facts and the character of the men involved is that each of the four – Slim, Baldwin, Wingate and Calvert – were utterly resolved that THURSDAY should be mounted that night.[4]

The crisis was surmounted, but Wingate's trials on this, his first night in high command, had only begun. The glider parties contained the engineers and plant required to convert the landing-zones into airstrips big and smooth enough for the landing of C-47s by the evening of D plus one. With them went also the fighting troops to cover the operation and the air control group. The troubles began at once. The flight plan had been designed to ensure the fastest possible build-up, but an over-hasty trial had resulted in each C-47 being allotted two gliders to tow at once. The best pilots, given good weather, could manage a double tow, but many were inexperienced and had not had enough practice, and the route lay over the mountain-ranges bordering the Chindwin, where conditions were bumpy and the aircraft had to climb to 10,000 feet to clear them. Moreover, though later experience showed that the Waco glider could only take a load of 3,500 pounds, each now was loaded to 4,500 pounds, on top of which again, because of inadequate briefing and training, some troops ignored their loading tables and slipped even more extra gear on board. The gliders lurched and yawed in the rough conditions, endangering each other, sometimes hanging back to stretch their elastic nylon tow lines severely and then as suddenly riding up on to the tug. All that night Wingate and Tulloch had grimly to endure the reports of gliders parting from their tows or being cast off by alarmed pilots, crashing or disappearing into the night all along the route from three miles from the edge of Lalaghat airfield to somewhere far away in the dark forests east of the Chindwin.

The first sorties should have arrived at Broadway at least by half past nine, but midnight came and then one and two o'clock in the morning without any word from Calvert. Radio conditions at night were always bad, but at two thirty a.m. the radio operators at last faintly picked up advanced HQ, 77th Brigade through the roar of static, and the news was not good. The pre-arranged code word to stop all flying was heard: 'Soya Link, Soya Link, Soya Link!' After that nothing. Nine tows in the air were recalled and eight came safely back to Lalaghat; the ninth, as it turned out, delivered its gliders. Wingate was left to speculate what horrors Calvert had encountered at Broadway, and to taste in advance the bitterness of failure and the glee of his real or imaginary enemies. At Broadway Calvert had a cup of cocoa and went to sleep.

Tulloch remained calm and indomitable; Slim has recorded his continued calm from the moment that the American pilot had rushed up to Cochran with the revealing photographs. If he ever had had to justify his appointment he could claim his conduct on that trying night as sufficient in itself. Taking the attitude (like Haig at First Ypres) that in war the news was never as bad as it sounded, he remarked that all would be well in the morning, and advised Wingate to go to bed and get some much-needed rest. Wingate, replying that his chief-of-staff was 'a bloody optimist', meekly obeyed. Tulloch was perfectly correct. At half past six next morning, to everyone's relief and joy, came another laconic code-word – 'Pork Sausage' – asking for flying to be resumed that night, when the strip would be ready for lightly-loaded C-47s. By ten in the morning conditions were good enough for Wingate and Calvert to talk on the radio. There were no Japanese near the landing zone, but the earliest gliders had run into deep logging ruts overgrown by long grass, and into some of these the later sorties had crashed and caused a hazard before they could be pulled out of the way. Thirty men had been killed and twenty-eight injured, many of them belonging to the United States Engineers airfield construction parties. Only thirty-four of the sixty-one gliders despatched had arrived, but there were sufficient troops to get on with the work, Colonel John Alison of the Air Commando had arrived safely with a cargo of gear to exercise flying control, and the lift could go forward at nightfall on the 6th, as planned. That morning Major Rebori, USAAF, set off with a large covey of unarmed L-5s over occupied Burma, flying low, and brought out all the injured in a display of cold-blooded courage that was to be the hallmark of the light plane pilots and would later be taken almost for granted by the Chindits. At nightfall Brigadier-General Old, piloting the lead aircraft, led sixty-one C-47s into Broadway.

So much for drama. The great men and the pilots, and even the adventures of the parties rudely decanted into the jungle miles off target, stole the limelight but THURSDAY in fact was a *tour de force* of staff work. That this has gone unrecorded is partly because staff work, wrongly, is believed to be dull. Certainly few will bother to understand its technicalities. No one in India had had any previous experience of an air-transported operation on so vast a scale. All the techniques had to be worked out by common sense from first principles and by inspired improvisations, like using the command posts and communications of the artillery units, who were the last in the order of fly-in, to provide the ground control organisations on the airfields. Nine battalions had to be brought up from hundreds of miles away and bivouacked, fed and kept amused without any amenities in remote areas in Assam and Manipur to await the great day. Lengthy schedules of movement and loading tables, in which tactical desirability had to be reconciled with air force constraints, were compiled and argued over with brigade staffs and altered and re-altered. On the air side General Old's staff had to assemble a mass of aircraft in the three forward fields. (The Air Commando had nothing like sufficient powered aircraft for the lift. The actual sorties flown in the first phase were RAF, 331, USAAF of Eastern Air Command, 197 and USAAF of the Air Commando, 132.) Administrative backing, radio-communications, specialist flying control staff and huge quantities of fuel had to be positioned. Procedural differences between the two air forces and the army had to be sorted out, and quite apart from the troop lift, food and ammunition for re-supply had to be positioned near airfields and aircraft earmarked to supply the strong-hold and sixteen separate columns in the field. The army and air force had worked out an elaborate communication network, drills for marking supply dropping-zones and an ingenious code for indenting for supplies and stores.

The skill and flexibility of the staffs concerned can be established by a single example. The alterations found necessary on D-day were made so rapidly that the first glider tows to conform to the new plan were airborne *only forty-two minutes late*. The subsequent repercussions then involved re-routing the whole of 111th Brigade which in turn demanded that the necessary assault boats and outboard engines had to be speedily located, shipped to the airfield, loaded into the air commando gliders and delivered to Lentaigne at the point where he had to cross the mile-wide Irrawaddy which, as a result of being landed at Chowinghee instead of Piccadilly, barred his route to his operational area south-east of Indaw. The new plan was then altered again to fly Lentaigne's two British battalions into Broadway, not Chowinghee. Broadway from D plus one onwards was a sight amazing to the incoming columns, braced as they were for danger: the C-47s coming in with their landing lights on, the bright flare-path and the bustle of 'passengers' and cargo were like the scene at a great civil airport.

It was by no means all plain sailing, however. There were the inevitable clashes between forceful and hard-worked officers, which required much tact and diplomacy on the part of the staff to smooth over. It was particularly exasperating for the brigade and column staffs, their nerves worn thin by waiting, who suddenly and without explanation had to unload all the troops and weapons so carefully stowed in gliders and tear up their laboriously exact manifests and start again: maddening alterations made necessary by the enforced change of plan. Brigadier Lentaigne was pardonably angry when his plans were changed twice, and to make matters worse he had to shift his columns from one airfield to another.

On their side, the staff officers of the air force and Special Force headquarters found the brigades equally exasperating. There is always friction between the staff and the fighting troops, and the junior executive officers on the spot become the target of abuse from the colonels and brigadiers in a 'Catch-22' situation. As Mead records, the staff were accused of allowing insufficient time for one hundred per cent training for airborne operations and many columns had yet to discover how to lead mules into a glider or a C-47 or how to control them in flight. Many novice mule-drivers, when thousands of feet in the air over the Chin Hills, found themselves trying to control their terrified animals, some of whom fell down, or threw themselves down, or tried to kick their way to freedom through the side of the aircraft. Column commanders evaded the loading schedules, piling on extra stores, or refused to arrive as far in advance as the staff demanded for emplaning. When the 14th Brigade were flown in, the well-rehearsed Black Watch at first stood around haughtily expecting soldiers of lesser worth to act as porters and load their animals and stores for them, until disabused of this notion.

These, however, were all minor irritations and obstacles, overcome by the tact and firmness of the staff and by the skill and courage of the pilots. When the first phase of THURSDAY was complete (the West Africans and the 14th Brigade were to follow later) 9,000 fighting men, 1,300 animals and 500,000 pounds of weapons and warlike stores had been flown into Burma without the loss of a single man or aircraft by enemy action.[5] It was a great feat, and Wingate was understandably cock-a-hoop. On March 12th, when the first phase, strictly THURSDAY, was complete, he sent off a signal to the Supreme Allied Commander for onward transmission to Churchill summing up the situation and radiating success. It ended, significantly, with the words: *'situation most promising if exploited'* (author's italics) and the clear implication that there were those who were reluctant to do so. But the signal was not a strictly literal statement of fact. It was a political document designed to impress a susceptible Prime Minister and to strengthen Wingate's position in case his enemies tried to obstruct his grand design. It read as follows:

At a total cost of 120 all ranks approximately twelve thousand men of Special Force are now within a circle of 50 miles radius centre Indaw area. 9250 men and 1200 animals were introduced by air to Broadway, lat 24° 40 long 96° 45 and Chowringhee sixty miles south of Broadway. Broadway is now an airdrome occupied by American and British fighters and defended by two troops artillery and a dug in Stronghold. This Stronghold will be held. Chowringhee was attacked enemy bombers 10th and 11th after clearance by all Columns. No casualties. Intention. 77 Brigade is marching on Mawlu 20 miles north of Indaw to block permanently all road and rail communications to the north. One Column on Irrawaddy. One on Katha. 111 Brigade is now crossing Irrawaddy at mouth Shweli river directed on roads and railway Wuntho-Indaw. Two

Columns are now crossing Shweli to east to block Mandalay-Bhamo communications. A special Patriot force is raising Kachins around Broadway thence east to Bhamo area. 16 Bde is entering upper Meza valley descending on Banmauk and Indaw. Already encountered and ambushed successfully several enemy patrols. At Stilwell's request two Columns detached for attack on Lonkin lat 25° 40 long 96° 20. Forty light planes are using Broadway Stronghold. Further Strongholds to be established earliest by 16 and 111 Bdes. Enemy completely surprised. Situation most promising if exploited. Special Sit Rep gives fuller pictures.
12 March '44.[6]

Outwardly Wingate had every reason to be jubilant and to rub in the news of his success, but inwardly he was alarmed and anxious. He had good reason to believe that Slim, who could also be devious when necessary, had designs on his reserve brigades for the impending battle west of the Chindwin. What his situation report to Churchill did not disclose, naturally enough, was that Fergusson was badly behind schedule, as was Lentaigne, and that both their brigades were split and required time to concentrate. Moreover Dah Force was not in truth raising Kachin 'patriots' around Broadway as Wingate's signal stated, for indeed this was not its mission. It was plodding along on foot to its distant rendez-vous on the far side of the Irrawaddy. Templecombe had not been declared free of the enemy, and Herring had been landed at Broadway. Everything, as things stood on March 12th, hinged on Calvert, who was two days march from the vital Railway Valley. The situation was 'promising', but the test of battle was yet to come.

Wingate had now reached that most trying moment for any commander, when there was nothing more that he could do except wait for news and trust that fighting soldiers in the sections and platoons would turn his plans into reality.

7

Emphasis in the Railway Valley

THE VARIOUS CRISES on D-day of Operation THURSDAY – the late discovery that Piccadilly was blocked, the loss of gliders, the accidents at Broadway with the consequent delays and alterations to the time-table for the fly-in – had an adverse effect on that ambitious part of Wingate's plan which depended on the prompt capture of the airfields at Indaw. Calvert's brigade, instead of having two airfields available, had to use Broadway only, which meant a slower build-up, and his forward concentration was not complete until the night of March 9th. Lentaigne's headquarters and his leading battalion, 3rd/4th Gurkha Rifles, had to be sent to Chowringhee, east of the Irrawaddy. Chowringhee, intended only as the port of entry of Morris' 4th/9th Gurkha Rifles, was not a stronghold and had no anti-aircraft defences. It was discovered by the Japanese air force, and so Lentaigne's two other battalions were flown in to Broadway after Calvert was clear of it, and had some three days extra marching before they could join their commander. In consequence the 111th Brigade arrived too late to interfere with the northward move of the Japanese reserves, made in response to the intelligence that 'British airborne troops' had cut the railway, and that another group of them – Fergusson's brigade, in fact – was moving southward towards the same area. The Indaw operation, as it turned out, was dislocated beyond remedy.

Fortunately for General Stilwell and the future of the whole campaign, all this was peripheral to Wingate's *legitimate* mission. The key to the impending battles was control of the railway supplying the Japanese 18th Division in the Hukawng Valley, 150 miles to the north. Wingate had, with fine tactical sense, chosen the point where the railway could best be blocked, and had allotted this crucial task to his most trusted lieutenant, Calvert. The code-name of the 77th Brigade was apt: 'Emphasis' was indeed on the railway. Ten days after Calvert had arrived at Broadway he debouched from the forest with three battalions and prepared to squeeze General Shinichi Tanaka's logistic life-line.

The 'Railway Valley',[1] as the British called it, was ideally suitable either as a target for guerrilla harassment from the adjacent jungles or as the site for a defended block. From the area of Mawlu to a point some sixty miles to the north where it opened out into the broad valley of the Mogaung River, it was flanked by jungle-clad mountain ranges whose slopes, descending in places to the very edge of the railway on the valley floor, were threaded only by the footpaths between the forest villages, passable to men, mules, elephants or sometimes bullock carts but to no motorised transport. The abrupt Gangaw range, rising to 4,500 feet where the peak of Loi Maw towers above the pass leading from the Kyawkwe River to Mawlu, formed the valley's eastern wall. To the west lay a complication of forest-covered peaks and ridges stretching away for mile upon mile like the crests of a turbulent green-blue sea to the valley of the distant Chindwin. A network of mountain torrents drained the slopes on each side to feed the north-flowing Namyin and the south-flowing Ledan rivers; the watershed being at Mawlu. Like all Asian rivers these placid, winding streams became raging torrents in the monsoon, impossible to ford.

The valley floor was scrub-covered, opening out into plantations and wet-rice cultivation: 'paddy fields', liquid mud in the wet season, but now, in March, iron hard and criss-crossed by the little retaining banks or 'bunds'. When these were laboriously hacked down, the paddy fields provided landing-strips for the ubiquitous American L-5 light aircraft used to evacuate the wounded. There was no continuous road running through the valley, although there were stretches of dirt track motorable in the dry season. Its life-line and only through route was the railway. This was a little, toy, single-track, metre-gauge affair, with a station every ten miles or so and an abundance of bridges to provide the only crossing points when the *chaungs*, or watercourses, were in flood. It was an amenity for the villagers who lived along it, a convenience for government officials and traders, and had just sufficient capacity to serve the commercial needs of a simple, rural economy. It was also big enough, if allowed to work uninter-rupted, to supply the modest requirements of a Japanese infantry division in the field: a little petrol, a few hundred rounds of artillery ammunition per month, small arms ammunition and the frugal Japanese rations.

Calvert's 77th Brigade was concentrated in Broadway by first light on March 8th, and at noon its leading columns began their march to the Railway Valley, stirred by Wingate's rousing order of the day: 'Our columns are inserted in the enemy's guts . . . Let us thank God for the great success he has vouchsafed us and press forward with our sword in the enemy's ribs to expel him from our territory of Burma . . .' All the orders had been given, and all the troops rehearsed during training in their detailed tasks down to practice in mining, booby-trapping, and the construction of the little fortress which was to become known as 'The White City'.

The commando engineer party tasked with blowing the Mawhun railway bridge had exercised on one of identical size and structure found in India. It had, indeed, possibly exercised too well. At a final rehearsal, the officer in charge, Lieutenant Patterson, Royal Engineers, had insisted on maximum realism. Covering parties of infantry were posted to protect the working parties from interference, the charges were laid and connected, the working parties withdrawn and all was ready for the final order to 'fire'. The actual explosive charges were, of course, dummies, but the fuse connecting the detonator with them was real Primacord, stretching like a web over the bridge. An unexpected train crossed the bridge at this moment and set it off, with results like a Chinese firework festival. Public opinion in India was jumpy at the time and the explosion combined with the sight of armed men was too much for both drivers and passengers. The train came abruptly to a halt and all on it descended unanimously and fled for safety in the neighbouring jungle. It took some time to persuade them to emerge and allow the train to continue on its way.[2]

Calvert's plan was to leave Broadway, securely protected by the 3rd/9th Gurkha Rifles, in position as the garrison, and both columns of the King's 'floating', to use the vapid jargon term in vogue for a mobile force used to patrol outside the perimeter of a stronghold and counter-attack an attacker.

He himself was to set out with a powerful column for Mawlu to establish a block on the railway. This column, consisting of his brigade headquarters, his personal assault company, the 1st South Staffords and the 3rd/6th Gurkha Rifles, were to make for Mawlu, near which there was a suitable blocking position where the foothills of the Gangaw range came right down to the railway. Intelligence had forecast that there were some 500 guard and administrative Japanese troops that might be met in the area, so No. 50 Column of the Lancashire Fusiliers was to act as right flank guard to the north, blowing up the railway bridge over the Ledan River at Mawhun, and No. 20 Column as left flank guard at Pinwe. When the block had been secured and fortified the two Fusilier columns were to 'float', harrying and ambushing any traffic that sought to by-pass the block or Japanese troops approaching it. The Chindits were to prove unsurpassed as marchers, but fit and fresh as the brigade was, it took the task force six days to traverse the jungles and scramble with their laden mules over the Gangaw range. It was not until the 16th that they arrived at the site of the block.

As a military instrument Calvert's 77th Brigade was to prove as sharp and durable as any in the history of the British Army, and its anatomy, a compound of the British 'regimental system' and Wingate's peculiar methods, is of abiding interest. We have seen how in the 5307th, or 'Galahad', the rich variety of America from Red Indians to real-estate agents was ironed out by the United States Army system to form a standard regiment; uniform, all-American and efficient and, indeed, one whose spirit and response was such that not even Stilwell's rough hands could completely spoil its mouth. The British obtained the same results in a different way. The Americans frowned on any class or regional or ethnic differences and, above all, on élitism, but the British seized on them and exploited them. Illogically every British regiment considered itself an élite, whether they were the 'Jocks' of the Black Watch in Brodie's 14th Brigade with their Eton-educated, Scottish aristocrats as officers, or the dour 'South Staffs', whose officers were more work-a-day.

It was an odd system because it led to regiments* arranging themselves in a pecking order in no way related to their prowess or efficiency. Some regiments were notoriously bad, and they were found equally at the top and the bottom of the pile, and the same was true of the good ones. From the middle came the 'stolid, enduring, regiments of the line', the backbone of the British infantry. The system was based partly on regional peculiarities and, in the case of the officers, on social origin. These were cherished. No Black Watch officer would cheerfully have accepted a posting to the South Staffords: few officer cadets acceptable to the South Staffords would have been considered in peacetime for a commission in the Black Watch by the colonel of that excellent regiment. No one would admit publicly to the fact that, say, the Bedfordshire and Hertfordshire, the South Staffords or the King's (Liverpool), whose 13th Battalion, formed only for static guard duties from unfit men, had under Wingate's spur fought so hard in LONGCLOTH, were judged by these meretricious standards or that in peacetime they found it difficult to attract their share of the better officers being commissioned from the Royal Military College at Sandhurst.

Officers and privates alike in all regiments could close their ranks to outsiders. The chronicler of the Black Watch records, without

* It must be understood that the Americans, the Chinese and the Japanese were organised in 'regiments' that were tactical entities, of three battalions, distinguishable by the roman number for the battalion and the arabic for the regiment, e.g., III/113. The equivalent British tactical formation is a 'brigade'. The British 'Regiment' is a regional grouping, county or national, raising or training battalions for 'brigading' with others: e.g., the 1st South Staffs was the regular 1st battalion of the South Staffordshire Regiment; the 7th Leicesters a Territorial battalion of the Leicestershire Regiment.

enthusiasm, that due to casualties one of their columns was briefly commanded by the attached Burma Rifles officer, the only 'outsider' ever to achieve such a privileged position. Norman Durant, a volunteer for the Chindits from the Royal Artillery posted to the South Staffords, had a protracted battle of wills before he could make his platoon accept him. But an officer from Kent, another volunteer for the Chindits who had found himself cold-shouldered by the Yorkshiremen in his battalion, was happy to find himself kindly and cordially welcomed by the Lancastrians in No. 50 Column. The 'regimental system', like all human behaviour, is never consistent or simple. The luckless 26th Hussars, a newly-raised tank unit, were broken up to swell the numbers of the regular infantry battalions, who gave them a chilly welcome, and vomited out as many as possible when ordered to post out men to form the new defence platoons in the brigade headquarters.

In other brigade headquarters such men were no more than a pool for labour: digging trenches for the brigade staff, acting as orderlies and sentries. In 77th Brigade Calvert expanded his defence platoon into his personal, élite assault force, with a specially selected Gurkha officer, Ian Macpherson, to command it, and another, Rook, as his second-in-command.

Wingate, with his irregular background and coming from a regiment whose officers might be as snobbish as those in any battalion of foot but which had throughout its history always been open to talent, and professional and technical in its approach, understood little about these infantry eccentricities and cared less: he believed in the best men for the job. At first he proposed to discard the entire regimental system, numbering the columns from No. 1 onwards as they were formed and to call the brigades 'groups' with fresh titles, thus ensuring the total separation of the Chindits from an army he despised. Major-General Symes dissuaded him from so drastic a step, which would have caused great resentment in every rank and weakened the sense of identity which binds all effective fighting units together. Columns developed their own *esprit de corps*, but the cap-badge and the regimental identity was retained, to be fiercely cherished.

The Gurkha regiments were different again. The Gurkhas, or *Ghorkas*, of Nepal are Mongolian by race and Hindu by religion, but by an accident of history already accustomed to be ruled by Indians of the highest caste, and so had accepted, in their military life, the leadership of another kind of outsider, provided he came up to their own pitiless standard of courage. ('A good officer, saheb, but not a Gurkha officer,' was the polite formula by which the native Gurkha officers would invite their commanding officer to get rid of a British officer whom they had tried and found wanting.) The Gurkhas were recruited into their several regiments after careful selection by officers who had knowledge of every shade of clan and sect and their qualities as soldiers at their finger tips; Magars and Gurungs from Western Nepal; Rais and Limbus from the east; Puns, Thakurs and Chettris. The 3rd/6th were westerners. The 3rd/9th in Broadway and the 4th/9th who at that moment were trudging from Chowringhee to their operational area on the Chinese frontier were Thakurs and Chettris: these names indicating a claim to membership of the Rajput caste, famous for its military tradition. They were stricter in their adherence to the Hindu religion and so known to the other British Gurkha officers as 'the High Church party'. As a class, the British officers in the Gurkha regiments tended to be exclusive, narrow-minded, as professional as Prussians or the officers of the French Foreign Legion. Among them was a strong Scottish element, who had taught their mountaineers to accept the bagpipe as their regimental music. The biblical rhetoric of Wingate, though it struck a chord in the breasts of the British officers (the adjutant of the 3rd/9th recorded his famous order of the day verbatim in the war diary) meant little to the Gurkha officers and riflemen. By their own tradition fighting was an end in itself. The 'ninety-day contract' meant nothing to them; they were sworn, like the Legion, to 'march, fight and die', and as long as their officers, British and Gurkha, led, they were prepared to follow them until they dropped, as many did.

To these powerful forces of ancient regimental tradition and the new-found sense of belonging to the Chindit élite, the 77th Brigade added two more. It was conscious of being Wingate's own favourite brigade, although every unit within it had changed after the return from Burma in 1943 and only the title remained. Wingate resented adverse criticisms of it during exercises, even by umpires appointed for the very purpose of reporting on faults. It was strong in his LONGCLOTH veterans: Walter Scott of the King's, Robert Thompson the colonial administrator turned airman, Astell, Burma Rifles and, above all, Calvert. Calvert as a military commander is best judged by his own statements and his own signals made at the time and not by any external criteria. He was inventive, inconsistent, intelligent yet naive, calm in action yet highly strung, argumentative and dis-respectful to the point of indiscipline. At a first glance (and perhaps in his own estimation) he appears a rebel and a maverick, railing against military dogma and 'staff officers': paradoxically, his every military action conforms with the 'principles of war' and as for staff work, the administration of his brigade from the air base forward was a model of its kind. Under the panache he was always the thoughtful engineer officer.

In the twentieth century the unromantic fact is that even brigadiers are forced by the nature of war to command from a headquarters, for on a modern battlefield a general in a forward battalion position is no more than a battalion commander, and whatever he may try to achieve, all he can do for the fleeting moment when in front is judge the temper of the commander on the spot, advise him, encourage him, or boot him onwards as the circumstances and his 'feel' for the battle dictate. Calvert, spiritually belonging to the generation of conquerors of the Indian Empire, Clive, Adams, Flint and Monro, instinctively led from the front: there is a temptation to use the phrase 'sword in hand', but the actual gesture was with rifle and fixed bayonet slung over the shoulder.

In this context it is worth noting Calvert's heterodox solution to an orthodox command problem. Apart from the Railway Valley he was responsible, by Wingate's written orders, for the Irrawaddy, two separate forces beside his own (Morris Force and Dah Force), and the security of Broadway. His total command, later to be augmented, was already six and a half battalions and the rank appropriate to his span of authority was major-general. Had he been an orthodox American or British officer he would have seen that the conventional and unassailable solution was to sit in Broadway at the reliable centre of communications, flying in an L-5 to visit his various fronts in turn. His second-in-command, Rome, a highly capable soldier, could have been placed in command of the Mawlu task force, just as Merrill employed Hunter in a similar position. As Wingate had emphasised to Calvert, however, the emphasis for 'Emphasis' was on Mawlu, Rome could look after Broadway and Morris Force could look after itself. On March 16th he arrived with the Gurkha Rifles and the South Staffordshire columns at the little village of Henu, just north of Mawlu, where, as a close study of air photographs had shown him, a cluster of foothills abutting on the railway track offered a perfect site for a blocking position. It was held by some Japanese pickets, but these he wasted no time in driving off, leading the attack himself.

There is more than one account of the capture of the site of 'The White City' block at Henu, including Calvert's own, but the best, as so often, is by a junior officer: Lieutenant Norman Durant, who had been given command of the machine-gun platoon in No. 80 Column, 1st South Staffordshire. He, apart from writing a vivid account of his experiences while events were still fresh in his mind, was a sharp observer of personalities, as this comment on his brigade commander shows:

His [Calvert's] hair flops over his forehead, and he has a disconcerting habit of staring at you when you speak to him and yet not appearing to hear a word. His lectures were always painfully slow and hesitant and during training he gave the impression of taking a long time to make up his mind; in action things were very different. He knows all the officers in the brigade and many of the senior NCOs, and his manner and attitude are always the same if he is talking to a CO, a subaltern or a private . . .

Durant had had a rough time with his Staffords. All the 'old sweats' – the pre-war long service soldiers recalled from the reserve – seemed to be concentrated in the machine-gun platoon, but by dint of throwing out the platoon sergeant and two others, bringing in some young, intelligent soldiers to learn the Vickers gun, and reducing the rest first to tears and then to a state of discipline, he had his platoon so much in hand that it was enough to threaten a man with relegation to the rifle company to restore order without reference to the Army Act. The White City position at Henu, so called because of the scores of white supply parachutes later draping the trees, was on seven little hills, and on the evening of the 16th Durant's guns were posted on one with two platoons of the rifle company at its foot. Nearby was a dominating feature, 'Pagoda Hill', unoccupied by the British and not, as so far seen, by the enemy. The night was spent strenuously in digging in. At first light a lot of 'yammering' was heard and Sergeant Jenkins remarked to his platoon commander that the 'locals seemed to be a bit chatty this morning'. Durant went down to have a look from the two rifle platoon positions at the foot of their little hill. The 'locals' were a few Japanese soldiers oblivious of their presence, a short distance off at the foot of the neighbouring Pagoda Hill. Unknown to each other, they and the South Staffords had dug in peaceably as neighbours. Durant snatched up a Bren and shot at them, thus opening a brisk fire-fight which rose to disagreeable intensity as the Japanese heavy machine-guns and medium mortars joined in.

His own account of the fight that followed can hardly be improved:

At about 1100 hrs. [he records], heavy rifle fire and L.M.G. fire opened up on us from hill C. – Pagoda Hill – and at the same time we came under grenade and mortar fire from hill D where a Jap Pl. had taken up position. For the next 4 hours we had a very unpleasant time indeed. We couldn't see the Jap and there were very few parts of the hill that weren't under fire. Casualties were mounting up. I had to move the Vickers every half hour or so as the Jap was doing his best to knock them out. He put a burst across one gun which hit the man firing it in the thigh, another in the foot and ripped the box of ammunition which was being made into shreds.

However we silenced one of their L.M.G.s and from occasional screams knew that we were also inflicting casualties. By now a third of us were casualties, including the rifle Coy. 2nd-in-C who was hit in both feet, and one of the Pl. commanders who got a bullet through the buttocks, and we were extremely glad to get a message over the wireless to say that the Brigadier was on his way with 2 companies of Gurkhas and would counter attack any feature held by the Japs. The next hour was absolute hell. The Japs stepped up their mortaring and grenading and it became quite obvious that at any moment they might rush the road and attack from Pagoda Hill. Consequently the arrival of the Brigadier at 1600 hrs. resembled the moment in an American film when the police with sirens screaming speed up in time to help the hero, whilst the audience applauds wildly. The first we knew of his arrival was when the firing on our left stopped and we saw the Gurkhas were attacking the hill D. and then the Brigadier himself came striding up our hill, rifle and bayonet in hand, took a quick look round and then said to Major Jefferies, 'How many men can you spare to attack Pagoda Hill?' 'About 20.' 'Right we'll go straight up.' George Cairns, the mortar officer and I, hearing this, picked up some grenades, got out our revolvers and prepared to go too. We had been shot at all day, and everyone felt like getting into the Japs and exacting a bit of retribution, besides which I was very keen to see just how many casualties my guns had inflicted on the enemy. Seeing me ready to go my Pl. Sergeant (Jenkins) picked up a Sten and I knew it was no good ordering him not to come. The Japs on Pagoda Hill were now a bit concerned over the arrival of the Gurkhas and we were not fired on as we doubled down the forward slopes of our hill on to the road. As we got to the bottom the Brigadier said to me, 'Take a party round to the left and clear the houses', and to Jefferies, 'Take the right side and the Pagoda.'

I went up the hill like a two year old and halfway up met a path which led round the left of the hill, about 12 feet below the Pagoda, obviously finishing by the houses. I shouted over my shoulder to my sergeant to follow up with the party and, unencumbered by any equipment, I doubled along the path, rounded a corner and came into view of the houses.

To this day I'm not quite certain what I expected to see – the place deserted, or the Japs on the run, I suppose – but what I actually saw was a Jap section climbing out of their trenches under the nearest house and coming straight for me, the leading two, with bayonets fixed and rather unfriendly expressions, being about 20 yds. on my right. I fired my revolver and nothing happened – I was later to find that the hammer had worked loose.

It is strange how at a moment like that the mind can think of a hundred things during the space of a split second. I remember that even as I ran forward my brain was working faster than it has ever done before or since. I realised that my sergeant was a good 30 yds. behind me, out of sight round the corner, and the men with him were probably a bit behind that; time was too short for them to be of any help. I had a 4 second grenade in my hand but it was obviously useless against the two leading Japs because in considerably less than 4 seconds they were going to be embarrassingly close. I also knew that if I stopped or turned round I was asking to be shot.

This didn't leave me very much choice of action, so I took the pin out of the grenade and, still running forward, threw it over the heads of the first two amongst the Japs who were scrambling out from under the house, did a swerve to the left which Ian Smith* would have envied and took a flying leap over the side of the hill. As I swerved I felt as if I had been violently kicked on the knee and although I never heard the shot, I realised that I had been hit. I was only about 12 feet down the hill with no cover at all and for a ghastly moment I imagined myself crippled and unable to move, having to lie there whilst the Japs, following up, got to work on me with their bayonets. I remember saying to myself as I anxiously looked up the hill, 'What the hell did I volunteer to come here for? This is the last time I'll do anything like this unasked!' But no one appeared and I moved back along the hill about 30 yards and climbed on to the path just below the Pagoda.

My sergeant later told me what happened after I'd jumped. He had come round the corner with 2 or 3 men and they had shot the leading 2 Japs. The grenade I had thrown had caused casualties and the remaining Japs were moving back round to the west side of the hill. Seeing no sign of me the sergeant thought I had been captured and was being bustled away by the returning Japs. So he went quite berserk, grenading like a lunatic until the area of the huts was clear; he then moved back round the side of the hill and was relieved to see me there.

The first thing I saw on reaching the path was a horrible hand-to-hand struggle going on further up the hill. George Cairns and a Jap were struggling and choking on the ground, and as I picked up a Jap rifle and climbed up towards them I saw George break free and, picking up a rifle bayonet, stab the Jap again and again like a madman. It was only when I got near that I saw he himself had already been bayoneted twice through the side and

* A famous footballer.

that his left arm was hanging on by a few strips of muscle. How he had found the strength to fight was a miracle, but the effort had been too much and he died the next morning.* There were now a lot of our dead and Jap dead lying about, and our wounded were crying for help. But the Japs still held the top of the hill and things were looking critical; in fact we might have been pushed back if the Brigadier's voice had not shouted out, 'Come on now, one more effort, you've got them on the run'.

The last few grenades were produced and thrown and then with bayonet, kukri, machete and revolver we stumbled up the last few yards and before we knew what was happening the Japs were running. It was almost dusk and as the men began to dig in ready to face an expected counter-attack, I sat down whilst someone put a field dressing on my leg. The hill was a horrid sight, littered with Jap dead, and already the ones who had been killed there earlier in the day were black with flies. Stretcher-bearers were removing our wounded and our mercifully very few dead. Noel Day had been killed, shot through the back of the head by a Jap feigning dead, but on trying to repeat the ruse he was spotted by Noel's platoon sergeant who promptly kicked his head in. We found out then what we were never afterwards to forget – it doesn't pay to leave wounded Japs breathing.

I made my way back to the RAP had my leg dressed, was given a shot of morphia and told to rest.[3]

It speaks volumes for the uniform quality of the Japanese Army that the hammering inflicted on the defenders of Pagoda Hill did not deter a fierce attempt to dislodge the South Staffords on the night of the 18th. The Japanese obviously thought that the block only faced south, and encircled it to put in a sharp attack from the north down the railway. Shouting somewhat unconvincingly in English and Urdu such rote-learned phrases as 'Cease fire', '*Thik hai*, Johnny (i.e., 'It's OK, it's me, Johnny Gurkha'), 'OK, Bill' and 'Stand down now', they rushed the perimeter and made a lodgment, overrunning a platoon, but suffering many casualties. A Japanese-speaker on the British side heard them shouting to each other about withdrawing, and other authoritative shouts ordering the attack to be pressed home. A sporadic and savage close-quarter fight went on all night, and at dawn the commanding officer of the South Staffords led the first of the Chindit counter-attacks in person, and after some hard fighting the Japanese intruders were thrown out, but at the cost of

* Cairns received one of the three Victoria Crosses awarded to British officers in the Chindit campaign. All were posthumous.

Colonel Richards mortally wounded and his Royal Engineer officer killed. This only pushed the Japanese back into the jungle on the edge of the perimeter and the rifle company of Durant's column was ordered to clear them out.

Direct air support was called for and the system devised by Robert Thompson, by which an air-force pilot on the ground directed the strike aircraft by radio – on this occasion Thompson himself – was used in battle for the first time with devastating results. The Japanese were driven out of the perimeter but at the cost of the life of an officer leading the attack, Major Jefferies. Durant listened to him – 'one of the nicest men you could hope to know' – speaking on his portable radio and ending with, 'I'm going in now, so will close down', to have one of those unaccountable but sickening moments of prescience that occur in moments of high tension: his friend was doomed. There were fifty-nine casualties in the South Staffords, seven of them officers. The Japanese left sixty dead.

As a butcher's bill it does not compare with the hecatombs of Russia or Western Europe, but the fighting in Asia had an intense personal quality only rarely seen in more civilised theatres, where battles between hundreds of tanks were prefaced by vast bombardments and where it was possible to fight all day with little more than the glimpse of a distant enemy: a group of scurrying manikins in the distance, or tank turrets sliding like beads sideways along the facing ridge. As a much-decorated infantryman put it at the Staff College in 1944, where he was enjoying a rest from his exertions in Italy, 'An infantryman is a chap who when he's told, gets out of a hole in the ground, walks up a hill (here he imitated the action with two fingers on the syndicate table) and there he digs another hole and gets into it.' 'Artillerie conquiert, l'infanterie occupe'. in short.

Mid-twentieth century warfare was largely an exchange of fire-power, carefully orchestrated to bring the infantry alive and un-damaged on the objective, or to protect the defenders by placing a dense belt of bursting shells across the route an attacker must follow. Even 'close' or more direct conflict was often in reality across a space of hundreds of yards and between the tanks, anti-tank guns and machine-guns. There were indeed many bloody and bitter clashes when infantry fought infantry and in Russia there was a fierce hatred of the Nazi invader which added a peculiarly savage quality to the fighting. But without underestimating the ordeal of those who fought in Europe, there was an impersonal element about that war. The soldiers subjected to torrents of artillery fire or the even more demoralising attacks by aircraft felt almost as if they were the victims of some terrible natural disaster. As for the Germans and Italians, they were at least human beings.

In Burma in 1944 there was a scarcity of artillery and the refinements of artillery–infantry tactics were not understood: the best that either side could do was a preliminary softening-up process from a few guns and mortars or, peculiar to 77th Brigade, the massed, close-range fire of Vickers machine-guns combing the jungle just ahead. Combat, at Nphum Ga, at Henu, at Mogaung, was an exchange of lives; the two sides closing until in the ensuing mêlée men shouting war-cries and insults threw grenades at each other, shot each other at ranges so close that the sub-machine guns cut them to pieces and, to use the old obsolete phrase, 'bayonets were crossed', in the literal act. The savagery of the contest was intensified by the physical aversion and moral horror the British felt for the Japanese soldier. 'Somehow one can imagine that one could have a drink and a cigarette and a cup of tea with a (German) prisoner, but once having met the Japs one can only imagine kicking their heads in. They look like animals, they behave like animals, and they can be killed unemotionally as swatting flies. And they need to be killed, not wounded, for as long as they breathe they're dangerous.'[4]

The repulse of the first attack by the Japanese on The White City gave Calvert a fortnight's breathing space to fortify his stronghold. He surrounded it with a deep belt of barbed wire, mines and booby traps and the troops burrowed into the hills until they were honeycombed with shelters, all except the fire positions being covered with logs and earth, thus making the position proof against any artillery the Japanese were able to deploy. A defensive fire-plan combining all the machine-guns to cover the approaches to the wire and mortars was carefully worked out. Control was through a web of buried telephone lines. On March 29th some 2-pounder anti-tank guns arrived by glider followed later by engineers and plant to build a strip big enough for C-47s, which flew in more artillery until the block was defended by four anti-tank guns, six 40 mm Bofors light anti-aircraft guns and a battery of four 25-pounders. In the meantime the two Lancashire Fusilier columns, which, like the claws of a lobster, had reached out into the valley to the north and south, were making themselves felt.

The task of No. 50 Column, led by the commander of the Lancashire Fusiliers, Lieutenant-Colonel Christie, was to prevent any move by the Japanese to the north of the proposed site of the block interfering with Calvert while he set it up. On March 15th Christie cut his way out of the jungle into the Railway Valley and ran into a party of Japanese and Burmese of the Burma National Army. (Called the 'Burma Traitor Army' by the British. Who was a 'patriot' and who was a 'traitor' depended upon the point of view.) These were easily dispersed, and Lieutenant Hugh Patterson with his commando platoon and a rifle platoon to cover him set off for the railway bridge over the Ledan River. By nine o'clock that night 350 pounds of high explosive had been placed and the Primacord connected up to the time fuses. Having lit them, Patterson withdrew with his sergeant who, in a mood reminiscent of Stilwell urging Doorn to burn down the police station, remarked with satisfaction, 'This is something I've wanted to do all my life, sir,' upon which both were blown flat on the ground by the blast and bombarded with bits of metal and masonry, having underestimated the effect of a charge far bigger than they had ever fired in training. All the spans and piers went down and Patterson laid traps and time bombs to discourage repairs. He then went on to wreck the water-tower, pumps, repair crane, points and rolling stock in Mawhun railway station and mined the permanent way and roads leading into it. Not satisfied with this, he asked permission to take a smaller and less conspicuous party without mules to the next bridge at Kadu, which he blew and then made a rapid get-away as there was a Japanese guard post in the village. This involved a round trip of forty miles in twenty-four hours and he recorded that he 'found the strain of wandering about Jap-infested territory in a small party quite considerable'. It was a permanent feature of life for the Burma Rifles officers of the brigade, who were fully occupied in enlisting the aid of the pro-British, anti-Burman Kachins in the district, whose best use was to provide an unrivalled local intelligence net. One of them, Musgrave-Wood (better known later as the cartoonist 'Emwood' of the *Daily Mail*) had provided Patterson with a guide to take him to the Kadu bridge.

No. 20 Column did not make as positive a break in the valley communications but was able to impose a threat to any road traffic from the south, the alternative routes offered by the railway and the network of forest tracks being too extensive for a single column to block completely, although it could harass movement. All in all, the situation was now good enough to encourage Calvert, whose tactical instinct warned him against anything resembling a passive or static defence, to move out from his jungle fortress and, as a first step, evict the strong Japanese garrison a mere 2,300 yards south of him in Mawlu before it could be reinforced. He boldly left the South Staffords in The White City and moved out with the 3rd/6th complete, ordering No. 20 Column to put an ambush on the road and railway in their area near Tonlon, and No. 50 Column, summoned from their blocking position in the north, to circle the little town and take up a cut-off position immediately south of it. Lieutenant-Colonel Skone and Major Shaw with their two columns of Gurkhas were to attack from the north and drive the garrison on to Christie's waiting machine-guns.

Unfortunately March 27th was not one of the Lancashire Fusilier's best days. Christie was delayed when the point of his column ran into a Japanese patrol and the officer in the lead was killed. Christie took some time to get going again, so the cut-off position was not occupied in time, while 20 Column remained 'unaccountably inactive' and 'it was bad luck that Shuttleworth [its commander] had just removed his ambush from the road and railway'. Admittedly the fighting garrison of Mawlu was no more than a company, the rest being a military administrative section for the railway and the staff of a 'records office' (i.e., for detailed personnel administration, whose crates of individual records proved a rich intelligence haul) but in the Japanese Army the clerks could fight with the same suicidal tenacity as the riflemen, apart from which all Japanese soldiers were adept at digging themselves in. Given a little time, they covered their trenches with logs and earth until they were proof against anything smaller than a medium artillery shell. They had turned Mawlu into a little redoubt, and when the Gurkhas advanced unsupported they were badly shot up. Only their peculiar combination of doggedness and dash carried them on until their flame-thrower parties were near enough to set fire to the houses in the village. Even then they were still checked. Help was on the way, however, and the Mustangs of the Air Commando once again demonstrated the extraordinary accuracy of their bombing and cannon fire on positions barely a rifle shot ahead of the leading troops. Encouraged, the Gurkhas dashed into the smoke with grenades and kukris at the ready, and then was seen a sight rare at that stage of the war.

'Then the Japanese broke . . . They ran! I saw them run,' wrote a liaison officer from Special Force Headquarters, who was watching the action from close behind and at this point abandoned the severe, unemotional military style. 'They abandoned everything – dead, documents, equipment, weapons. They fled out through the village, across the paddy-fields and into the woods beyond . . . 77th Brigade became in that hour the Lord Paramount of all the area around the block (The White City).'[5] The fugitives carried with them the few Japanese occupying the nearby village of Sepein. They did not stop until they reached Indaw. Patrols reported no enemy between Monhyin in the north and Indaw twenty-five miles down the line in the south.

Unfortunately in that sector everything had gone awry for the Chindits and there was nothing to prevent the Japanese, now fully alive to the dangerous position of the 18th Division, from assembling a counter-offensive force, coming north again and re-establishing themselves with artillery, this time around Sepein, in preparation for a properly organised operation to smash The White City block. Two more fierce engagements were to be fought in this stretch of the Railway Valley between March 27th and mid-April, after which the Japanese paused to lick their wounds.

Broadway meanwhile had been built up into the perfect stronghold and base on the lines laid down by Wingate. If it had a defect it was that its very inaccessibility made it unsuitable, when compared with Aberdeen, as a safe harbour and resting place for columns; the outside world could only be reached after four or five days difficult marching through jungle. Its chief value lay in the large airfield with two runways the United States Army engineers had built. This could accept C-47s from India which could carry out the sick and wounded brought in by light aircraft from the columns. For a time half a dozen Hurricane aircraft of the Royal Air Force were based there, complete with early-warning radar, but this only served to attract air attack and was uneconomical and they were withdrawn. It was an expensive establishment in military terms, requiring two battalions, a battery of four 25-pounders, one of 40 mm Bofors light anti-aircraft guns and a number of 0.5 American air defence machine-guns, but apart from its military value Broadway was a splendid gesture of defiance. Visitors never failed to marvel at the sight of this busy depot and airport functioning unimpeded and unharrassed except for the occasional air raid in the heart of Japanese-held Northern Burma. It was not until three weeks after THURSDAY had been launched that a Japanese force succeeded in approaching it, to be severely trounced by the castellan of this astonishing establishment, the fiery Colonel Rome.

The force sent to attack Broadway was Major Wakayuma's battalion of the 146th Regiment from the 56th Division, based on Lungling in Yunnan. It appears to have approached from the east, having reached Broadway by a circuitous route through Mogaung and down the Railway Valley. Near the railway it had ambushed and dispersed the 6th Battalion of the Nigeria Regiment. This luckless unit was marching from Broadway to Aberdeen, to provide the garrison for the stronghold which 16th Brigade had established twenty-five miles north-east of Indaw.

One of the West African prisoners taken on this encounter was impressed as a guide. Another account related that a British prisoner-of-war identifiable now only by his nickname of 'Dodger', was also being used as guide to the defences of Broadway and actually led the attack up to the wire, where he was wounded but managed to escape into the defensive perimeter.

The first indication of Wakayuma's approach came from the local Kachins, and then on March 27th the reconnaissance platoon of No. 41 Column (King's Own) jumped a company of Japanese infantry

127

bivouacked near the Kyaukwe river. Lieutenant Hart, who was to have an adventurous tour with the Chindits, had lost his way on the march from Broadway to Indaw. and been picked up by Scott. He had been ordered to take the place of one of the reconnaissance platoons of the King's in No. 82 Column and was retained temporarily in the Broadway area where he took part in the battle. (He eventually caught up with his battalion in Blackpool.) Later in the afternoon of the same day, Major George Astell, of the Burma Rifles, who had a patrol watching the only track leading through the jungle to the Broadway airstrip, signalled to the garrison that a large party of Japanese going south had just passed him and overshot the airfield. He gave its strength, quite correctly, as a 'weak battalion': it was 300 strong.

This was Colonel Rome's first positive intimation that he was about to be attacked, but he was by no means surprised, as the Japanese bombers and fighters had located the stronghold and raided it on the 13th, the 16th and the 26th, and it was only a matter of time before the Japanese ground troops found him. He was well prepared. The stronghold was surrounded by a belt of wire covered by 'bunkers' in imitation of the Japanese style, roofed in with logs eight inches in diameter. Inside the stronghold were the artillery and various signals and engineer detachments and the 3rd/9th Gurkha Rifles with two of its rifle companies. The third, 'D' Company (Major Pickett) was detached to patrol round the airfield, to provide early warning of any attack. No. 82 Column of the King's was ordered to keep well clear of Broadway and out of trouble until called, but to be prepared to act promptly when summoned for action against any Japanese attacking the stronghold. Colonel Scott with his No. 81 Column was on a separate mission twenty-five miles away to the south and out of direct contact. Rome immediately sent a signal cancelling all flying for the night, and told the light aircraft pilots to be ready to fly out at dawn the following morning, as it was too late for them to take off and land in daylight in India. They were to spend an alarming night or two in the stronghold.

Rome posted 'D' Company at the western end of the airstrip, where the track joined it, pulled in the half-dozen 0.5 inch anti-aircraft machine-guns emplaced around the strip with their crews into the stronghold perimeter, and signalled Major Gaitley to move his No. 82 Column closer to Broadway, lie low, and await further orders. All he had to do then was to wait for some action, and he was not to wait long.

It was a pitch-black night and towards midnight 'all hell cut loose at the airfield entrance'. Wakayuma seems to have marched in a complete circle through the teak jungle around Broadway until he stumbled on the track leading into the airstrip and there he collided with two platoons of Major Pickett's 'D' Company. The Japanese, by design, were very noisy in the attack, shouting and knocking tin cans together, so as to draw fire and thus discover the fire-positions, and calling out scraps of English and Urdu to confuse the defenders. The night rang with cries of '*Thik hai*, Johnny! *Ham Hindu hai!*' ('We're Indians'), 'Charge!' and, less convincingly, 'Where is the AA sentry?' and 'Halt, right turn!' After a fierce and confused fight of about forty minutes they drove in the forward platoons, who rallied on Pickett's headquarters. This the Japanese located and a dog-fight continued at close-quarters until dawn, showers of grenades being exchanged. Major Pickett was mortally wounded, the Japanese caught a party of stretcher-bearers and killed them all, together with the wounded, and the company lost fifty men. Most of the survivors found their way back into the stronghold, but on looking round at dawn Rome saw Gurkhas by twos and threes who had taken cover in the bomb craters on the airfield with their weapons pointing in the direction of the enemy. He called them in, and refused the plea of 'D' Company's subedar (the senior Gurkha officer of the company) to take out a patrol and recover Major Pickett's body.

The Japanese in the meanwhile were able to examine the geography of the stronghold in daylight and Rome did nothing to disturb them. He had no intention of leaving his defences. What he wanted was the Japanese to come to him, and they did. Soon after dark they began a series of suicidal attacks on the stronghold perimeter and kept them up all night, howling and screaming in their usual way, to be met by short-range rifle and machine-gun fire, mortar fire and showers of grenades. None succeeded in forcing an entry but many were left dead on or near the wire. How many, it was difficult to tell, because Wakayuma had brought a large number of coolies with him who were were made to remove the dead, which the Japanese regarded as ritually important. One of these 'coolies' who managed to escape and take refuge with the garrison proved to be a Captain Chai Shuh-ming of the Chun Li Pu, or Chinese military intelligence service, who had been captured some time before, but being able to speak Burmese had passed himself off as a coolie and been impressed by the Japanese. Apart from encouraging details about the weakness of Wakayuma's force, he brought with him much valuable information.

One of the L-5 sergeant-pilots later wrote a lurid but by no means exaggerated account of the night's events. He had taken refuge in one of the Gurkha bunkers 'with eight fox-hole-like positions linked with each other by a communication ditch' where he was given a weapon post to man in an emergency, but rashly he and his companions elected to sleep above ground in their 'sacks'. Some distant explosions and shots soon awakened them and they dived for the nearest fox-hole, but that was fully occupied, so they scrambled about looking for their proper positions. 'All of a sudden there was the most blood-curdling yelling and screaming I have ever heard. It sounded like hundreds of Indians on the war-path. The Nipponese (sic) had found our kitchen and were raiding it. We had booby-trapped it. The poor guys never had a chance . . .'

The next day Sergeant Prather and two other Americans asked permission to try to reach some of the L-5s in the dispersal. These, they found, were undamaged except for some bayonet thrusts through the fabric, and by the afternoon they were able to take off with three aircraft and a number of wounded, although not without some excitement and being shot at by a Japanese machine-gun while preparing the aircraft, for a brisk engagement was being fought in the jungle all round the airstrip. 'One of the boys,' he recorded, 'dove into a fox-hole and wouldn't come out for anything. I even tried staying outside while the mortars were firing to show that there was little danger. I'll never forget him, because he cried like a baby.' Courage is a strange quality. There was a youth, scared out of his manhood by a few explosions, who nonetheless was perfectly prepared to fly a slow, unarmed aircraft, probably overloaded with wounded, through Japanese airspace over mountains in some of the most dangerous flying conditions in the world.

That day Rome felt able to go over to the offensive. The subedar of 'D' Company was allowed to collect Pickett's body. A strong fighting patrol went out led by Major Twelvetrees of 'A' Company and clashed with a Japanese platoon. Reading between the lines of the flat prose of the war diary, one gets the impression that the untried young riflemen of the 3rd/9th had been a trifle dismayed by their first encounter, but now, to use the infantryman's expressive phrase, they began to 'go', responding to the war-cry – '*Ayo Gurkhali*' – and the vehement urging of their under-officers. The platoon was routed, leaving sixteen dead in exchange for two killed and seven wounded. 'They leapt upon their foes,' says the regimental history, 'plying bayonet and kukri.' Nor is this an exaggeration. The use of steel persisted in Gurkha regiments, and the heavy kukri, a leaf-shaped blade, heavy and awkward to a European hand and used for anything from clearing brushwood to building a hut, was a terrible weapon. (A Gurkha officer of the 9th in Africa once took the head off a German, steel helmet and all.)

While all this was going on the Gurkha patrols searching for Wakayuma's main position encountered a new menace. The Japanese had established a screen of observers and snipers up trees, usually tied to a branch so that they did not fall, even if hit. It was one of their favourite tricks in jungle warfare and a lethal one, for they remained silent until the forward troops had passed, and shot, at very close range, officers, runners carrying messages, or the radio-operators in headquarters following up the attack. Hunting them was a task exactly suited to the Gurkha temperament and the 29th was spent skirmishing and shooting the Japanese on their perches, and gradually winning control over the forest area immediately outside the stronghold.

Rome now sensed that Wakayuma was ripe for a counter-stroke, so he summoned the outlying column of the King's Regiment and ordered it to be ready to attack on the morning of the 30th. That night the Japanese attacked again but not with the same spirit, and once more they were beaten off.

Rome was now to encounter a communication difficulty that was to bedevil all Chindit operations involving the coordination of widely separated columns throughout the campaign. The radio network was designed to work 'up and down', and the lateral links were unreliable. Thus a message to an outlying column only a few miles away often had to be passed to brigade headquarters or right back to India for retransmission: Gaitley received the message, but he was not able to tell Rome that he had just fought a company of Japanese and was in some disarray. However, he sent part of his rifle company under Captain Coultart to Broadway, who duly attacked from the west up to the stronghold wire, only to be badly cut up by Japanese, who had stealthily occupied the air-raid trenches dug outside the perimeter by the light aircraft pilots (against orders). Coultart, a good and brave officer, was killed. The attack failed and Rome pulled the King's inside the stronghold. A third night attack was beaten off without difficulty. Wakayuma, in fact, had shot his bolt.[6]

On the 31st Rome called in the Air Commando, and mounted a strong attack to follow up the strike, using a company of Gurkhas and the group of King's, whose attack he led personally. The Gurkhas soon over-ran their objective. In fact the Japanese fled, but the King's had been badly shaken in their two previous encounters, having lost, besides Captain Coultart, some thirty-six killed and wounded. Nothing Rome could do would persuade them to follow up. 'They saturated the jungle with bullets and made a lot of noise, all sound and fury and not much else.' Not that it mattered. The persistent Astell was on the trail of the Japanese and he reported them retiring to the north and in poor shape. That was that. Broadway re-opened for business.

At this moment the Chindits appeared to be in disarray, both in the Indaw and the eastern sector, and so far had drawn nothing like the numbers they had deployed on themselves away from Stilwell or, for that matter, from the Fourteenth Army. Large numbers of élite troops imported with great effort behind the enemy lines were not engaging the Japanese at all. Stilwell was for the moment on the defensive. Only the 77th Brigade dug in grimly in the valley offered any threat at all. And yet, when the Japanese set aside their fanatical belief in their superiority and analysed the situation on their side, they could not but conclude that they were in deadly peril. It was not only the stout-hearted Tanaka who was in a fix, although his position was bad enough, with his supplies of ammunition and the barest necessities of life for his troops dwindling. Overall the Japanese were hopelessly outnumbered, and the qualitative superiority of their infantry had mysteriously been matched by their enemies. In the Hukawng Valley, Arakan and inside Burma Japanese troops had been beaten from the field. The Japanese air force, the only modern component of their simple, flexible but primitive war-machine, was being steadily ground down into impotence. Already the morale of the Japanese soldier was being eroded by the terrible rain of blows that descended on them from the sky. They were still able to attack and as patient and enduring under hardship as ever, but the marvellous weapon was losing its edge. Then, at the very moment that the high command had committed the bulk of its best troops to the desperate adventure of challenging the British forces west of the Chindwin, a veritable army had descended across all their lines of communication.

Wingate's scheme of operations involved landing his columns at widely dispersed points, remote from their objectives. All the Japanese could obtain at first were reports of British troops marching in every direction in a manner which concealed their goal. They were at first baffled, and slow therefore to react. Where there were roads they could move rapidly to counter a threat, using motor transport. But the bulk of their units had to rely on marching and horse and bullock transport, and could only pursue men on foot at the pace of men on foot. Reserves were hard to find, and the counter-attack forces were scraped together from every quarter: the Chindits were beginning to identify detachments and battalions from half a dozen different regiments. The best hope for the Japanese was the monsoon rain, due to arrive in mid-May, which might conceal them from the Allied air forces and cut off the Chindits from their air supply. But the rain descends on the just and the unjust, on Chindit and Japanese, and mud and malaria would slow them down alike. What the Japanese had most to fear at this juncture was a sustained offensive by the Chinese in the north. A victory lay within Stilwell's grasp.

At this moment Stilwell had halted. This was at least prudent. Until he met Slim at Jorhat on April 3rd he was gloomily convinced that a British defeat might leave him cut off and isolated in his northern base without land communications. The puny counter-thrust by Marayuma up the Tanai route had alarmed him. Stilwell was always to be alarmed at the faintest threat of a counter-attack. He was constantly obstructed by the secret orders of Chiang Kai-shek to his divisional commanders, and as it turned out he had put a veto on any further advance south of Shadazup. All the same Stilwell was and remained obstinately oblivious to the real extent of the Chindit success.

There were no American liaison officers with the brigades, and only one at Special Forces in India and his views carried little weight.[7] Had Stilwell been aware of Calvert's success to date, and of the crushing defeat he was to inflict on the Japanese 24th Brigade in the next fortnight he could not, had he been the great aggressive soldier of his myth, have failed to make one desperate heave southwards. As it was, he did nothing, and blamed others for not fighting, and so missed the opportunity to crush Tanaka before the monsoon rains began.

8

Enterprise at Indaw

WHEN FERGUSSON WAS ordered to take his 16th Brigade on foot into Burma with the mission of capturing the airfields at Indaw, he was faced with a choice between impossibilities. To be successful he had to arrive in the area unopposed and undetected. This ruled out infiltration across the Chindwin on the pattern so skilfully employed by Wingate in 1943, because the Japanese patrols and outposts were now deployed in greater strength and closer to IVth Corps. To follow the route through Stilwell's front in the Hukawng Valley or across the Taro plain was to court certain detection even if a premature engagement was avoided. Fergusson then examined a horrific alternative. Between Ledo and the upper Chindwin lay two parallel ranges rising to over 8,500 feet in places, the Patkai Bum and the Sangpaw Bum. Even on the maps of today Fergusson's route crosses a blank white area marked 'relief data incomplete'. A tentative reconnaissance by an American had suggested that its inner fastnesses were impassable even by small patrols. The slopes were one in two, the height of the passes ran up to 5,000 feet, so the soldiers who had toiled sweating and ever upwards through the tropical rain forests of the lower slopes would bivouac in the freezing cold of the heights. The jungles swarmed with leeches, tropical storms regularly lashed the ranges and turned the hillsides into muddy glissades, and so abrupt was the relief that a supply drop lacking in pin-point accuracy might deliver the precious rations beyond hope of recovery, far above on a crest or a thousand feet in the valley below. The absurdity of an attempt to traverse this wilderness and then cross the Chindwin River with 3,000 heavily-laden infantry and some 560 mules offered the best prospect for surprise and secrecy. The 16th Brigade was well-named 'Enterprise': the first stage of seventy miles to the Chindwin as an enterprise outdid even the passage of Wellington's Peninsula Army over the Tras-O-Montes in 1812.

On January 29th Major Robinson, the chief Royal Engineer of the brigade, with three of the Commando Engineer platoons and a rifle platoon, started to reconnoitre a route, cut and revet flights of steps and traverses and build bridges. Their skill and heroic labour and the sheer determination of the troops enabled the brigade to force its passage through the mountains. Even Wingate had his doubts about the route, as he confessed later. He left an indelible impression on the minds of some of the men of main column as they set out. As they scrambled up the steep northern glacis of the Patkai Bum they passed that strange, unkempt figure standing by the trail, anchored by an arm hooked over the branch of a tree, saying nothing, but as each man passed turning the laser beam of his daemonic stare full in his face, as if trying to fathom if his will was strong enough to meet the challenge of the march and the battle that lay at its end.

The 16th was a good marching brigade, even by Chindit standards, but that first seventy miles came as a shock. Needham wrote:

Men would make a few laborious yards only to slip on the greasy slope and be precipitated to a point below that at which they took their last breather. Mules would make a prodigious effort only to lose their footing and go plunging backwards, head over heels, hooves lashing wildly in all directions, loads flung dangerously to all sides. The dangers were prodigious, the labours stupendous. In four hours the column reached the top of a 500-foot hill. Many of the loads had been manhandled to the top – wireless sets, chore horses (portable charging engines), ammunition, petrol . . .
The march was torment and hell. We noticed it because of its novelty. Soon it was to become so much a daily routine that our pain-racked bodies gave it no particular thought. It was to be our daily lot . . .
'The terrain was quite unsuited to the landing of light planes . . . [A sick man's] only chance was to recover and catch up, or make his way back alone to the Ledo road . . . there he sat . . . head in hands, his whole body shaken with malaria. We passed him by without a word . . .
Up and up we went . . . to the top of one peak. Then just as abruptly down, and even this was no alleviation, for it was often as difficult to keep your feet going down as it was to heave yourself forward going up. And as soon as the valley was reached another grim height towered ahead.[1]

Fergusson, more laconic, wrote later that the march was 'a fair stinker'.

The leading battalion started on February 10th and arrived at the chosen crossing point of the Chindwin on the 28th, to earn the signal from Wingate: 'Well done, Leicesters, Hannibal eclipsed!' The next obstacle was the great river. With memories of scrambling across the Chindwin and the Irrawaddy in 1943 Fergusson had paid particular attention to the art of river-crossing when training his brigade. Gliders landed assault boats and outboard motors on a convenient sandbank, everyone knew what to do and the crossing was completed with brisk efficiency. Both columns of the Queen's Regiment were over in two hours and ten minutes. A delighted Wingate flew in with a posse of war correspondents on the 29th to watch the operation. He found a hatch of turtle eggs in the sandbank (who else but Wingate would have noticed such a trifle at such a moment?) which he pressed on as many soldiers as he could persuade to eat the disgusting objects raw, as an object lesson in jungle survival.

Indaw lay another 150 miles ahead, perhaps 400 measured along the route actually followed, and the brigade, faced with another stretch in the hill tracts west of the railway valley, gradually fell behind the scheduled date for its arrival in its operational area. This had been set by Wingate as March 15th. Stilwell, moreover, had asked for a diversion to attack the Japanese outpost at Lonkin, which resulted in two columns, No. 51 and No. 69, falling ten days behind the main body for little visible result: Lonkin had already been abandoned by the Japanese, probably because of things going badly for them on the Hukawng front. After Tanaka had wriggled free from the trap set for him by Stilwell at Walawbum there was no point in his keeping 300 men guarding an unthreatened flank. The Lonkin detour resulted only in a skirmish with the rear party of the Japanese garrison. This, as it turned out, was the only action these two columns were ever to engage in, except for a tiny patrol clash some weeks later.

The remaining six columns trudged on to the south, full of spirit but with the fine edge of their physical fitness already dulled by fatigue and malaria, which began to hit them in the low lying country east of the Chindwin. Discipline began to suffer, and on March 10th the commander of No. 51 Column had to resort to the disciplinary code peculiar to the Chindits ordered by Wingate and circulated by word of mouth. Punishments were to be summarily awarded and draconian: flogging, banishment into the jungle, and death by shooting. The full implications of this development will be discussed in a later chapter. All that need be said here is that the soldiers had been forewarned and had stoically accepted the code, and the officers believed, wrongly, that it had the force of law and had been sanctioned by the Commander-in-Chief, India. On this early occasion, two men had been found asleep and absent from their sentry posts in the night bivouac, thus endangering the safety of the whole column, and one had been detected helping himself to rations when collecting supplies after an air drop. These, as can be imagined, became the prevalent Chindit offences as fatigue began to wear down the weaker men and bad weather prevented supply drops so that men went short of food, sometimes for as much as five days. No commander used his power of punishment lightly. In the case of the delinquent sentries, their commanding officer went away by himself, as was his habit, to read a chapter of the Bible he carried with him, and having considered the matter carefully, ordered the pair to be beaten by the column sergeant-major and the man who had pilfered rations to be tied to a tree in the sun during a mid-day halt, a variation of the long-abolished 'field-punishment' of the First World War.[2]

During this second stage of his march Wingate's latest directive on the subject of 'strongholds' reached Fergusson, who was impressed by the vigour of its language and the text at its head: 'Turn ye to the stronghold, ye prisoners of hope.' (It is from Zechariah 9:12 and according to the Standard Revised Version is '*Return* to the stronghold . . .' Zechariah, poetical, full of obscure allegories and images of death and war, naturally appealed to Wingate.)[3] Fergusson sallied out in a light aircraft and chose a site near a little village called Taungle, twenty-five miles north-west of Indaw on the head waters of the Meza. Like Broadway, ABERDEEN, as this place was to be code-named, was remote and difficult of access by formed bodies of conventional troops, the terrain lent itself to defence, there was a good water supply and the surrounding villages were friendly to the British and could provide a screen of scouts or observers to give early warning of the approach of Japanese patrols. Its only snag was that it lay in a deep mountain valley, closed at the northern end by a high and abrupt ridge. Its airstrip was to prove a terror to the C-47 pilots and even the lighter liaison aircraft, there being no chance of a second circuit if the first approach to land went wrong, and all take-offs had to take the form of a hair-raising climbing turn at full throttle.

On March 20th Wingate flew into Burma, by B-25 to Broadway and from there by light aircraft in a couple of hops via the White City to Aberdeen to meet Fergusson and approve the site and lay-out of the defences. There he broke the news of two important changes in his plans.[4] He intended to bring his reserve brigades into Burma forthwith, beginning with the 14th, as soon as Aberdeen was ready to accept the C-47 transports, and Fergusson, who according to his original orders from Wingate was to precede his attack on Indaw 'by some weeks of preying on the enemy in that and the Banmauk area', was to continue his march without a pause with the immediate task of seizing and holding Indaw East airfield. This was a surprising change, at least as far as Fergusson was concerned, but in any case his orders from Wingate had so far been in such broad terms as to amount to vagueness. He knew that he had ultimately to capture

Indaw, after some days or weeks of preliminary skirmishing, but by this stage in his march he felt his instructions should have greater precision. On March 11th he signalled Force Headquarters:

> Would appreciate detailed orders about 15 March. Otherwise propose surrounding Banmauk and harassing all roads and neighbourhood. Propose also feint against Mansi on way past without incurring delay. Does this meet spirit of (your) instructions, or would you like me to move against Indaw earlier? Presume movement of 111 Brigade and 16 Brigade will be co-ordinated? What are inter-brigade recognition signals? . . .

It might be asked why, if Wingate was so determined to revive the TARZAN plan, of which the early capture of Indaw and use of its two airfields was the very core, he did not direct Fergusson on this objective from the beginning. Indeed, why did he not make it the objective of a glider-borne *coup-de-main*? Why the remote landing, the cat-like circling round the prize, followed by a long-delayed pounce? Both courses required the Chindit columns to hold the area against counter-attack until the 26th Division could be flown in, for which there had been no staff planning by the air forces whatsoever.

Re-arguing the case and mounting the operation would be a slow process. As it was, it took sixteen days to bring in the 14th and 3rd West African Brigades. But the *coup-de-main* would have at least ensured that the Japanese would not be able to put Indaw into a state of defence. Calvert has a recollection that some such move was discussed, but discarded. It can only be conjecture, but possibly the underlying reason was that 'deep penetration' or 'long-range penetration', together with its in-built version of the 'indirect approach', was felt by Wingate to be his unique contribution to the theories of strategy, and that his Special Force, after many administrative struggles, had been created especially to carry it out. He was therefore chained to his guerrilla-type operations to justify its existence. It is, perhaps, significant that when Wingate visited Calvert in the White City, that officer, flushed with success, proposed that the White City should be secured by another part of the Force while he drove up the Railway Valley and attacked the rear of the Japanese 18th Division. Wingate's response was to snub him rather severely, bidding him to 'remember the principles of long-range penetration'. What Wingate clearly had in mind was a screen of guerrilla-minded columns orbiting round Indaw and keeping off the Japanese reserves, while part of the force seized the airfields and held them. Unfortunately the situation had now changed for the worse.

Fergusson's brigade, in spite of heroic marching, was five days behind schedule, and 111th Brigade, owing to its re-routing, was still east of the railway, which it should have blocked, and intelligence reports revealed that the Japanese were rushing troops north. (They were, but to attack Calvert, although they were by this time aware that a British force of undetermined size was coming down from the north-west.) It was therefore essential to beat them to Indaw.

There was also another consideration. The trouble with Wingate as a commander was that he could never confine himself to one objective at a time. If Indaw was all-important, then it would have made good strategic sense to add Brodie's 14th Brigade, fresh and well-trained, to the effort to capture it, but Wingate ignored this elementary principle. At this precise date events west of the Chindwin, where Mutaguchi was developing the 'U-Go' offensive with his Fifteenth Army and caught the British IV Corps off-balance as it changed from an offensive to a defensive posture, attracted his attention. Slim's crisis was Wingate's opportunity. Now, he thought, was the moment to strike an impressive blow that might well decide the fate of the hard-pressed Slim and his Fourteenth Army. His written operation order to Brodie was to move south-west from Aberdeen as soon as he had landed, establish a stronghold and airstrip of his own, and harry the supply routed from the many small supply depots in the Indaw area which fed, via Homalin, Mutaguchi's right-hand or northern division, now threatening Kohima.[5]

Wingate was therefore pursuing three distinct aims at once. If 'Plan B', as he called it, was all-important, then Fergusson was on the spot, and could have set to work at once, and Brodie could join in as his columns arrived. The capture of Indaw, whatever its possibilities for Wingate's long-term strategy, would have been more than half way to 'Plan B'. From it Mutaguchi's northern supply routes could be conveniently raided. Wingate, acting on impulse and intuition, as he so often did, in the event sent Brodie off in one direction, where he achieved nothing until mid-April, and Fergusson in another, where he was defeated; while Calvert, whose grip on the White City was crucial to the Chindit mission to aid Stilwell, was left to fend for himself. It was characteristic of Wingate, however, that when he heard that the White City was under heavy attack and the Japanese had penetrated his perimeter, he suddenly gave an order to Fergusson to turn his line of march eastward and rush to Calvert's assistance, and then as quickly countermanded it. The result was that two of the already tired columns of 16th Brigade had to make an unnecessary detour when they could have been closing up on the site of the new stronghold of Aberdeen, resting and re-supplying for the battle that lay ahead.

Wingate's order to Fergusson to move on Indaw at once found him

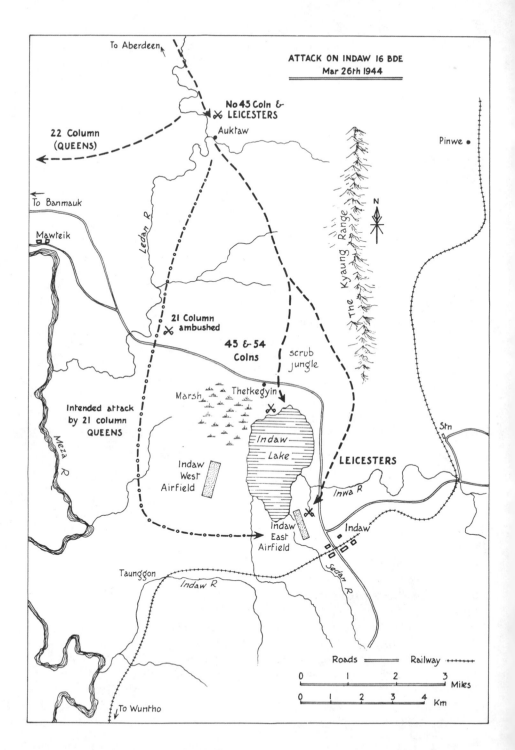

ATTACK ON INDAW 16 BDE
Mar 26th 1944

To Aberdeen

No 45 Coln &
LEICESTERS

Auktaw

22 Column
(QUEENS)

Pinwe •

To Banmauk

Mawteik

Ledan R

The Kyaung Range

N

21 Column
ambushed

45 & 54
Colns

scrub
jungle

Marsh   Thetkegyin

Indaw
Lake

Stn

Intended attack
by 21 column
QUEENS

Meza R

Indaw
West
Airfield

LEICESTERS

Inwa R

Indaw
East
Airfield

Indaw

Taunggon

Indaw R

Sedan R

To Wuntho

Roads ═══ Railway ┼┼┼┼

0   1   2   3
└────────┴────────┴────────┘ Miles

0   1   2   3   4
└────┴────┴────┴────┘ Km

in an awkward posture. His columns were spread out over a great distance. On March 20th his own headquarter column, No. 22 (Queen's) and No. 71 (Leicesters) had arrived in the area of Aberdeen, with their sister columns a short way behind. Nos. 45 and 54 were two days' march behind, and Nos. 51 and 69, who had waited long and vainly for Stilwell's Chinese to come and take over Lonkin, had left there (to Stilwell's annoyance) only on the 18th and were ten whole days behind. Fergusson would therefore have to do without two columns altogether. Nor would Wingate allow him any time to rest his tired troops, who, after their epic 450-mile trek would, he said, only 'stiffen up'. But Wingate, a man of quite extraordinary self-discipline and proof against any fatigue, had no time for human weaknesses. In his view malaria, dysentry, hunger, physical exhaustion, could all be overcome by will-power and faith in Jehovah, the God of Battles.

Fergusson was in a difficult position, but one common enough in war. An attack in form on entrenched Japanese was a serious matter and no degree of preparation could be enough, but he was a well-educated soldier who could balance the dangers of a premature or over-hasty attack against those of delay, which might well be fatal to his lightly armed columns, not trained or equipped for a direct assault on a strong position the enemy had had time to prepare. Moreover, at that moment, Fergusson believed that Indaw was the focal point of a triple, concentric Allied offensive into Burma, and that the 26th Division was ready poised to take over on his success.[6] The arguments for attacking at once were strong. He put his case for a rest to Wingate, as was his duty, and then obeyed his orders, as was also his duty.

Fergusson still remembers vividly what was to be his last meeting with his strange chief; a 'paladin', as he always declares, and a man who had enhanced his life by giving him the opportunity of taking part in two searing but splendid adventures. The scene was a beautiful and remote valley, as yet undisturbed by the bulldozers of the engineers, the roar of aircraft or the staccato rapping of the anti-aircraft guns. The two men were quite alone, except for Wingate's aide-de-camp. Fergusson was one of the men who had no fear of Wingate – who could be terrible in his wrath – and he had stood up to him more than once, but on this occasion their discussion was calm and businesslike, as befitted the occasion. They had only one misunderstanding, to become the subject of heated debate long after the war was over. Fergusson parted from Wingate convinced that Brodie's 14th Brigade, about to fly in to the new stronghold, Aberdeen, might be able to come to his assistance in some manner not exactly specified.[7] (It remains a matter for conjecture, but the

14th Brigade could, possibly, have reinforced the 16th if the attack on Indaw East airfield had not gone well or, more important, helped to consolidate its defence after capture, as the Japanese were bound to react violently.) Clearly Brodie could not be of immediate assistance, as it would take some time to fly in the whole of his brigade. Fergusson certainly understood that Brodie had first of all to establish himself in his assigned area of operations west of Banmauk, while Wingate's orders to Fergusson were to move as rapidly as possible. The United States Army Engineers, as usual, worked wonders in levelling the Aberdeen airstrip, and the first column of 14th Brigade, the Black Watch, arrived as early as March 23rd. But by that time Fergusson had already left and so had no opportunity of meeting Brodie and discussing his forthcoming operation with him.

Neither Wingate nor Fergusson can be blamed for a misunderstanding which did not, in fact, affect the course of events. The prosaic explanation must be the lack of written orders to confirm Wingate's instructions to Fergusson, or at least a confirmatory signal in cipher. The reason for this lapse was almost certainly the temporary interruption to the Special Force radio-network caused by the unplanned move of Wingate's forward headquarters which, as will be seen, also interfered with Fergusson's ability to control his own columns at a critical moment in his attack. Whatever the cause, no confirmatory copy of the operation order issued to Brodie reached Headquarters 16th Brigade or was ever seen, then or later, by Fergusson or his brigade-major.[8] Yet this document makes it perfectly clear Brodie's mission did not include any task in support of Fergusson's impending attack on Indaw.

The consequence of Wingate's insistence on an immediate attack was that Fergusson could not wait for Nos. 51 and 69 columns, ten days' march behind after their diversion against Lonkin. Even so, it took him four days to collect the remainder of his strung-out columns, who had to move into position as they arrived without rest, adequate reconnaissance, or formal orders, for what was a somewhat complicated manoeuvre. Fergusson's plan, using widely dispersed columns coming in on the objective from different directions, had a strong Chindit and guerrilla flavour. The Leicesters and the 45th Reconnaissance Regiment were to assemble at the villge of Auktaw, where Fergusson intended to give their commanding officers their final orders personally, and then creep stealthily along the narrow, forest-clad crest of the Kyaung ridge which provided a covered approach to Indaw West airfield. One column of the Queen's was to make a long detour round the west side of Indaw Lake and attack Indaw (or the airfield, it is not at all clear which) from the south-east. The other column of the Queen's was to go off two days' march to the west and ambush the road near Banmauk, with the mission of preventing any move towards Indaw by the scattered parties of Japanese believed to be in that area.

There is a 'marked contrast between the operations of Calvert's brigade and Fergusson's. The difference was not of skill, but of style. General Symes, it will be remembered, had asked Wingate during the preparatory period if he was clear in his mind between the guerrilla rôle and the conventional one. Calvert had veered more and more towards the conventional. He closely controlled his columns, had trained them to dig and fortify positions and was fully prepared to assault the Japanese, controlling his vital air support through his brigade Royal Air Force officer.[9] (He has described his method as moving and probing with outspread fingers, but clenching his fist before striking his enemy.) The 16th Brigade represented an earlier phase in the evolution of Wingate's tactics. Fergusson commanded loosely, leaving the details to his widely dispersed column commanders. It was the only sort of warfare that Fergusson had experienced, and it is worth noting that his plan had been approved in advance by Wingate, at least in outline. As a result, Fergusson was to fight under two disabling handicaps, neither of which was the result of any neglect on his part. Ideally he should have detached the reconnaissance platoons of the columns and sent them questing ahead of his route to Indaw to locate the enemy and pinpoint his fixed positions, if any. He had no time to allow them the necessary start of ten or fifteen miles which they required if they were to give accurate information of routes and conditions, and the location of the enemy. Even so there was some mismanagement. There seems to have been no short-range reconnaissance, and the columns stumbled on the Japanese without warning on at least three occasions, with serious consequences. There was another unpredictable factor. A water-supply for men and mules was absolutely essential, and the second half of the route to Indaw was waterless, with disastrous results.

The second handicap has been briefly mentioned in the account of Rome's defence of Broadway. The complex Special Force radio-network was exactly designed for the command and control of Chindit tactics. The main channels ran like the spokes of a wheel from hub to rim. A battery of powerful sets, located at Imphal, picked up the weak signals from the portable sets in the field, amplified them and retransmitted them back again. If the columns in a brigade were outside the effective range of the feeble No. 22 radio-set, about 5,000 yards under the best conditions, it was surer, for technical reasons, to sent the message back to India. Even in the best of conditions the times for transmission were limited and required the headquarters concerned to halt and put up their aerials, and in the worst ferocious static caused the passage of even a short signal to take a long time. (The American air-support net used by the Air Commando was proof against this, but the base equipment was located at the airfield and not at Special Force Headquarters.) Fergusson was faced at this critical moment in his operation with another obstacle no one could have foreseen – although Wingate might have done so if he had had the prescience some of his disciples continue to claim for him, and maintain he showed in his 'Plan B'. Forward headquarters was at Imphal, threatened at exactly that moment by the Japanese offensive, so Wingate himself had at short notice to move back to Sylhet and take the whole base radio complex with him. The compound effect of these various factors was that Fergusson was blind for lack of intelligence of the Japanese, and at crucial moments he was also deaf and dumb as well.

All the same, war lies in the domain of chance, and the dice have rolled favourably for commanders who have made worse plans and faced bigger obstacles. Fergusson, however, was dead out of luck in his first, and last, battle. On the 25th the leading column of his main striking force, the 45th, blundered into Auktaw hoping to water the men and animals, only to find it held by a strong post of the Burma National Army stiffened by Japanese. The Japanese had put out no sentries and the 45th had not reconnoitred the village, so surprise was mutual and there was some 'confused fighting'. Into this imbroglio arrived Colonel Wilkinson of the Leicesters and part of his No. 17 Column. There was a 'lively engagement', which ended with the Leicesters clearing the village at bayonet-point. 'They ran as fast as Italians,' remarked a private, proving to his own satisfaction that the reports of Japanese prowess had been exaggerated. It was not a cheap victory. Two officers of the 45th were killed and Wilkinson's elbow was shattered by a bullet. This upset all plans for a tidy approach to the impending battle, but it was a satisfactory little skirmish. Fergusson, to avoid delay, sent out his final orders by liaison officer and ordered the four columns to press on.

Then emerged the horrible fact that the Auktaw forest, through which they were moving, in spite of the streams and lakelets shown on the map, was in March as dry as the Sahara. There was water miles away in the Ledan River and water in the Indaw Lake, but between the two nothing except the meagre supply of the forest villages, and such moisture a solitary traveller might find in a stagnant pool in the bed of a dry watercourse or, at a pinch, by digging in the stream bed. Four columns and headquarters column needed approximately 3,000 gallons of water a day to keep man and beast in fighting trim in the tropics. A survival ration for the men could be included in a supply drop, and this brigade headquarters and the Leicesters hastily arranged for themselves, but the 45th failed to do so, and there still remained the mules.'

Fergusson was now beset by acute difficulties but he did not hesitate, His orders were clear: to take every risk in the hope of capturing Indaw East as soon as possible, so he decided to go on at once with the Leicesters alone. Colonel Cumberledge, the commander of the 45th Reconnaissance Regiment, was to take his two columns to the village of Thetkegyin, which stood in open paddy-fields between the edge of the forest and the north shore of the lake, water his animals and men and then press on as fast as he could in the wake of the Leicesters.

Unfortunately Thetkegyin proved to be stoutly held by a small force of Japanese. A disjointed and grim little battle took place; the Japanese, in their usual way, not content with holding on but coming out of their defences and counter-attacking, while their patrols, perhaps guessing what the battle was about, held off the desperate attempts by Cumberledge's men to reach the lake shore in what came to be known as the 'Battle of the Waterbottles'. Cumberledge was frustrated, and eventually pulled out his No. 45 Column and with commendable tenacity – he himself was over the forty-year age limit and in the last stages of physical exhaustion after the rigours of the long march from Ledo – set off with two platoons he had rallied from the confusion of the scattered fight in the jungle to see if he could help Wilkinson.

Varcoe, commanding No. 54 Column, alone and out of touch with Cumberledge and Fergusson, came hard up against the Japanese positions round the village. He hung on, beating off one Japanese counter-attack after another; his men scratching around in stream beds, often under fire, to fill a *chagal* or a waterbottle to bring round to their comrades for a sip each in mid-battle.

A vivid and unadorned account of the action from the pen of Trooper Aylen of No. 54 Column describes how his platoon came up to reinforce the attack, and the sinking of the spirits he felt at the first horrid evidence of real battle after all the months of training and marching, as he and his comrades moved up through the smoke and flame of the burning forest towards the sound of firing ahead. Mortar fire had hit the mules carrying the flame-throwers, and they lay roasting in the flames, which had spread to the ammunition. The engineer explosives had gone up, the forest was on fire, and the grenades and mortar bombs were exploding intermittently in the burning undergrowth. Here were the scorched corpses of Japanese; there lay comrades they had seen speaking and laughing with not long before. Discipline, however, conquers fear and morbid reflections. 'We fixed our bayonets and loosened the pins in our grenades,'

145

says Aylen, and in a moment he has passed that mental barrier dividing a soldier who has fought and been in action, if only for an hour, from one who has not. There is close fighting with rifle and grenade among the trees. Then the Japanese bring up a machine-gun at close range and pin his section: a man rash enough to lift his head could see the faces and expressions of the Japanese machine-gunners, who traversed to fire through the undergrowth at every sound: Aylen's troop-sergeant lies in a dip, shot through the ankle, stifling his groans lest they should bring another burst in their direction. Then the fight turns a little in their favour: Aylen hears the 'masterly' note of one of their own Vickers guns in reply. All but one of its crew are killed, but the remaining man serves the gun until the Japanese are driven off. (He earned the Military Medal.) Aylen watches the column mortar officer standing erect and cool amid the flying bullets on the little ridge they are holding; calling out his orders and fighting a bizarre duel with the Japanese machine-gunners as each fire blind at the sound of the other.

Aylen, jungle-wise, found a banana tree and cut a length of its sappy stem, and on the way back to his section saw men from another platoon, 'their eyes protruding and their flesh sunken from acute thirst'. One begged him for a piece, and he gave him half. After two days and a night of this, and having accounted for eighty-six Japanese killed, Varcoe pulled out. Five days of thirst was followed by enough water, at last. Having had food and tea Aylen lay down with a further supply of water to hand and, 'for curiosity', kept a tally of the mugfuls he drank in the night: he absorbed fifteen pints.

Thetkegyin was hardly a model operation. The 45th blundered into the enemy, this time an alert one, without adequate reconnaissance. The powerful aid of the air commando was not summoned, the two columns fought an uncoordinated battle, and the upshot was that the whole 45th was written off for the time as an effective force. The two columns were later combined into one, Cumberledge was relieved and flown out, and command given to the Burma Rifles officer, Major Astell, who had shown such spirit in the fighting round Broadway.

The luck of the Queen's was mixed. No. 22 Column at Banmauk ambushed a small Japanese lorry convoy, and interrupted road traffic effectively, but this had no relevance to the fight for Indaw East, and they were too far away to come to Fergusson's help. No. 21 on its way to its objective had bivouacked unwittingly close to a road (not marked on the map) when a company of Japanese in lorries, to the great surprise of both sides, drove into their camp. There was a violent fire-fight with showers of grenades in which the mules were caught. They were shot or stampeded, so the unfortunate Lieutenant-Colonel Metcalfe lost all his radios, heavy weapons and reserve ammunition and was forced to disperse. In this way, before the battle had started, the five columns of the striking force were reduced to three, of which only two were near the objective, and the brigade commander was out of touch and no longer able to influence the battle.[10]

All now rested on Colonel Wilkinson and the 2nd Battalion of the Leicesters, not inappropriately known as 'the Tigers'.

The Leicesters were a perfect example of an old-fashioned regiment of the British infantry line; élite, self-regarding, self-confident. They were not particularly honoured by being Chindits: if asked, they might have answered that the Chindits were honoured by the inclusion of the Leicesters. Nor were they impressed by the Wingate mystique.[11] When Wingate signalled that by their crossing of the mountains and the Chindwin they had 'eclipsed Hannibal', Wilkinson remarked that such references were over his head. Wingate's stirring order of the day to all ranks when they had safely arrived in Burma is recorded in the war diary as 'long corrupt message from Force, impossible to decipher, but something in it about guts and God'.[12]

Wilkinson, a highly professional infantryman, had devised his own method of Chindit fighting. His columns were organised so that the fighting elements could quickly be divorced from the transport and amalgamated into a single, compact battalion of some 300 riflemen and a heavy-weapons group of four Vickers machine-guns and four mortars. Such a group was capable of hard, sustained fighting. He led the attack himself, his broken arm dressed and in a sling. Wilkinson nearly won the battle alone, the Japanese being unable to dislodge him. Had the cards not fallen so badly, had there been any support for his efforts, had the 45th not been diverted to find water, the day could well have been his and the airfield in Fergusson's hands. He reached its very edge before he ran into the Japanese and decided to dig in and await their attack on the banks of a flowing stream, the Inwa *chaung*. There, with an assured water supply and a good defensive position, Wilkinson fought the battle he wanted; one in which the fire discipline and marksmanship of his veteran battalion could mow down the repeated, frontal, banzai attacks of the Japanese who hurried to meet him. He held out for two days and three nights, killing (at a modest estimate) some ninety Japanese for the loss of two officers and nine men killed, and six men wounded. The aircraft of the First Air Commando, supplying the most daring and accurate close support – the bomb splinters whirring into the Leicesters' forward posts – killed many more, and finally enabled Wilkinson to bring off that trickiest and most dangerous of infantry manoeuvres – breaking from close contact with a determined enemy – when Fergusson finally decided to call a halt to the whole operation and ordered a general withdrawal to the vicinity of Aberdeen.[13] Alarming fragments of radio messages had been heard by Headquarters, 16th Brigade through the deafening static to the effect that 1,000 Japanese were approaching the stronghold, and later that Aberdeen had actually fallen to the enemy. These proved false, and the 16th Brigade paused to rest and lick its wounds.

The fiasco at Indaw remains the only example of Wingate in personal control of a large-scale operation in the field and reveals all his daring, and all his weakness, as a commander. If he is to be judged by the strictest criteria laid down by Liddell Hart for the 'indirect approach', he emerges well. The element of surprise, the choice of a point of attack remote from the main battlefield where the opponent would be forced to fight but where he would be weakest, the multiplicity of objectives so that his plan would have two or three branches – all were achieved. (But it must be said that Wingate was no 'Liddell-Hartist'. He was a 'Wingate-ist': in his arrogance he admitted no mentor.) He had judged the logistic factors correctly and also the capability of his much-abused staff when he brought in two brigades at the shortest of notice. He must, however, be judged not by theory but by results. His bounding imagination and energy had brought altogether 8,200 fighting men converging on the goal of his hopes and dreams, from whence he would embark on the liberation of North Burma. Only 300 of them, the Leicesters, arrived on the objective. The 'indirect approach' may be a useful concept and a corrective for those generals who rely exclusively on a bloody frontal attack, but it is an *ignus fatuus*, a fool's lantern, for amateurs of warfare. Even the indirect approach demands that the general focus his whole mind and intellect on his chosen goal. No chance of this with Wingate. No sooner had he completed the final preparations for his great enterprise of THURSDAY than his restless imagination was seizing on new combinations and new goals. Already, before battle had been really joined, he was dashing off reports converting the successful fly-in into a great victory, hinting to the Prime Minister that all that had been gained might be lost by failure to exploit by the chief Allied commanders, crying up the work of the Air Commando and suggesting that if only he had two or three such formations he could win even greater victories.[14] Nor did he stop there. He amazed Slim and Mountbatten with a fantastic proposal to raise twenty-five more Chindit brigades and advance overland – to Bangkok![15] He then imagined that he held the key of the great battle about to break out west of the Chindwin and darted off on that new tack. As a first step he considered that if he could bring some of his reserve units into this area he could assist Slim, but, as he thought further, his imagination carried him on and he saw this move as ensuring Mutaguchi's total defeat. He said as much in his signal to the Prime Minister, throwing in the destruction of Tanaka's 18th Division facing Stilwell for good measure.

He revealed these new perspectives to the faithful Tulloch, but only in private conversations. Symes and Marks, on whom the burden of working out the logistic details would fall, were kept in the dark until the last moment and there was never any forward planning. Everything was undertaken at the last minute. The brigade commanders likely to be involved were never consulted or informed or given the opportunity to study the areas in which they were likely to be operating. It proved a great surprise to the 14th Brigade and to the battalions of the 3rd West African Brigade when they were suddenly called forward. No calculations were made at that stage to see if General Old's transport force could maintain any extra units in the field. The highly efficient airfield organisation set up by Special Force Headquarters to supervise the fly-in for THURSDAY had been dismantled on March 12th.

In the meantime Wingate was revolving another idea in his mind. Later in the month there appears in the 77th Brigade war diary a significant signal from Calvert to Tulloch. He suggests, on March 30th, that as soon as Indaw has fallen a local, superior commander should establish himself in the Indaw-Mawlu region to coordinate the activities of the five brigades by that date milling about in the area. Calvert himself, with three battalions at the White City, two at Broadway and Morris and Dah Forces away on the Chinese border, was already carrying a burden of responsibility appropriate to a major-general. It was a thoroughly sensible and practical suggestion, and Wingate's ideas were often prompted by his ablest lieutenant.

On March 3rd Wingate had written a letter marked 'Private, confidential and most secret' to Symes outlining his ideas for rationalising his command and control structure. He wanted Symes to study how, without asking for any additional resources, Special Force could be reorganised as 'an army corps for LRP', of two divisions. 'If we have been successful in the next crucial fortnight there will be no grounds whatever for refusing it,' he said, indicating how each success was to be used as a launching pad for a further expansion of the Force and of its rôle and status. When he sent a certain signal to Symes (he said), which was to be the reference number and date of this particular letter, Symes was to go himself and negotiate the change with Headquarters, South-East Asia Command. This mission was given to Symes, not Tulloch (who does not appear ever to have heard of this plan), and Symes was to go not to Slim, Wingate's operational commander, but over his head to Giffard, who was the British land forces commander overall. In addition, Symes himself was to organise a divisional headquarters for the 'second division' (there is no mention of who was to have first division, but Wingate may have been thinking of Calvert) and take command of the three reserve brigades, that is, the 14th, 23rd and the West Africans.[16]

This gives an important insight into Wingate's developing ideas, for it implied that he would, following the normal hierarchical structure, have to be promoted lieutenant-general, and a lieutenant-general in command of a semi-independent corps would occupy a very different and more powerful status than a mere major-general in command of a force of guerrillas. However, this scheme was shot out of his mind by the next emotional crisis to hit him.

Slim at this moment was hard pressed by the anxieties of the opening moves of the great battle developing at Imphal-Kohima, and on March 8th he discussed with Tulloch the prospects of diverting the reserve Chindit brigades from their legitimate object of assisting Stilwell, to assisting him. He told Tulloch not to pass on his thoughts on this to Wingate, because he did not want to distract his attention from the operation he already had in hand. Slim trusted Tulloch, having been impressed by his calmness and common sense during the trauma of the early hours of THURSDAY. His instruction as an army commander to a senior staff officer, that his remarks were in strict confidence, were perfectly privileged, and binding. His object was to give Tulloch the opportunity for some discreet forward planning. He had, however, mistaken his man. Tulloch blurted the confidence out to his chief on his return, with the result Slim had feared. Wingate, scribbling an authority for Tulloch to command in his absence, flew off on the 9th in a passion to see Slim and to threaten his resignation (yet again) if thieving hands were ever laid on his precious brigades.[17] He had not paused to consider that for once he and his superior were in agreement, for both men, for a brief moment, perceived that the Chindit effort might be better employed in cutting Mutaguchi's supply lines than in awaiting Stilwell's advance. Slim blandly calmed him down and Wingate returned mollified, if not wholly reassured. He now saw the opportunity to implement his 'Plan B' but his true feelings were revealed in a phrase he used to members of staff: that he was determined to introduce his remaining brigades into Burma 'before the rats got at them'.[18]

On March 10th Symes learned of Wingate's latest proposals. What Wingate had in mind was to redirect Lentaigne's 111th Brigade from its primary mission of blocking the approaches to Indaw from the south to a harassing rôle on the routes leading west from Indaw and

Wuntho. To this end two more columns, chosen by Wingate because he thought they were the best, were to be flown in to reinforce Lentaigne. The Black Watch had done some impressive exercises with gliders and were a fine battalion and war-hardened, so Rose's No. 42 Column was one of those selected and the other, No. 77 Column of the 7th Leicesters, was commanded by one of the 'old guard' from the 77th Brigade of LONGCLOTH, Major Geoffrey Lockett.

Symes was alarmed on both counts. He and Marks would have great difficulty in persuading a reluctant air force to provide the extra planes, not only for the fly-in, which was only a temporary diversion of resources, but for the increased burden of maintenance in the field. C-47s were like gold world-wide, and the existing transport force was already stretched. Also, Symes was perturbed by Wingate's apparent inclination to revert to using Special Force in fragments and not stick to established brigade and battalion grouping. He thought he had won this argument the previous year, and he protested vigorously.

In the meantime it soon became apparent that 111th Brigade would be too late to carry out either rôle. The alteration in the flight plan for THURSDAY had put Lentaigne behind schedule. The two battalions landed at Broadway had had further to march, and Lentaigne had had a bad crossing of the Irrawaddy. After taking two days he still had all the heavy weapons and part of the mules of No. 30 Column and all No. 40 Column on the left bank, so he had sent them to join Morris and pressed on westwards with his headquarter column and No. 30 amalgamated into one. His brigade was not to reach the area of Wuntho and cross the railway until March 26th.

Wingate meanwhile examined the possibilities of landing the 14th Brigade complete south-west of Pinlebu, and the 23rd in the area of Pakkoku 200 miles south of Indaw to sever the main Japanese supply line to Imphal. These ideas were discarded as impractical. (Pakkoku was a mistaken objective in any case. The natural route to Imphal and the one in use by the Fifteenth Army was from Mandalay to Kalewa.) Wingate next called for Symes and Marks to meet him at Comilla, Headquarters, Fourteenth Army, on March 20th, to brief him on the logistics of flying the 14th Brigade in through Aberdeen, and then went in to see Slim alone. Slim agreed to release the 14th Brigade from reserve, and there can be no doubt that at this stage and until April 9th he fully agreed that the rôle of the brigade was to harass Mutaguchi's communications. The operation order to that effect, issued by Headquarters, Special Force on March 23rd, directed Brodie to the south-west and instructed him to establish his own stronghold in his operational area. Wingate then flew off (on 20th) to launch Fergusson on his venture to Indaw East airfield. On the 22nd the American airfield construction engineers were landed by glider at

Aberdeen to level the C-47 airstrip while the staff of Special Force, in a brilliant piece of improvisation, reconstructed the airfield control machinery. (Mead, a young major at the time, recalls visiting a recalcitrant full colonel at Headquarters, Fourteenth Army, thumping the table in the best Chindit style, and uttering the word of power, *Wingate*, so as to extract the necessary men and resources.) The Aberdeen strip was ready for use and the Black Watch columns began to assemble there on the 23rd and 24th. It was a fine feat of organisation and good staff work, but rapid as it was, it would still be some time before Brodie would be able to exert any pressure on the Japanese supply routes, whereas the 16th Brigade were already on the spot and poised to do the task which they had been originally given.

The air maintenance burden was by this date becoming heavy beyond all the original estimates, because as well as the 14th Brigade two battalions of the 3rd West African Brigade were entering Burma. When Wingate conceived his 'stronghold' policy in February he asked for garrison troops, and was grudgingly allotted the 3rd/9th Gurkhas, for Broadway. Any more, he was told, must be found from his own resources, and the 6th Nigerian Regiment was flown into Broadway to march to Aberdeen. This had encountered the Japanese battalion on the way to Broadway and in the fight that followed it had been scattered and badly demoralised. The commanding officer had been removed, and Major Upjohn, the brigade-major, promoted to take charge and pull it together in Aberdeen. To take its place meanwhile, the 12th Battalion was also to fly in. By the end of the month, therefore, there would be five fresh battalions to feed in Burma, and there was still the 23rd to be brought in 'before the rats got at it,' as in the event they did.

Tulloch had reminded Wingate of his right to communicate direct with the Prime Minister, so he drafted one of his flamboyant signals asking for more transport aircraft. Wingate had told Slim of his intention to do this, probably on the morning of the 20th, and Slim agreed in principle, on the grounds that extra aircraft were in great demand by the whole theatre, but he did not agree the draft. On the 21st it was sent to Headquarters, South East Asia Command, to Mountbatten's Assistant Chief of Staff. It contained the words that the text was to be forwarded to Churchill 'verbatim repeat verbatim', with a copy to Slim. In it Wingate asked Churchill to obtain four squadrons of C-47s – a hundred aircraft – for the exclusive use of Special Force, promising in exchange a great victory, 'no more Hump', the destruction of four Japanese Divisions (three in Fifteenth Army and the one facing Stilwell) and 'all Burma north of the 24th parallel'. He added that 'Slim gives me his full backing', which annoyed Slim, for neither he nor any other senior commander was going to part with a hundred of these precious aircraft to any major-general for his exclusive use; Slim least of all. The four squadrons did in fact arrive in India, and proved to be a great boon, although they were not used for the purpose Wingate had had in mind.

The whole transaction is a perfect example of Wingate's methods. A situation is created, with Machevellian skill, in which he has to be supported or exposed to disaster: the troops are sent in first and how they are to be supplied is left to be considered later. A verbal agreement in principle is rapidly converted to 'the full backing' in an explicit text; and so on. The question that remains concerns the nature of Wingate's generalship.

There is no doubt about the transcendent qualities which had enabled him to scale the heights, convert the great men he found there to his views, create a unique type of army and transport it to the battlefield of his choice. But was he a second Marlborough, as one of his followers called him, or a commander 'whose reputation will live on long after the names of other generals of that war are forgotten', in the words of another?

If Wingate's conduct of affairs during that last month of his period of command is any guide, he appears to have lacked that middle level of military experience and skill where all the dull, laborious slog of staff work, nine-tenths administration, is done, and without which all the brilliant strategic plans and the courage and battle-craft of the fighting soldiers come to nothing. A Napoleon may be permitted to exclaim, '*Ne m'en parlez pas des vivres*'. A Wingate can be excused when he produces a raw onion from his shirt pocket, presses it on a reluctant soldier, and makes him eat it. ('That will keep you going for a week, my man', he said). Eccentricity is one thing, but to signal to brigades in the field threatening to deprive whole columns of their rations as a punishment for alleged faults in not reporting locations or for the incorrect marking of supply drop zones was absurd.[19] It is one thing to believe that formal staff training produces officers of rigid orthodoxy unable to deviate from regulations, but quite another to damn all trained staff officers as useless. Wingate was extremely well served by his staff from the top down, but he treated them, except those in his own select circle, with rudeness and contempt. Unlike the troops in the field, many of them hated and feared him. He regarded them as so many clerks, when each man should have been regarded as a specialist – as happened in other, happier headquarters – and given his head once the main lines of the mission had been laid down. It is an indictment of Wingate's lack of system that, having evolved his Indaw plan, he failed to order the one, essential, preliminary reconnaissance which would establish whether it was workable: that is, by discovering the state of the Indaw airfields. When, in April, the 16th Brigade finally overran Indaw West unopposed, it was discovered to be unusable, even in the dry weather, without extensive engineer work. The Japanese did not even bother to defend it. Such neglect was criminal. Wingate did not understand the need to open his mind to all his staff, not just to one or two officers unknown to each other, and allow them to plan ahead for contingencies.

He had no 'plans' at all in the accepted, military, sense of the word: only flights of strategical fantasy. Admittedly his fantasies were sometimes creative with a germ of a valuable idea, but what is to be made of such proposals as his original plan for the 77th Brigade – to fly to Yunnan and march back into Burma fording the Salween en route – or to send the 23rd Brigade on a suicide mission to Pakkoku, or for IVth Corps to invade lower Burma by floating on rafts down the Chindwin, or to raise twenty-five more Chindit brigades? His mind was like the kitchen of an alchemist, full of retorts, alembics and crucibles all bubbling with strange potions, some full of dross, others with traces of pure gold, to which Wingate turned from moment to moment for a specific as each fresh scene in the battle unfolding in front of him caught his eye.

Nevertheless, Wingate had one supreme virtue as a military commander, greater even than his gift of inspiring his followers: he never admitted defeat. He would have seen the fiasco at Indaw as only a set-back. Greater generals have survived many worse.

The casualties had been a trifle and there would be no great difficulty in concentrating for a second attempt. He had two strongholds in working order, and all attacks on them by land and air had been repelled. Calvert was ensconced in the Railway Valley near Mawlu, had won a tangible and much-needed victory and was about to win another. Wingate had the unique Air Commando at his private disposal and also the enthusiastic support of Air Vice-Marshal Vincent of 221 Group Royal Air Force who (on March 11th) had even deployed a flight of Spitfires in Broadway. He had exercised his right to communicate directly with Churchill for the purpose of appealing for more transport aircraft and he could reasonably hope that any resulting additions to the transport fleet in the command must inevitably benefit his own plans. In a few days time all his brigades bar one would be inside Burma and under his own hand and three of them – a divisional-sized force of ten and a half battalions – correctly deployed in what he firmly believed to be the area vital to his strategy. His conviction, that under his guiding hand the Japanese could be defeated inside Burma or on the Imphal plain by indirect action, was not likely to falter. He had seven weeks, before the monsoon rains began, to make and implement fresh plans.

He was perfectly capable of switching from one plan to another without the least regard for his official mission. He might have marched westward in strength on to the Chindwin crossings. He might have concentrated three brigades around Indaw for an attack to seize the airfield complex and hold it under Symes as a divisional commander. All this, however, remains speculation, and what he would have done and how it would have turned out will never be known.

On March 24th he paid another visit to his strongholds in Burma and, during the last leg of his return journey, the B-25 bomber in which he was travelling crashed in the mountain range west of Imphal, killing everyone on board.

9

Lentaigne Succeeds Wingate

THE NEWS OF Wingate's death was a profound shock to every Chindit in the field down to the humblest mule-driver. For many who had only seen him once and many more not at all he was their inspired leader in war, their chieftain, their protector, their champion against the unfeeling, invisible bureaucracy of the 'staff'. 'If they listened to me,' said Wingate, seeing some men of No. 59 Column weighing their equipment, 'you would be carrying thirty-five, not seventy-five pounds.' They knew that he had obtained the best rations for them, and the best weapons. If they were sick or wounded they would be picked up in the light aircraft he had obtained from the Americans and treated in the hospital he had set up especially for Chindits.

This unquestioning faith in Wingate was by no means confined to the private soldiers: the hard-marching, much-enduring 'other ranks'. Many officers had equal faith in him and believe to this day that had he survived he would have retained the White City, captured Indaw, and obtained the promised extra division to secure their gains; that he would never have allowed the Air Commando to be so abruptly disbanded on May 1st, his whole plan of campaign to be perverted, all their gains abandoned, or permitted Special Force to be delivered into the hands of Stilwell. The Chindits were to fight on valiantly long after the ninety days Wingate had declared was the most that troops in deep penetration operations could stand without relief, groaning that Wingate would never have allowed such suffering, but using the last dregs of their energy and courage in the bitter days at the end of July, when the survivors, mere skeletons racked with fever, were finally relieved.

The non-commissioned officers of the British Army, and this was particularly true of the citizen army of 1939–1945 with its wealth and variety of talent, who were the very emblem of authority and the instrument by which discipline was maintained, were proof against inflated rhetoric, and possessed a keen nose for the bogus. They were the severest and most just critics of their officers, but even they were not proof against Wingate's spell. One, trudging along with Head-quarters, 111th Brigade, on learning that their new mission was to go to the aid of the IVth Corps, growled something to the effect that he knew that those non-Chindits would sooner or later be squealing for help, but that Wingate would never have allowed it (little realising that the new orders reflected Wingate's last expressed wish).[1]

One night towards the very end of the campaign Sergeant Shaw of No. 12 Column was sitting with his friends round a camp-fire, absorbing a welcome rum ration and discussing the burning question of relief and, with some cynicism, the larger problem of Britain's war aims.

'"The War Office won't care a bugger if we're all dead."

"Bloody Burma Oil. *That's* why they're keeping us in."'

Then one of them produced from his haversack a stained order of the day, issued by Wingate, and read it out:

'"We need not, as we go forward into conflict, suspect ourselves of selfish or interested motives. We have all had the opportunity of withdrawing, and that which has led each one of us to devote ourselves to that which lies ahead cannot have been a bad motive."'

This produced silence for a few seconds and then the argument started again.

'"But Wingate's dead now. If he weren't, we wouldn't bloody well be here."

"You're right. We're not Chindits now."'[2]

Such regret was not universal. There were many on the staff in Fourteenth Army and Eastern Air Command whose unforgiving enmity Wingate had fairly earned. The news of his disappearance gave rise to a curious scene in the mess of his own main headquarters, whose members had so often felt the lash of his anger – a lash applied equally to the backs of the efficient and the inefficient and to victims whose only fault was to be within range. When the news that their commander was missing spread, the officers, instead of going in to snatch a hasty meal as was the practice in that hard-working organisation, stood around in groups in a babble of speculation, ordering round after round of drinks. Their mood was not callous, but neither was there any indication of gloom, let alone dismay. All present knew, and none better than those former members of the 70th Division headquarters, that the unique organisation into which they had been drawn or dragooned was Wingate's own creation and without him its future, and therefore their own, hung in the balance. Naturally there was excited discussion. There was also a detectable mood of relief, as if a gloomy shadow had been lifted by the disappearance of a dreaded taskmaster. The mess sergeant was shocked. He said to an officer who was also standing apart from the throng and watching, that it didn't seem right to be, as it were *celebrating*, when their general was lying somewhere in the jungle cold and dead.[3]

That was the staff reaction. It was Calvert who spoke for the Chindits when Tulloch's signal announcing Wingate 'missing, believed killed' was handed to him in the White City. Putting his head in his hands he said forlornly: 'Oh, who will look after us now?'[4]

Wingate, that ruthless man, whose repeated message to the Chindits had been that their lot was to be toil, suffering and death, had in a few brief months become a legend. The grave danger of such a style of leadership lay in the impossibility of producing a comparable successor. With the Chindits now scattered over upper Burma and embroiled with the enemy, the new man would have no chance to visit commanding officers, talk to the men, reassure them and impress his personality on them. Wingate was a terrible loss, but a change in the style of leadership was not necessarily harmful. On the contrary, with Special Force created, animated and fairly launched into battle it would be a good thing to entrust it to a general less tempestuous in his relations with the rest of the army and air forces and more systematic in his conduct of operations. But the nature of Special Force was such that choosing Wingate's replacement was not simply a matter of picking a capable man from the short list of high-ranking officers kept for such emergencies by the Military Secretary. He had to be someone known to the Chindits; someone for whom they would 'go'. He had, therefore, to be some officer with an established reputation as a fighter, or someone from the ranks of the Special Force who had carried a pack and fought in the jungle.

Wingate's own appointment had been the work of the Prime Minister, overriding all normal procedures and objections, but that brief period of sunshine for Special Force was over. Winston Churchill's attention was now focused on other more pressing matters, such as the invasion of Nazi-occupied France. Nor was it the business of the Commander-in-Chief in India, Giffard, the Army Group Commander, or even the Supreme Commander, Mountbatten. Special Force was in effect a division commanded by a major-general acting under the command of Fourteenth Army, and by normal army practice the task of choosing a successor fell on Slim. Army commanders are selected on the grounds that, among their other qualities, they are sound judges of men and can be entrusted to hire and fire their subordinates. Slim was not a man to waste time, in spite of his ponderous and even stolid appearance, apart from which he had at that moment no time to waste. Special Force needed a sure pair of hands on the reins immediately, and all his own attention was required for the nerve-racking opening moves of the Kohima-Imphal battle. Time also prevented him from looking any further afield than Special Force itself.

There were four possible candidates. The obvious one was the deputy commander, Symes. Wingate's own choice might have been the faithful Tulloch, to whom he had delegated command when he was about to resign, and Tulloch believed that he was Wingate's nominee. Lentaigne was next in seniority, and Calvert was rapidly establishing a reputation as a fighting commander that had spread outside his brigade. Brigadier Perowne, it is said, was also considered.

Symes may not have been a jungle-fighting ex-Chindit, but he was an exceptionally able commander: had he not been he would not have passed the close scrutiny used in choosing a general officer to command a British regular division at that late stage in the Second World War. He had rapidly absorbed the Chindit idea and had begun re-training his units even before Wingate had returned from Quebec; he had continued in full command during Wingate's serious illness and had brought his wide knowledge of administration and staff duties to the complex task of setting up the new force and the machinery required to train it. Wingate had breathed life and fire into Special Force, but Symes had moulded the form. He had also reconstructed the whole staff machine and no one understood its workings better. The bulk of the staff of the new headquarters of Special Force were from the 70th Division, unhappy at the break up of their battle-tested formation, but under Symes' guidance and following his example they loyally devoted themselves to their new rôle and their new master. Symes had also persuaded the died-in-the-wool infantry, that conservative and jealous body, to accept the new, scallywag rôle of guerrillas, and he had been successful even with the Royal Artillery, who keenly disliked giving up their guns to become infantry, and the 45th Reconnaissance Corps, many of whose soldiers had only just reconciled themselves to the change from infantry to their new, Armoured Corps rôle. Compared with Wingate, Symes may have seemed somewhat drab and lacking in panache, but that applied to all eligible successors. He knew the units well, as he was a great believer in visiting them regularly and talking to the men. He had kept himself in touch with the progress of operations and had visited Broadway. He laboured under only one disadvantage. Being based on Rear Headquarters of Special Force far away in Gwalior in Central India, he was better known in Delhi than in Headquarters, Fourteenth Army. Symes had no doubt that he was Wingate's legitimate heir, and when he heard that Wingate was missing immediately came forward to take control at main headquarters at Sylhet.

Another option was to appoint one of the brigade commanders. The Chindits were engaged in a testing and unique type of operation and one of the advantages their commanders in the field had was that they shared the discomforts and dangers of the men in the columns.

They marched on foot as their men did, they carried the same crushing weight, they ate the same meagre ration and they shared the same dangers. There was obviously something to be said for a commander who knew from personal experience what would be the effect of any order he gave from a remote headquarters: a Chindit to command Chindits.

Wingate was killed on March 24th. On the 25th when there was no trace of him or his aircraft and hope that he had made one of his unexpected detours was given up, everyone was duly informed. A patrol went to examine the wreckage of a crashed aircraft reported in the mountains west of Imphal but was not able to make its report of a positive identification until the 27th, but on the 26th Slim consulted Tulloch by telephone on the choice of a successor; Tulloch, it will be observed, not Symes. He respected Tulloch because of his steadiness and common sense and perceived that he would receive his disinterested advice. How mistaken Tulloch was events would reveal.

Tulloch himself had a letter from Wingate authorising him to take command in the event of his death, although this carried little weight, as the appointment was not in Wingate's gift, but Slim's. But he excluded himself because he had never trained or commanded a Chindit column and was strongly of the opinion that the new commander must have experience in the field. For this reason he ruled out Symes as well. He then discussed the merits of the brigadiers and firmly recommended Lentaigne, giving as his main reason that of all the commanders he was the one most in tune with Wingate. Slim agreed, and added that Tulloch was to control operations until Lentaigne could take command. It would have been a happier arrangement if Slim had followed the usual protocol and announced his choice personally to the officers concerned, but those were tense days for Slim and there was much else on his mind, so he left it to Tulloch to break the news to Symes.[5]

Tulloch was in an awkward position because Symes was his senior and he had to explain to him why he, Tulloch, was now in temporary command and what had happened. Characteristically, he was completely candid about his own part. Symes was naturally furious, and with good reason: brigadiers are not normally consulted about the fitness of their immediate superiors for command. He protested formally to Giffard and to Slim, who were sympathetic to the point of writing to the Chief of the Imperial General Staff in London (Brooke) to make it clear that their passing over Symes was due entirely to the peculiar nature of the appointment and in no way a reflection on his ability, but otherwise they were adamant.

After due reflection Symes saw there was no hope of realising his ardent wish to command at least a part of his old division in active operations, as promised by Wingate, and therefore no point in producing his letter of March 3rd, and that the dignified course of submitting to Slim's decision without further protest was also the correct one. Moreover, as he confided to his diary:

> There was no one else [i.e., besides Wingate] who had the special ear of Winston, and without it Special Force was doomed. Not straight away, of course, but as soon as it could decently be interred. Leaving aside the tragic manner of his death and the gloom of the men under his command, it was obvious that there would be more than a slight sigh of relief in the upper echelons of command, the majority of which had been thwarted in one way or another by Wingate's ruthlessness and duplicity.

He understandably asked to be relieved of his post of deputy commander and this was agreed. So passed from the Chindit saga the modest officer who had in his practical way done so much to enable Wingate to realise his dream.[6]

The transaction was not without its ironies. Tulloch, however innocent and upright had been his reasons, had by getting rid of Symes saved his own skin. Symes, a highly-trained and experienced staff officer, had formed a poor opinion of Tulloch's abilities and had determined, if ever he was appointed to command, to be rid of him and appoint Neville Marks in his place. Tulloch, moreover, was mistaken over Lentaigne. Far from being the officer most in Wingate's mind and the natural choice to translate his ideas into future action, he despised both Wingate and his theories.[7] Nor had Lentaigne any use for Tulloch, who by Slim's decision became deputy commander, but without promotion to major-general. When Lentaigne decided to re-establish a small forward headquarters to deal purely with the control of operations, he brought the young and very able Henry Alexander, the Colonel, General Staff (Training), from Gwalior to be his chief-of-staff and gradually reduced Tulloch to a position of obscurity and impotence, leaving him to concern himself with purely administrative matters; a position which he bore with patience and dignity. The subject of Wingate became Tulloch's obsession, and he was to devote much of his time and mental energy for the next twenty-seven years to assembling the material and composing an apologia for his friend, patron and hero.

The advancement of 'Joe' Lentaigne illustrates the difficulty for selecting men for high command in war. Outwardly Lentaigne was suitable in every respect. He was an educated soldier whose qualities of heart and mind were amply proved after the war was over, when the military authorities of newly independent India asked for him to establish their new Staff College. There he commanded both the respect and the affection of the Indian officers; so much so that he was invited to remain for a second tour of duty. He had led a battalion in hard-fought and prolonged fighting in an adverse situation and when gallantry is combined with sound military knowledge it earns a sure footing on the ladder to high command. He was an Irishman, volatile and vital, who could make up his mind quickly; too quickly, some said, but in war a rapid decision is often better than one made after weighing every factor while the opportunity slips away. He had rapidly grasped the principles of Chindit warfare and trained his brigade in them before ever he had met Wingate, and when Wingate had been ill and Symes had commanded, Lentaigne had effectively filled the post of deputy commander. He was experienced in fighting the Japanese. At forty-five he was seasoned wood and ready for higher responsibility. After the war when Slim was checking his Despatches he was asked, rather boldly, by the officer who wrote the draft, why he had appointed Lentaigne to command the Chindits. Slim gave one of his rare, loud laughs: 'Ha! Ha! Because he was the only one who wasn't mad!' He then added: 'And I knew with him in command that there wouldn't be any nonsense about writing direct to Churchill and Mountbatten.' There may have been something in this, for no general, even of Slim's outward calm and patience, could easily tolerate a subordinate like Wingate. Slim, however, with his burdens crowding in on him, wanted something more than a commander who would not pique or irritate him and distract him from his own battle. He wanted a sensible, orthodox man who could be given a mission and left alone to do it. Lentaigne possessed these admirable characteristics in ample measure, but this good officer had a soft centre, unperceived by almost everyone.

The position of a brigadier is a testing one. At the lowest level of command, in a battalion, the acutely difficult art of thinking and fighting at the same time, and the strain of giving orders face to face which may send men to their death, is mitigated by the fact that the commander is among officers with whom he has grown up, and who will support him as the head of family and tribal chief he in fact is. When he relaxes he is among friends and in the mess only the first among equals. At the other, highest, level the general is not altogether isolated. He can usually find among his senior staff, or sometimes in his senior chaplain or medical officer, someone in whom he can confide, or simply chat with privately over a whisky and soda. By contrast a brigadier is in the position of the captain of a warship who has to live in the ward-room and not in the splendid loneliness of his cabin, and he has to strike a balance between aloofness and familiarity. Jack Masters, Lentaigne's dedicated 'brigade-major', had welded his diverse staff in the 111th Brigade into an efficient headquarters and also a jolly one. The conversation in the mess ranged widely and was intelligent, sometimes irreverent and occasionally ribald when the drink flowed. There was a tendency to mock the apocalyptic style of their formidable but weird force commander. At one post-exercise conference, when the audience braced themselves for the usual verbal flaying Wingate was in the habit of inflicting on these occasions, an Indian mess-waiter, unaware of the solemnity of the occasion, suddenly appeared and placed an enormous teapot on the table where Wingate sat with his entourage. The association of ideas with the Mad Hatter's Tea Party was irresistible to the 111th Brigade staff and there was much reprehensible giggling.

Lentaigne entered into the spirit of his young men. He was lonely, having recently separated from his wife. He loved good company and good talk, and had a store of diverting anecdotes which he told well. 'He drank a lot, but held it well,' it was said of him. Later, under the strain of high command, he perhaps drank rather more, and held it less well.[8]

In open combat where he could see his enemy he had proved a paladin, but even in the few days he spent in the field he had found the physical and mental strain of Chindit fighting too much for him. Masters, his brigade-major, friend and loyal subordinate, has described his reaction to a reported Japanese threat to his column, and his panicky signal to Headquarters, Special Force, which Masters suppressed.[9] His military judgment may have led him to justified pessimism about the whole Chindit venture, but it was indiscreet to reveal to a column commander (Major Lockett, an 'old' Chindit) he met on his way out to take over command that in his opinion all the strongholds were doomed and must soon fall.[10] Such readiness to chat on equal terms with a junior officer was part of his charm and the reason why he was so popular, but he was too genial by half to be a senior commander. A general may be liked and this may be part of his equipment for leadership, but he must also have an element of steel in his make-up, and abrasiveness as well. He must relish confrontation even if he does not seek it and, as Lord Butler once said of prime ministers, 'he must sometimes be a good butcher and know the joints'. Lentaigne's military judgment was excellent and it is probable that he could have commanded an orthodox Indian infantry division with distinction. But the troubles he was to meet in Burma, above all from Stilwell, were to pain him deeply and wear him down until he was ineffective.

All this, however, lay in the future.

His immediate task was to bring his considerable gifts as a trained staff officer to imposing order and direction and giving a fresh impetus to the Chindit brigades chaotically embroiled round Indaw: 14th Brigade deploying for a task for which they had been given but the scantiest of notice to prepare, 16th Brigade recoiling in defeat, the West Africans queueing to follow the 14th in to Burma, the 6th Nigeria Regiment scattered, and the commander of the 12th putting Aberdeen into a state of emergency on the basis of an unconfirmed rumour of a Japanese attack, and withholding the Black Watch for defence of the stronghold.

In the meantime Tulloch, as acting commander, continued what he believed to be Wingate's policy, 'Plan B', which, to his satisfaction, coincided with Slim's wishes. There has since been much debate between Wingate's supporters and his detractors over Slim's precise intentions for 14th Brigade when he released it to Wingate on March 20th but on March 27th when he summoned Tulloch to brief him on the latest situation around Indaw there can be no doubt that at the front of his mind was the intention to use the Chindits to harass the supply lines of the Japanese Fifteenth Army without prejudice to Special Force's legitimate mission of assisting Stilwell. Slim's analysis of his position was perfectly correct. The whole campaign of South-East Asia depended on the outcome of the great battle that had begun between the British Fourteenth and the Japanese Fifteenth Armies, because that was where the main Japanese striking force had been committed. Accordingly, every resource he possessed should be devoted to the destruction, of the Japanese Army, and these included the reserve brigades of Special Force. As the commander-in-chief exercising operational control over both Stilwell and Wingate he was fully entitled to make any dispositions he chose, bearing in mind only his obligation to Stilwell and his right to redeploy Special Force in as he thought best. At the end of March the position of his army was delicate, because the IVth Corps looked as if it might be caught and gripped while changing from its forward deployment to its defensive positions, and an unexpectedly strong thrust by the Japanese 31st Division threatened Kohima and the Fourteenth Army's maintenance area and the vital communication which served both it and Stilwell's military complex in Assam: the airfields, Chih Hui Pu, and General Pick's army of United States Army Engineers and labourers working on the road.

The first stages of Imphal-Kohima looked extremely alarming from the Allied side. It was the only time that Slim's impassive, gun-turret-like features were observed to show signs of anxiety. Stilwell's pleasure at the prospect of another humiliating defeat for the Limeys – 'Louis (Mountbatten) to put it mildly had his hind leg over his neck . . . What a mess the Limeys can make of it in short order . . .' – was quite spoiled by the thought of the appalling consequences if Dimapur, the vital supply centre, fell to the Japanese. He asked for an early meeting with Slim. At that fraught moment Slim confided to a friend who was visiting his headquarters that his chief anxiety as regards Special Force was that if he diverted it from its legitimate mission it might end up 'like Grouchy at Waterloo' – he probably meant d'Erlon at Quatre-Bras-Ligny – wasting its effort by marching backwards and forwards and being of no use to him or Stilwell. In fact he made good use of Special Force and returned it to Stilwell as soon as the immediate danger was past.

On March 27th Slim discussed 'Plan B', including the proposal to land the 23rd Brigade some 200 miles to the south, at Pakkoku. This was absurdly impractical on grounds of time, distance and air supply, and in any case there was no need to go as far south as that. There were a number of small dumps and depots dispersed over the Indaw area and Slim agreed that all three Chindit brigades already there should be directed to locate and destroy them and harry the obvious supply routes leading westwards to the Chindwin. Lentaigne's 111th Brigade, now under the command of Jack Masters, the brigade-major, was to cease blocking and cutting the railway and move west, so that Brodie and Fergusson were spread out north and west of the Indaw Lake and Masters to the south and south-west of it.

Slim had next to ensure that the Japanese at Kohima did not by-pass or break through his defences there and capture Dimapur. Stilwell, convinced that the Limeys were sure to break and run under Japanese pressure as usual, called urgently for a conference with Slim to coordinate defence measures and the two generals met on April 3rd at Jorhat. Lentaigne and Tulloch were ordered to attend.

Stilwell, who for all his iron will was on his own admission a 'worrier', had taken counsel of his fears. He had an exaggerated idea of the strength of the Japanese counter-stroke in the upper Tanai, where at that moment Hunter was hotly engaged at Nphum Ga, and now he had horrible visions of the Japanese ravaging his defenceless base. He halted his offensive in the upper Mogaung Valley, hastily organised a task force to defend his base, and offered Slim the use of the Chinese 38th Division for the defence of Dimapur. Much to Stilwell's relief, and his surprise, Slim told him that he was confident the measures he had already put in hand would enable him to hold Mutaguchi's drive without Stilwell's assistance. He was in the process of deploying a fresh corps, the XXXIIIrd, forward of Dimapur for the defence of Kohima, and he had ordered the one remaining reserve Chindit brigade, the 23rd, which was handily placed, into action to cover its assembly area. The Chindit brigades inside Burma were already attacking Mutaguchi's communications, with the aim of putting a brake on his offensive towards Kohima.

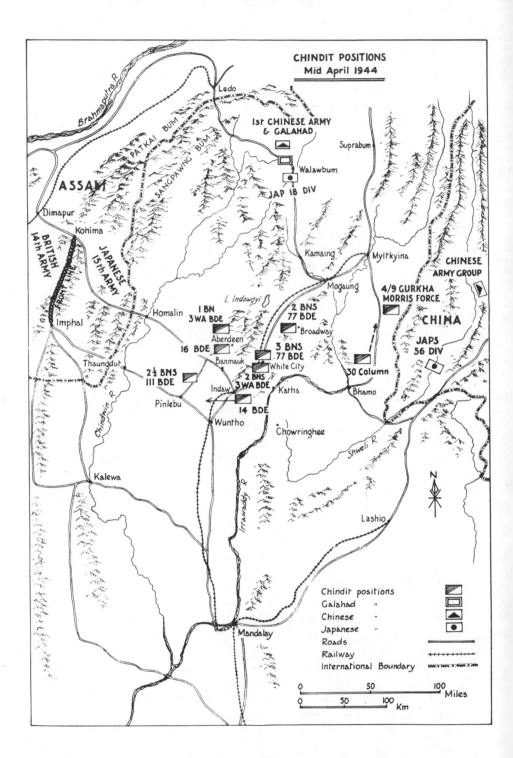

CHINDIT POSITIONS
Mid April 1944

Brahmaputra R

Ledo

1st CHINESE ARMY
& GALAHAD

Suprabum

PATKAI BUM

SANGPAWNG BUM

Walawbum

JAP 18 DIV

ASSAM

Dimapur

Kamaing

Myitkyina

CHINESE
ARMY GROUP

Kohima

Mogaung

4/9 GURKHA
MORRIS FORCE

CHINA

BRITISH
14th ARMY

JAPANESE
15th ARMY

FRONT LINE

Homalin

L Indawgyi

1 BN
3 WA BDE

2 BNS
77 BDE

JAPS
56 DIV

Imphal

Aberdeen

Broadway

Thaungdut

16 BDE

3 BNS
77 BDE

30 Column

Chindwin R

2½ BNS
III BDE

Banmauk

White City

Bhamo

Indaw

2 BNS
3 WA BDE

Karha

Pinlebu

14 BDE

Wuntho

Chowringhee

Shweli R

N

Kalewa

Irrawaddy R

Lashio

Chindit positions
Galahad   "
Chinese   "
Japanese   "
Roads
Railway
International Boundary

Mandalay

0   50   100   Miles
0   50   100   Km

Stilwell, said Slim, with all due courtesy, should stop looking over his shoulder and press on with his own offensive towards Myitkyina. (Obviously. It was part of the main plan, and the harder he pressed the more it would have the secondary effect of exerting leverage on the Imphal-Kohima front.) Stilwell showed no adverse reaction to the switch in the objectives given to part of Special Force. As it transpired, apart from any scepticism he felt about the fighting ability of the British, his only requirement was that they should continue to block the Railway Valley as far south as possible.

Then, six days later, on April 9th, Slim cancelled the orders he had given Lentaigne and transferred the whole Chindit effort back again to assisting Stilwell. He felt considerable misgivings about the propriety of detaching Special Force from its agreed rôle, except in an emergency, and the situation on his front, although still delicate, had shifted distinctly in his favour. Kohima was holding, and on the 10th he felt able to order the XIVth Corps to begin a counter-offensive. On the 13th the most dangerous Japanese penetration at Imphal was driven back. He retained the 23rd Brigade permanently for more local operations on the rear of the Fifteenth Army on the Chindwin front, for which it was well suited. As the operations of Special Force and the Chinese First Army were so closely connected and inter-dependent they should come, Slim felt, under a single command, and in spite of Stilwell's protests that such a move would only embarrass him and he was not confident that the British would carry out his orders, the Chindits were transferred to his operational command. In due course, when Lentaigne was firmly in the saddle and had made the new plans which he felt were necessary, he was to set up a forward headquarters next door to Stilwell's 'Northern Combat Area Command' headquarters, at Shaduzup in the Mogaung Valley. The moves that were to result from this took some time to arrange and were not effective until mid-May, and the harrying of the Japanese supply arrangements went on for some time after April 9th, the 14th Brigade being still at work as late as April 22nd.

Lentaigne went from the conference at Jorhat straight to a conference of Chindit brigadiers he had called at Aberdeen. This was more in the nature of a council of war between equals than the occasion on which a new general takes the measure of his subordinates, impresses his personality on them and gives them their orders.

Perhaps the Chindit style was different. An illuminating anecdote concerning the 77th Brigade relates how, in No. 50 Column, the fire-eating Lieutenant Patterson, the blower-up of bridges, had the audacity to complain to Calvert, his brigade commander, that the commander of his column, Colonel Christie, had refused him permission to go off on another bridge-blowing jaunt, and worse, his complaint contained the implication, contrary to all good order and military discipline, that under Colonel Christie's direction the column, which was 'floating', lacked offensive spirit. Calvert, instead of squashing Patterson flat, sat down with plaintiff and respondent on the ground like the guerrilla chief he was in spirit, and heard them both. His impartial judgment was that there were no grounds for the complaint, but Patterson could leave the column and join the élite assault force that was part of his own headquarters column, where he would have all the dangerous jobs he wanted.

So Lentaigne may have justly appreciated that the Chindit commanders in the field, only occasionally in touch with headquarters and each other, already accustomed to act on their own ..iitiative without constant direction from above or precisely worded orders, were men to whom no one but Wingate could dictate or lay down the law: and that he, Lentaigne, certainly could not. It would be tactless to assert himself too strongly over his former colleagues, two of whom were veteran Chindits. Accordingly, at Aberdeen, the discussion was easy and informal. Lentaigne confined himself to asking Fergusson and Calvert, of Wingate's 'Old Guard', how they thought operations ought to develop and pointed out some of the logistic obstacles to what they proposed. No one else spoke. Only Brodie of the remaining brigade commanders is reported as present, and Lentaigne does not appear to have brought a staff officer from Special Force headquarters with him. The only member of the general staff present was the journalist and travel-writer Peter Fleming, then in the guise of a lieutenant-colonel in the Grenadier Guards, who had some obscure rôle connected with deception. He was unconnected with Special Force, to which he seems to have attached himself as he smelt the prospect of amusement combined with danger. He contributed what Calvert calls 'acid' and 'cryptic' remarks, which heightened the informality of the occasion.

Fergusson's suggestion, based on his belief that the TARZAN plan was still in existence, was to make another attempt to secure Indaw East, while Calvert repeated (for the third time, he had already signalled Special Force headquarters on the subject and had been rebuffed by Lentaigne as well as by Wingate) that two brigades should secure the White City block while he with his 77th forced his way up the Railway Valley and fell on the rear of Tanaka's division, so breaking open a way for the Chinese First Army to advance. Nothing was decided except negatives. Fergusson, as the castellan of the stronghold of Aberdeen, dispensed lordly hospitality in the shape of Burmese curry and rice and ration rum – a welcome contrast to the privations of column life – and Lentaigne went back to Sylhet to ponder on his next moves. It was an odd affair, and a portent for the future.[11] Except for an occasional flash of anger Lentaigne was rarely to command in the accepted sense but, rather, to advise, invite, exhort or chide – by signal. He was to make only one more visit to the troops in the field.

Lentaigne's new position as commander of the élite and revolutionary Chindit corps was glorious, but fraught with difficulties great enough to baffle the best of commanders. In a month the monsoon rains were due to break and would make all the air operations on which he depended difficult and at times impossible, even for light aircraft. Flying conditions apart, the dirt strips would be reduced to quagmires, and his urgent enquiries had already met with the answer that there were no engineer resources available to convert them to all-weather airfields. There was a momentary flash of hope when patrols from the 16th Brigade reached Indaw West airfield, but it was found to be unusable.

The Special Force staff heard with shock and indignation that the demands on the transport aircraft for the main battle-front were so great that no empty sorties were to be allowed to run into the strongholds: the only space for evacuation was in aircraft returning after delivering rations and ammunition. This information reached them at the moment when the flow of casualties was increasing and the whole of 16th Brigade were due to be flown out, being physically exhausted. Worst of all, in conformity with the ninety-day term General Arnold had placed on the existence of the No. 1 Air Commando, that splendid unit would cease to exist on May 1st and the Chindits would then have to stand in the queue, competing for operational priority for air support, like all the other divisions.

It should in all fairness be emphasised that some Chindit accounts are biased in favour of the United States Army Air Force, and the Air Commando in particular. In fact the Royal Air Force made a substantial contribution, notably No. 221 Group, and the supply dropping 194 Squadron, whose pilots became trusted allies of the Chindits. Nonetheless, No. 1 Air Commando's disbandment was seen as a severe blow, because the Chindit brigades, without artillery, could call on Cochran's fighter bombers without formality and they would be overhead in half-an-hour, or they might even be patrolling ready in anticipation of a call.

The method in the Eastern Air Command was for requests for sorties for the whole front, which always exceeded the number available, to be submitted twenty-four hours before, so that resources could be distributed according to operational necessity (at a desk far from the battlefield), air photos studied, pilots briefed and so on, which was suitable for conventional operations but useless for the Chindits, who lurched from one opportunity or emergency to another.

Cochran on several occasions had tipped the balance of a doubtful battle in their favour at the last moment. It only added to Lentaigne's difficulties in command that there were murmurs among his staff that he did not fight for the peculiar requirements of the Chindits and acquiesced in these alterations too readily. Wingate, they felt, would not have allowed such enormities. Lentaigne had not the same arrogance: nor of course had he Wingate's access to the Prime Minister. And even if he had, orthodox and obedient officer that he was, he never would have used it.

These were all trying developments, but looming above Lentaigne's other problems was the question of the health of the troops. No one understood the stresses of jungle fighting in the monsoon better than he. He remembered the plight of his brigade during training in India in 1943, when some eighty per cent of its strength, including the Gurkhas, had gone down with a combination of malnutrition and malaria, causing a medical panic in general headquarters in Delhi, the despatch of medical consultants, enforced rest and mass medication. Lentaigne now had no troops available for relief. Wingate may have saved his brigades (except the 23rd) from the 'rats' of the staff, but the anopheles mosquito carrying malaria, some of it of a fatal strain, water-borne spirochaetes carrying a fatal jaundice-like disease, and the tiny tick or mite bearing the infection of 'scrub-typhus', as deadly as a bullet, were doing their work even better. The prognosis was that the whole of Special Force would be unfit for hard marching and fighting by the end of May, and after that date Lentaigne could expect a rapid decline in its efficiency from purely medical causes at an ever-increasing rate. The 16th Brigade, he was advised, should be relieved as soon as possible. That was the basis on which Lentaigne's future planning had to rest.

On April 10th, therefore, when he sat down to analyse his problem, he was beset by difficulties: the health of his troops, the impending monsoon, the famine in transport aircraft, the impossibility of maintaining the strongholds and the White City block on the one hand; and on the other the order, stated uncompromisingly by his new master, Stilwell, that he was to continue to block the Railway Valley for as long as possible. Stilwell did not seem to understand, or even to enquire, how this could be reconciled with the logistics of the Chindits' situation.

It was to take Lentaigne almost a month to resolve these difficult factors and make a new plan. In the meantime, although Slim had said that there was no further need for even the modified version of Wingate's 'Plan B' after April 9th, three brigades, the 14th, the 16th and the 111th, totalling ten and a half battalions, or twenty-one columns, continued to ravage the supply dumps and harry the supply routes of the Japanese from the Indaw-Banmauk-Pinlebu area to Homalin, on the east bank of the Chindwin, until the 26th. (As will be explained in Chapter 11, they could have been put to better use around the White City. There is no clue why they were kept on what was an obsolete mission, but it is not impossible that it was due to Tulloch who, as he says himself, strove for as long as he had any influence to continue Wingate's policies.) Both Tulloch and Calvert have asserted that 'Plan B' seriously hampered the Japanese, and some Japanese commanders, when interrogated as prisoners just after the war was over, have confirmed this view, or at least have confirmed that the supply situation was 'very bad'.[12] Lentaigne's new plans were not to take effect for nearly six weeks. This therefore is a convenient point at which to assess the direct Chindit contribution to Slim's great victory at Imphal-Kohima.

It will be understood that it was not Wingate's intention to attack the actual units of the Japanese Fifteenth Army in the rear but rather, in accordance with his own strategic principles for the use of long-range penetration forces, to sever its supply routes and so starve it to death. His plan, in short, was an attack on General Mutaguchi's logistic system, and it must be assessed in the factual, numerical logistic terms of transport and tonnages.

Mutuaguchi sent three divisions across the Chindwin, more or less in line, on a broad front from Imphal to Kohima. His main depots were far to the south, near Meiktila and Mandalay, with a subsidiary system near Indaw. One serviceable road led up from the south and continued on the west bank of the Chindwin up to Imphal, but even this was very poor and required a stupendous engineer effort to convert it into a line of communication suitable for the Fourteenth Army when Slim went over to the offensive in Burma in 1945. East of the Chindwin, which was unbridged throughout its length, there was, apart from this, only a dirt road and track system unfit for heavy motor traffic; 'motorable in dry weather' is a recurring legend on the maps. West of the Chindwin the only east-west communications were jungle trails, some sufficiently improved by the Fourteenth Army's engineers to be capable of taking jeeps.

It was clear to Mutaguchi that even the frugal Japanese Army – a simple affair, relying on the rifles, machine-guns and mortars of its sturdy infantry, and with only light artillery and hardly any motor transport – could not be maintained in the normal way once across the Chindwin. He therefore committed himself to a wild tactical and logistic gamble. He relied on the Japanese infantry's combination of ferocious frontal attack and encirclement once more to break the nerve of the British and Indian troops, as it had in Malaya and in Burma in 1941 (although the violent repulse of the preliminary

Japanese offensive in Arakan, in February of that year, might have warned him that he now had a different enemy to deal with). This battle, he considered, might take three weeks, after which he hoped to make use of captured British supplies. Accordingly he sent across, with the divisions, supplies of food and ammunition sufficient for twenty days' fighting: on the backs of the soldiers, in unit first line transport, on the heads of coolies, in such motor vehicles as he could ferry across the Chindwin, in country carts and on elephants. If he did not break through by D-day plus twenty Mutaguchi would be in serious difficulties, for while he could hope to keep his divisions resupplied by road, the balance of the rival logistic systems favoured the British, as they had well-developed communications behind them, while his were atrocious. Especially vulnerable were those leading to his right hand, or northern, division, the 31st, whose objective was Kohima, and which was to come under Chindit attack.

The difficulty of analysing the result of this attack lies in ascertaining the minimum Japanese requirement, and the stocks actually destroyed by the Chindits. (There is also the additional difficulty of assessing the exact share of the Allied air force, which was ranging deep into Burma over the whole of the Japanese communications zone and attacking the Chindwin ferries, but it can be assumed that air interdiction was among the decisive factors.) It is, therefore, necessary to guess. We know that during the advance of the Fourteenth Army over very similar country in 1945 the British-Indian divisions could make do with as little as 150 tons per division per day.* We also know that when Tanaka's depleted 18th Division was reduced to thirty tons per day by Chindit action in the Railway Valley and air attack it eventually broke down. Each of Mutaguchi's divisions therefore might have been able to fight an offensive battle on 100 tons per day, and simply hold their positions with rather less.

The last of the twenty days' supplies carried forward would have been consumed on March 30th, but at that date, and indeed for another week, the only brigade operating against the 31st Division's supply line was the 111th. Masters, in his methodical way, claims that he destroyed some 200 tons of stores and twenty motor vehicles, and inflicted 430 casualties in the process. (This was largely achieved by the Cameronians. The King's Own had less luck, and one of their

---

* In Europe, by way of contrast, a fully mechanised infantry division in 'intense' combat required some 450 tons per day, and an armoured division 900. In pursuit, the bulk of this was petrol; in fighting, it was artillery and tank-gun ammunition; the total remaining remarkably constant. Food is the least weighty item, but water, if required, is very heavy. Exclude these, and a rifle-and-bayonet army requiring basically rice and small-arms ammunition and mortar bombs might well do with 100–130 tons per division per day.

columns was in disarray for some time after being ambushed.) These are hardly decisive qualities.

Nor was the supply factor the decisive one. The Kohima garrison held on after a heroic defence until April 5th, on which date it was reinforced by an Indian infantry brigade. On that date and the 6th the last two assaults by the Japanese were repulsed, and on the 10th the leading troops of the British 2nd Division, whose mission was to begin a counter-offensive without delay, arrived, finally, to slam the door in the Japanese face. But the 14th Chindit Brigade was not able to begin full-scale operations against the rearward communications of the Japanese 31st Division until mid-April. Quite apart from the time it took to fly in the whole brigade, the movement of Chindit columns in the presence of the enemy was necessarily slow, and it took time to reconnoitre and locate the many small dumps concealed in the jungle or in villages. The 2nd Black Watch located one big dump and summoned the bombers of the Air Commando to deal with it. Their bag was a 'large' amount of ammunition, some petrol, medical and other stores, including an estimated one million doses of quinine, and three 75 mm guns. Altogether the 14th Brigade claimed the destruction of twenty-one dumps, tonnage unspecified, and a total of 15,000 gallons of petrol. The 16th Brigade was also active after it had reorganised, but the unit war diaries do not reveal any striking results.

Interrogation after the war revealed that the 31st Division during its long defence against the British counter-offensive was in dire straits, and was supplied only via Imphal. That the battle went on so long shows the extraordinary resolution of a Japanese Army whose heart continued to beat and which was still capable of inflicting savage wounds long past the point at which a European army would have collapsed from starvation. But was the Chindit intervention, in this defensive stage, in any way decisive? The Japanese generals, in the shock and humiliation of defeat, thought that it was. This is hard to believe. Even if the troops detached to deal with the Chindits had been free to reinforce the Fifteenth Army, it is difficult to see how more troops besides the three divisions already committed could be maintained west of the Chindwin, whereas Slim could, and did, reinforce his front. The real reason for the Japanese defeat was, surely, the new-found fighting spirit and skill of the British and Indian divisions, the crushing superiority of the Allied air forces, and, not least, the resolution and generalship of Slim and the Supreme Allied Commander, Mountbatten.

The Japanese post-war testimony is not to be discounted, by any means, but what is significant is not the opinions of Japanese generals, offered after the war, but what the Japanese high command did at the time. When they brought up their hastily assembled reserve division it was not committed against the 14th Brigade, but sent to clear the route through the Railway Valley. The Japanese were aware that there was a Chindit force coming down from the north (Fergusson), but all they did was to put out a flank guard to ensure free movement along the railway past Indaw.[13] No large detachment was sent to deal with Masters or Brodie. It is an ironical afterthought that had Wingate allowed Fergusson time to rest and reconnoitre for his attack he might have found less, not more Japanese in Indaw. The Japanese clearly perceived that the danger point was at Mawlu. If Tanaka's defence was broken because his supply route was blocked, it could bring the full strength of Stilwell's Chinese Army down on them, threatening not only the rear of the Fifteenth Army but their whole position in Burma. At Mawlu Calvert sat blocking the railway: like a fierce old boar of the jungle, his stern tucked into an impenetrable clump of bamboo, tusks bare and ready to rip up any opponent rash enough to venture within their sweep. It was he who had to be eliminated, and it was against the White City that the Japanese threw their only reserve division.

10

Blocking the Bhamo Road

WHILE ALL THESE stirring events had been taking place around Indaw and in the Railway Valley, the other limb of Wingate's plan began to unfold far away to the east on the Chinese border. It will be remembered that this was to consist of two distinct operations. The 4th/9th Gurkha Rifles organised into two columns, Nos. 49 and 94, under Lieutenant-Colonel Morris, were to be flown in to the Chowringhee landing strip in the bend of the Shweli River and make their way to a point north-east of Bhamo where they would establish a base (not a 'stronghold') in the spectacular range of mountains whose crest-line marks the boundary between Burma and Yunnan. From there Morris was to harry the motor road from Bhamo to the ferry over the Irrawaddy at Myitkyina. This was to be a Chindit operation on classical lines; demolitions, mines and occasional ambushes of Japanese convoys running supplies north to the 18th Division.

As has also been mentioned, Lieutenant-Colonel D. C. Herring, a former businessman and now an officer in the famous Burma Rifles, was to be flown to a landing strip (TEMPLECOMBE) east of the Irrawaddy and north of Bhamo. His mission was to raise a guerilla force from the warlike and anti-Japanese Kachins, who lived in the wild country along the Chinese border, for the purpose of supplementing the operations of Colonel Morris' Gurkhas.

To complicate matters, Lentaigne's headquarters column and both columns of the 3rd/4th Gurkha Rifles were flown to Chowringhee when it was found that Piccadilly was unusable. As will be shortly explained, No. 30 Column had to be sent east to join Morris.

Each of these distinct but interconnected movements must be described separately, and it is convenient to begin with Herring's group, code-named Dah Force. It must be explained that these initial moves all began shortly after D-day for THURSDAY and a fortnight before the death of Wingate.

The landings at Chowringhee went off smoothly and 'Morris Force', as it came to be called, marched off, crossed the Shweli and went on its way untroubled by the enemy. The Gurkha riflemen, with their capacity for being surprised by nothing, were neither moved by the flight or excited by being behind the enemy lines. Provided their officers seemed to know what they were doing, the sands of the Western desert, the crags of Tunisia and the forestclad mountains of Burma were all one to them. The officers were more impressed. Wingate, they marvelled, had said that he would put them down in the Burma where the Japanese 'were not', and he had. However far away he may have been in India, while his hands were on the controls everything, they believed, would go well.

Herring and his little band which was to be the nucleus and command element of Dah Force was less fortunate. His instructions were to coordinate his own operation with that of a rival clandestine organisation whose representatives were already in the area. There were already two officers of the 'Special Operations Executive' (SOE) already there with a similar mission, Major Shan Lone, A Kachin, and Major Campbell, and it had been agreed that they would reconnoitre a glider landing strip near Herring's proposed operational area, guard it and send a signal that it was clear of Japanese and safe to fly soon after D-day of THURSDAY. The signal never came and Herring and his party, after some delay, were put down by C-47 at Broadway to march seventy miles and make an unrehearsed crossing of the upper Irrawaddy north of Bhamo.

One of the many difficulties which arise in clandestine operations is reconciling control and coordination with the extreme secrecy on which the heads of the various agencies insist, their distrust of any 'regular' military commanders, and the jealousy with which they regard each other and the regular intelligence services. There is, of course, a fundamental difference between *intelligence* agencies and those for the conduct of *clandestine operations*. The business of the first is to collect information, remaining unnoticed and avoiding active or direct operations like sabotage at all costs; that of the second is active subversive operations and organising resistance movements. Both tend to attract the secretive, the intriguers, the paranoid and the conspiritorial.

The Kachins (as the British called them, their collective name for themselves was 'Jinghpaw') were an ethnic group quite distinct from and hostile to the Burmans of the lowlands. Their clans were spread throughout the forests of north and north-east Burma. They enlisted regularly in the Burma Rifles, and being martial, pro-British, and anti-Japanese, they were an attractive target for the various clandestine or irregular organisations, of which five are identifiable. On Stilwell's front the American OSS (Office of Strategic Services, equivalent to the SOE) had established themselves so discreetly that

Colonel Hunter, as already mentioned, only discovered by chance that this useful source of intelligence about the Japanese dispositions on his front existed. The. SOE were darkly pursuing their own objectives along the Yunnan border. Castens, a former Burma civil servant, had built up an intelligence network in the Aberdeen area, and Musgrave Wood, an army officer, another in the Railway Valley which proved of great assistance to Calvert. There was Dah Force, and in addition each of the columns had a locally enlisted element in the shape of a few invaluable Burma Rifles in each of its reconnaissance platoons, whose task it was to obtain Kachin assistance and set up their own intelligence links as circumstances dictated. There was also a highly effective force of irregulars, rather than guerrillas, under the command of an able British officer, Lieutenant-Colonel Ford, called the North Kachin Levies, based on Fort Hertz.

The SOE was for all practical purposes autonomous. Its headquarters was in London, with a local one in Calcutta, and it was cut off from the South-East Asia Command operational command except for liaison officers discreetly placed; one at Special Force Headquarters.

In a purely military operation the chain of command and who gives orders to whom is the proper business of the staff, who must 'button it up' so that there is no ambiguity or room for misunderstanding. This it seems, was never done with regard to SOE, partly because Special Force under Wingate and Tulloch did not set much store by such military pedantry and possibly, also, because the SOE disliked anything being put on paper at all. It seems clear that three agencies or forces were to be committed to the same area. Of these Morris was responsible to Special Force through Calvert, who was miles away at the end of a fragile radio link and locked in close and bloody fighting with the Japanese; Herring was responsible to Special Force direct; and Shan Lone and Campbell were responsible only to their own man in Calcutta. This did not worry Herring as a matter of principle. He was a civilian of flexible mind and had no great respect for the regular army. He had from the first been attracted by Wingate's imagination, verve and unorthodoxy. Tact and personal liaison, Herring felt, would resolve local difficulties better than any directive from a far-off headquarters. He had served in the famous Burma Rifles, he had an intimate knowledge of the Kachin peoples and spoke their language, was on good terms with Shan Lone who was a Kachin and also an officer of the Burma Rifles, and his target area was chosen because it was full of old soldiers and reservists of the same regiment. In the course of the operation Herring's confidence was justified, but the arrangements for his fly-in went adrift, as already described, because of this very lack of coordination.

The plan was for Shan Lone to select and prepare a glider landing strip in the jungle, remain in observation and send the message that it was all clear to fly in direct to Special Force on the SOE radio. All this had been agreed when, unknown to Special Force, SOE signalled to Major Campbell that on no account was he to bring the one precious SOE radio set down from his mountain fastness and risk its capture near Templecombe, the glider strip. This was perhaps an understandable order, for in clandestine operations the danger of losing a radio station in such circumstances with its frequencies and cipher books was great, but someone should have thought of this before. Had Wingate not set his face so rigidly against parachutists a pathfinder party, as developed in the British airborne forces, might have been dropped in to find out what was happening. But as it was, it was impossible to tell whether there had simply been a radio failure, or if Shan Lone had been forced to decamp or been captured and a Japanese ambush was waiting for Herring at Templecombe.

Herring was willing to take a chance, but Cochran refused to risk his gliders, understandably, and sent out a patrol of two light L-5s, with Herring as a passenger and navigator. They flew low over the proposed site of Templecombe and Herring waved, but no reply came. No one was in sight. Shan Lone, dumb for lack of radio, and with no means of finding out why Campbell had not arrived, mistook the American aircraft for Japanese, and he and his party hid until they went away. As a result Dah Force was switched to Broadway, and it was not until the end of April that Herring was able to begin operations. On March 12th Wingate in his euphoric signal to Churchill included the sentence, 'A Special Patriot force *is raising Kachins around Broadway* thence east to Bhamo area.' (Author's italics.) This was a double falsehood, for it was not Herring's rôle to raise Kachins in the Broadway area and never had been, nor, in fact, was he doing so. He had not even left India on the 12th, and was not to reach his operational area until 22nd.

Herring's little force consisted of seventy-four souls: himself and Captain Lazum Tang and ten Kachins of the 2nd Burma Rifles; Major Kennedy of the Poona Horse, Captain Nimmo of the Argyll and Sutherland Highlanders; a communication detachment of the Royal Corps of Signals nineteen strong under Captain Treckman; nine Hong Kong born Chinese of the Hong Kong Volunteers, for liaison with the Chinese guerrillas Herring expected to meet on the frontier; a defence platoon of the 1st South Staffords twenty-seven strong under Captain Railton; a demolition expert, Sergeant Cockling of the Grenadier Guards, possibly the most easterly deployed member of the Household troops in the Second World War; Captain Sherman P. Joost, USA, liaison officer; and Private Williams of the RAMC, who had the formidable task of looking after the wounded and sick. Herring could have done without the British rank and file who, in his opinion, were good enough in a column but quite unsuited to the tip-and-run, hand-to-mouth life of guerrillas working among aliens in a daunting jungle environment, forced to eat food strange and sometimes repellent to the conservative working-class palate, but Wingate had overruled him. In the event they turned out well, although at first they were depressed and took some time to become accustomed to the life.

Herring left Broadway on March 14th and on March 21st crossed the Irrawaddy, the most dangerous point of his journey, without difficulty, although not without being detected. The local boatmen were Shans, a Burmese tribe not ill-disposed to the British but siding with the occupying Japanese forces from sheer self-preservation. (Broadly speaking the Burmans proper were patriots seeking independence from the British and for that purpose hopefully sided with the Japanese. The Shans were neutral, although some were violently anti-British, while the Kachins and Karens were anti-Burmese and pro-British.) It so happened that Herring and Lazum Tang had crossed at this very place when east-bound during operation LONGCLOTH in 1943 after receiving Wingate's orders for a general dispersal and a return to India. The Shan boatmen recognised the two men on their return and duly informed the Japanese, but on March 21st, a week after leaving Broadway, Herring was able to cross the river and the Bhamo road into the safety of the jungles beyond without being intercepted. There he met with a reverse. His arrival at the road coincided with a passing Japanese motor convoy, but as it was dark he was able to slip a few men at a time through its intervals. He had only one radio set, carried on a mule, for the change of plan had forced him to leave the others behind at the airfield in India. Unfortunately the mule, in the perverse way of mules, was startled by an oncoming lorry, wrenched its reins from its driver and bolted, never to be seen again.

Herring was too experienced a hand to be upset by a minor set-back like this. At this last supply drop he had radioed a message for retransmission to the SOE for Shan Lone to meet him at a certain point. His troops were now starving and without rations, so having led them to a friendly Kachin village deep in the jungle where they would be safe and could obtain a little food he set off by himself to the rendezvous, only to find no one there, the signal having gone astray. But by dint of sending out Kachin messengers he arranged another and at last made contact with the SOE officers in their base.

There he just missed a brisk battle. Campbell and Shan Lone had made contact with a large band of 200 well-armed Chinese guerrillas-cum-bandits, the two activities being synonymous on the Yunnan border, who had been attacked by a patrol of Japanese troops sent up from one of the garrisons along the road to investigate why a number of C-47 aircraft were circling one of the peaks. The Chinese killed a large number and chased the rest back. When Herring arrived they had stuck the heads of the dead Japanese on poles around the village they occupied and were eating their livers; whether because they were cannibals by habit or as a victory ritual he was unable to discover. He was encouraged by their success and by the good progress made by Shan Lone and Campbell, who had collected some Kachin fighters as well as Chinese. The air drop which had attracted the Japanese patrol had brought supplies, many rifles and a few light machine-guns to equip them. A screen of Kachin observers had been organised to provide early intelligence of Japanese move-ments. All, therefore, was going well. A replacement radio was ordered and on the 25th the rest of the British nucleus of Dah Force arrived, but in poor spirits. Even the stiff Chindit training had not prepared the simple lads from Birmingham and Wolverton for the diet of roots and boiled leaves which was all they had had for the past few days, and the wilderness of precipice and forest on the Yunnan border daunted them. Fortunately they were immediately thrown into action, for the Japanese had reacted indignantly to the destruction of their patrol and had returned in strength, driving the Chinese guerrillas from their lair. There is no better cure for despondency in soldiers than a sharp and successful action.

Herring had collected Dah Force in the SOE base village, where some Chinese stragglers and Kachin volunteers on the run had rallied. Herring's own training told him not to engage in a stand-up fight, but as there had been much talk about the British returning to throw out the Japanese invaders, and as evasive action, however sensible, involved loss of face in front of the Chinese, he thought it was essential to make a stand – he 'felt bound to put up some sort of a show'. Nevertheless, he took the sound Chindit precaution of issuing precise dispersal instructions to everyone. This was providential, for the Japanese commander was cleverer than most. Instead of hurling his troops with shouts of *Banzai* into a headlong assault, he stealthily and silently infiltrated the defences at night, having given orders to his troops to use only the bayonet. A bloody little mêlée followed, impossible to control. Herring, unable to tell friend from foe, blew his whistle as the signal to disperse. This went off as smoothly as if it were an exercise: a tribute to Dah Force's training. Herring found a safe, remote mountain glen where his men could rest, receive a supply drop, eat some proper food and familiarise themselves with their environment. Meanwhile he held an operational *post mortem*.

Casualties proved to be a Kachin and four Chinese killed and fifteen wounded, including a number of British. A light plane strip would have to be constructed to take out the worst cases, among whom was the unfortunate Campbell, seriously injured when setting a booby trap. A British sergeant and a corporal were missing. As soon as the engagement was over the Kachin scouts, ghosting through their native jungle, deduced from the traces of the battle, among them the cremation fires the Japanese used to dispose of the dead whom they could not carry away, that they had suffered some twenty or thirty casualties inall. (The Japanese were scrupulous about the recovery and disposal of their dead, risking as much to drag back a dead comrade as Western soldiers would to rescue a wounded one. If they could not evacuate the corpse they burned it on the spot, cutting off a finger to send home so that at least a fragment of the deceased could rest in Japan.)

The British troops had behaved very well, especially the defence platoon from that fine regiment the South Staffords. Its commander, Railton, had proved cool and courageous during the fight and had extracted his men after the dispersal signal in an exemplary manner, being the last to leave and only just avoiding capture. So on balance things had not turned out too badly.

Major Campbell was evacuated by a light plane from the Air Command on March 27th, a remarkable feat which only ceased to be remarkable because sheer repetition made it commonplace. The use of tiny strips hacked out of flat jungle or on dry paddy was a tribute to the skill of the pilots. But the mountains on the Yunnan border were something vastly different: an alternation of peaks and precipices clothed in forest, subject even in good weather to turbulence and ferocious downdrafts, and with nothing but an inadequate strip on which it was just possible to land but from which every take-off was a gamble. Twenty years later when those fragile dragonflies the L-1s and L-5s had been replaced by powerful helicopters, able to fly through bad weather and set down on a patch the size of a basketball pitch, or brave the mountains of central Malaya or Borneo, it was frightening enough for a passenger. We can still marvel at the feats of the American light plane pilots of 1944. The same aircraft brought in a member of another corps equally respected by the Chindits for its devotion to duty. Herring had asked for a doctor, and the aircraft which took Campbell out brought in Major Faulkner of the Royal Army Medical Corps. He proved an outstanding officer whose presence immediately raised the morale of the British troops. Later, extending his practice to the Kachins, his jungle clinics did much to rally them under Herring's banner.

These preliminaries concluded, Herring was now free to devote his considerable talents to organising his guerrilla campaign, while Dah Force lay low to avoid enemy attention. It was not inactive, however. Officer patrols were sent out. Herring approved and extended Shan Lone's sound preliminary organisation of Kachin scouts. Communications with Special Force were restored and at this stage Herring sensibly took over the SOE operation without any formal orders, since obviously there was not room for two commanders in the same area. Next he had to establish liaison with Morris, whose columns were plodding their way up from the south into what was for them unknown territory, and would need all the local knowledge they could be given. Herring was anxious for their arrival, for he rightly believed that a guerrilla operation should have two fists; a mailed one of regulars who could engage the attention of the regulars on the enemy side, and the lightly armed, more mobile, more insidious, more penetrating and more elusive guerrillas: each should support the other.

A slight but unfortunate misunderstanding arose here. During the dispersal period Shan Lone sent off a signal direct to Special Force full of alarm and demanding help urgently. He was perhaps within his rights in sending off his message. He was certainly wrong in not clearing it with Herring. It caught the eye of Wingate, who banged off one of his thoughtless signals, 'as from the GOC'. He reassured Shan Lone, telling him that three powerful columns were on their way (Morris Force) to help him. Unfortunately Shan Lone was misled into believing that the rôle of Morris Force was meant to be defensive: a shield against Japanese reprisals. 'It was hard to make him realise after this that Morris Force was an operational force directed against the enemy,' said Herring, and not a protection for the levies and the SOE base area.[1]

That *three* columns were arriving was also news to Herring, and to see what had happened it is necessary to hark back to the Morris Force landing at Chowringhee. This, as has been said, had gone well. The 4th/9th landed intact and spread out to defend the perimeter, while Lentaigne's headquarters and his leading battalion, the 3rd/4th, deplaned and assembled in readiness for their westward march. Then Wingate arrived and sniffed the air. The smell was of danger. Taking one of his rapid decisions he ordered Chowringhee to be abandoned forthwith, and the rest of the 111th Brigade to be flown into Burma via Broadway, now functioning, as already described, as if it were a civilian airport. 'La Guardia has nothing on us,' Colonel Alison had said in an exultant signal.

Wingate's instinct was accurate. Just after the last troops had left Chowringhee and the Air Commando had snatched off the last undamaged glider, the Japanese air force arrived to bomb it. With a singular lack of inquisitiveness they failed to look over the Irrawaddy a few miles off, where they might have seen Lentaigne and his columns laboriously crossing the river, over a mile wide at that point.

Since the blocking of Piccadilly and the change of plan the much-abused 'staff' had been improvising desperately. Assault boats and outboard motors had been hastily collected from depots, despatched to airfields, and loaded into gliders. A flight plan had been made. All were standing by to land at the chosen crossing point. Lentaigne and Masters had chosen a place where there was a 300-yard-wide beach on which the gliders could land, with cover behind it where the columns could form up and wait their turn to cross. The beach and a mid-channel sand bar narrowed the water-gap to 900 yards, but this had the disadvantage of compressing the flow so that even in the dry season the waters ran strongly.

On March 11th the columns came up and hid in the scrub, No. 30 right and No. 40 left, each putting out a flank guard. An advance guard from No. 30 was crossed first to secure a bridge-head, then brigade headquarters were to follow, then No. 30 and finally No. 40. All the animals were grouped together to be swum across at the same time as the boat parties under Captain Mike Macgillicuddy. This remarkable Irishman had served in the ranks, and had won a Military Medal. Later he had been commissioned into the 3rd/4th and was now a holder of the Military Cross.[2] He was the mule-master of the battalion.

All the Chindit columns had practised river-crossings, but never over so wide a stretch of water. It proved an unlucky affair. As soon as it was dark Squadron-Leader Jennings, the brigade Royal Air Force Officer, marked out a landing-strip on the beach for the gliders with a line of bonfires. The Air Commando pilots, guided by their dim light, landed with their usual skill. No one could blame them for overshooting by half a mile. The heavy boats and engines had to be carried and dragged back to the proper embarkation point. It was then found that not all of the engines had been properly cleaned after coming out of 'preservation'. The air, already blue from polyglot oaths in English and Gurkhali, became bluer with the exhausts of motors with oil-clogged cylinder-heads, and bursts of renewed profanity as the inexperienced coxswains tugged vainly at the starting cords of motors that refused to fire at all. Boats were finally launched crowded with Gurkhas, who are poor and unenthusiastic watermen at best, only for the engines to stutter into silence in mid-stream and go floating helplessly down river. Fortunately it was bright moon-light, and by heroic exertions the bridge-head guard was put across and a trickle of riflemen followed. Daylight came with headquarters and most of the men of No. 30 Column across, but the whole operation was sabotaged by the mules.

Horses, treated kindly, swim well, and even enjoy it. Not so their illegitimate offspring. Mules, on land so docile, so footsure, so hardy, seldom frightened even by gunfire and the noise of battle, are unpredictable in the water. They may swim; they may not. On March 12th the mules of the 111th Brigade, infected by a collective hysteria, went on strike. Many refused to enter the water, even when beaten until the drivers could barely raise their arms. Those who did enter would at first swim off confidently enough, only to panic again and turn round halfway, or to be swept down river. In vain did Macgillicuddy and his men jump on willing mules and swim with them in the hope that the others would follow, or drive the more reluctant into the water. The sun rose on a crazy regatta; boatloads of men, some rowing, some motoring, some drifting; boats towing strings of terrified mules or, equally, strings of terrified mules towing boats whose motors had stalled yet again.

Overhead there was the heartening roar of the engines of P-51s, for Alison and Cochran had thrown every fighter aircraft they had into the task of protecting the crossing, Alison himself flying many hours on standing patrol. But it was only a matter of time before the Japanese awoke from their surprising torpor. The crossing was in fact discovered that morning by four Burmese policemen. Word had reached one of the Japanese local commanders that something untoward was going on, in the very area where Wingate had crossed in 1943, and he sent the Burmese to find out what it was, and stop it. These simple men were promptly arrested, interrogated and sent as prisoners to India by a method which to them must have seemed almost supernatural. This happened when the C-47s of the Air Commando came, as usual, to snatch away their used gliders. The technique for this was to stretch out the nylon tow-rope with its loop hooked between two upright spars stuck in the ground. The retrieving aircraft swooped down with its own towing gear trailing, roared at zero feet altitude along the line of flight and took the glider up; the elasticity of the nylon cushioning the shock of the glider's acceleration. No one seems ever to have sympathised with the Burmese in their plight; subjugated by the British, reconquered by the Japanese, their country ravaged by the Chinese Army in 1942, bombed by the Americans, and now carried off to India as 'traitors'. One can only hope that those unfortunate constables were one day restored to their homes and families.

Meanwhile the water-sports continued unabated, but in vain did Macgillicuddy, naked and in a frenzy, shout, encourage, swear and ride mules into the water and right over to the far bank, in the hope that they might attract their comrades to join them. Nothing on that day would induce the mules to launch themselves on what appeared to their myopic eyes a limitless expanse of water full of peril and lacking a farther shore.

A patrol sent upstream to obtain warning of any approaching Japanese, found some rafts moored to the bank and floated down on them. Macgillicuddy's last effort was to lash a motor to the biggest raft and start a mule ferry. Finally all these efforts succeeded in carrying a total of forty-seven mules to the far bank, but it was mid-afternoon, and dangerously late. Lentaigne had to weigh the risk of interception, increasing with every hour, and he decided to cut his losses then and there. His headquarters and the part of No. 30 Column already across would combine into a single column, jettisoning for lack of mules all heavy weapons and gear except two mortars and two heavy radios, and march off to the appointed rendez-vous where Lentaigne hoped to meet the Cameronians and King's Own columns who, after yet another change in the flight plan, were deplaning at Broadway. (This was a sensible alteration, as Broadway was already an airfield in full working order, strongly defended by anti-aircraft guns and Royal Air Force fighters, while Chowringhee was completely exposed to Japanese air attack; hourly expected, but fortunately made too late, after Chowringhee had been finally abandoned.)

Lentaigne was then faced with an acutely difficult decision. The whole of No. 40 Column was still on the east bank of the Irrawaddy, and he did not dare to linger in so exposed a position while it attempted the crossing. Accordingly he ordered it to march off eastward in the tracks of the 4th/9th and come under command of Colonel Morris. Wingate agreed, and the three columns on the Bhamo road were entitled 'Morris Force'.

This was a melancholy occasion for the 3rd/4th Gurkha Rifles. Battalions are closely-knit families, and the spirit of the 3rd/4th had not been affected by the split into columns: at least, the men felt, their friends were not far away. Now No. 40, already depressed by what was only too plainly a débâcle, were alone in Asia and separated from their friends in No. 30, nor was it much consolation to be joining another Gurkha battalion. The 9th Gurkhas were all very well, but they were not the *Fourth*. Major Monteith, the No. 40 Column commander, and his men trudged off glumly to cross the Shweli, to be out of the war for a month of steady and uneventful marching whose tedium was broken only by the interest of a supply drop.[3]

The loss of one whole column from 111th Brigade, reducing it to two and a half battalions, was not the only consequence of the diversion from Piccadilly to Broadway and Chowringhee. The whole timing of 111th Brigade's move was interrupted and it arrived late in its operational area. By the time it had reached the line of the railway south of Indaw the Japanese reserves, whose northward move it was Lentaigne's mission to block, had already arrived at Indaw and had thrown out a flank guard to keep off Fergusson. In consequence he had to fight, unsuccessfully, for possession of Indaw East airfield instead of being able to seize and defend it. All these set-backs flowed from a single, elementary error: the failure to order continuous high-level air surveillance over the Chindit landing-zones, which resulted in the last-minute discovery that Piccadilly was blocked.

Twelve days later Wingate was killed and Lentaigne, as has been stated, was whisked off to Sylhet to take command of Special Force. Before he left he had to appoint a new commander for 111th Brigade without delay. The obvious choice by seniority was Morris. Another Gurkha officer, Skone of the 3rd/6th in Calvert's brigade, was highly recommended, but there were obvious objections to shifting battalion commanders about in the middle of critical operations. There were equally strong objections to appointing some outsider, unfamiliar with the peculiar Chindit style. Lentaigne took one of his impulsive decisions. Morris, reinforced by No. 40 Column, had now some 1,300 men under him and an independent mission. He was promoted to the brigadier's vacancy, while retaining his present command, which then became known as Morris Force, and Russell, commanding No. 49 Column, stepped up to command the 4th/9th. Lentaigne wrote out a signal announcing his decisions, his first as the new General Officer Commanding, and handed it to his brigade-major, Jack Masters, for enciphering and despatch to Tulloch at Special Force Headquarters. Its second paragraph, Masters read with a shock, announced that he himself was to take command of the 111th Brigade and its five remaining columns.

Masters had a full measure of courage and self-confidence, but he was momentarily awed. He demurred, only to be genially overruled. He had been graded, Lentaigne told him, 'outstanding' as an officer, in the precise military connotation of that adjective, i.e., fit for high command. He had helped to train the brigade from its beginning, and he was completely in accord with the new general's ideas. Masters dutifully accepted the appointment, wondering how to make such a cock-eyed solution work, for he was not to be advanced in rank. Never one to fuss about protocol, he simply stripped off his major's insignia and wore none for the rest of the campaign.

Morris Force, with No. 40 Column trailing behind, crossed the Shweli neatly enough, although not without some grumbling about Morris's orders, which left No. 94 (Cane) guarding the crossing place and acting as a stop to prevent a Japanese follow-up until No. 49

(Russell), with which Morris himself was moving, was clear; an unpopular order because it meant that No. 94 missed a supply drop and went without food for five days. On 'column' everything revolved around food.

'Jumbo' Morris was a sound battalion commander and might have been eminently suitable to command a conventional Indian Army brigade. But he was overbearing, tactless and authoritarian, the last man to be entrusted with the political and military subtleties of clandestine warfare.[4]

But although he had his faults, he was resolute enough and his force soon took a firm grip of the Japanese supply line. By mid-April Cane and Russell, sometimes acting separately and sometimes by mutual agreement, had cut it in half-a-dozen places, brought the Japanese out to be ambushed, reduced their supply service to running separate convoys in the undamaged sections and manhandling and reloading the northbound stores at the gaps, and committed much effort to road repairs – all for very few casualties.

Wingate had, in fact, unerringly chosen a perfect setting for an operation along the lines of his original Chindit concept: a vulnerable target, a mountain sanctuary nearby, jungle cover and a friendly element in the population. Chindit warfare was a dangerous game, the hardships were considereable, and the marches – especially the evasive ones after a brush with the enemy, in darkness and up the steepest mountain trails over appalling going – tried even the Gurkhas. But the men were fit, the scenery glorious, often with open, rolling downs as a contrast to the steaming forests of the lower valleys, and there was a spirit of high adventure. The *via dolorosa* all the Chindit columns were fated to tread lay some weeks in the future. The morale of the force was undiminished even by the news of Wingate's death. Peter Cane's account contains a heart-felt valedictory passage, ending with 'there was never a more inspiring leader and the Battalion will never forget his influence over them'.

The first of the many adventures of the columns might be called the 'Affair of the Three Elephants'. On March 16th, emboldened by the total absence of any Japanese, No. 94 Column was marching openly along a road when it met an elephant carrying two Burmese, employees of the former Bombay-Burma Trading Corporation, now the Nippon-Burma Trading Corporation, and therefore technically 'traitors'. The wretches were terrified, as well they might be, because Cane was considering shooting them. One of them turned out to be a Shan *Thugyi*, or headman, who had openly espoused the Japanese cause and who, it was later learned, had rounded up and maltreated many ex-Burma Riflemen and British stragglers from LONGCLOTH. Killing them would ensure that they would not betray the column, and the elephant would be a useful addition to the baggage train. Wingate, however, had impressed on all column commanders the importance of winning over the Burmese by kindness and mercy, and while Cane was hesitating another elephant arrived, carrying a large load of passengers, also Nippon-Burma workers, from a logging camp. A single execution was repugnant; a mass execution even more so. The matter was settled when a third elephant arrived, this one carrying 'a sick but very beautiful Burmese girl'. While Cane wondered what on earth to do and the alarmed Burmese were shrieking in dismay at the sight of the Gurkhas and at each other, the young lady's elephant bolted, doubtless prompted by a surreptitious prod from its *soonkie's* ankus.* Cane decided the high road was no place to hang about in case anyone else turned up and swelled the party further. Suspicious of his first two prisoners, he kept them with the column. The remainder and the elephants he left behind under the guard of a section of riflemen and an officer, who were told to hold them for twelve hours nearby and then slip away and rejoin the column.

No. 94 Column then moved on to find food and a hearty welcome in a Kachin village. There the value of including experienced Burma Rifle officers in every column was underlined by a smart piece of detection by the reconnaissance officer. He recognised two aliens who, sure enough, turned out to be Shans. On interrogation they said that they had come to buy food, which was a thin story because the district was short of food and they were not carrying enough money. Two more Shans, telling the same story, were picked up the same day. There were all, in fact, Japanese spies, part of a large intelligence operation to locate the scattered Chindit columns and identify any of the local people who helped them. Cane picked up another suspicious pair and so had six whom he forced to accompany the column, with dire warnings of what would happen if they tried to escape. This the foolish men ignored. When the escort's vigilance was relaxed they made a concerted bolt for the jungle, downhill, a fatal mistake, for the speed of the Gurkha mountaineer on a steep slope has to be seen to be believed: '*khud*' or precipice racing is one of his sports. Dropping after them like lightning as if on invisible skis, kukri in hand, the riflemen caught five out of six and hacked them down. The sixth outstripped his pursuers and escaped screaming into the dense jungle. 'I had always heard,' recorded Cane, 'that the Gurkhas were very quick in using the kukri, but they must have been very blunt, or inexpert at finishing their victims off. . .' A grisly scene, but guerrilla warfare is a grisly affair and no one lost any sleep over the horrid end of the wicked Thugyi of Kwehaungdon, who had had two sick British

* The sharp-pointed, boathook-like weapon used by the rider to control his elephant.

soldiers, Chindits of 1943, stripped and publicly flogged. Dealing with informers was not a question of vengeance, however, but of sheer survival. Shortly afterwards a Kachin headman was betrayed for harbouring No. 94 Column. As a result the Japanese took him and his family and five of the other leading families, men, women and children, to Bhamo, where they were publicly executed. The iron laws of Kachin hospitality (and prudence) forced them to entertain travellers, whether Shans or Burmans, but from then on the Burma Rifle officers insisted that any strangers were shown to them and interrogated. Ten more spies were identified and duly shot in the course of the campaign.

Thus secured from detection, the columns were able to move freely and the first phase of the operations by Morris Force proved a model of the Chindit style. After crossing the Shweli River they headed east along the road leading to Bhamo, blowing the bridges on the way. They then circled round to the north, avoiding a Japanese garrison at Sinlumkaba, skirted the Chinese border and crossing the spectacular gorge of the Taiping River, a tributary of the Irrawaddy, moved downstream to destroy the suspension bridge and vehicle ferry on the Bhamo-Myitkyina road. Then, dodging from one side of the border to the other, they descended from the mountains to cut the road and ambush convoys as opportunity dictated using, in default of better topographical intelligence, *The Motorists Guide Book to Northern Burma*. By April 10th seven bridges and the ferry had already been destroyed, three of iron and one of stone. The Japanese, ignorant of where the next blow might fall, made futile dashes up and down the road, only to be ambushed from time to time, and were forced to divert some 1,000 men and engineer plant in constructing by-passes round the gaps. In this phase Dah Force exerted an indirect pressure by its mere existence. The Japanese, starved of intelligence, knew at least something was afoot in the hills along the border and sent strong patrols into the wilds to beat up the elusive Herring and Shan Lone instead of hanging on to the tracks of the Gurkha columns which, with their long trains of mules and their heavy resupply needs – explosives by the hundredweight and 45,000 rations every five days by air – were infinitely easier to pin down, or should have been. But Russell and Cane were masters of evasion, and aggressive and adventurous to a degree.

There was a typical action at Myothit where the road crosses the Taiping River. A long, hard night march brought No. 94 Column storming into the town at four o'clock in the morning to set about the demolitions, with 'stops' on the road to north and south to hold off any counter-action. The few Japanese in the town scampered off in terror. 'Not very *hara-kiri* like', remarked the column diarist. The

Gurkhas pulled down and burned the bamboo suspension bridge and blew up the cables and equipment of the vehicle ferry, booby-trapping the bank-seats and ruins to discourage the repair gangs. They also cut down and chopped up the telegraph line for five miles. They then wrecked the rice mill, which was a valuable source of Japanese rations, stuffing 'Nobel's excellent M808 explosive' into the cylinder-heads of the engines through the sparking-plug holes and finishing the job with sledge-hammers. There were twenty-three tons of rice on the site, some ready milled. The Gurkhas, who for a month had been subsisting on the miserable 'K' ration, had to burn this treasure. But first they stuffed as much as they could carry into pockets, packs and haversacks, weighing themselves down so much that they had sadly to jettison much of it on their withdrawal. They did however linger, with splendid impudence, to have a huge feast of boiled rice before pulling out at dusk.

On the north side Alec Harper, the second-in-command and rifle company commander, had set a neat ambush into which sailed a Japanese lorry full of soldiers, of whom nine were killed, Harper picking off one with the sporting rifle he always carried. The art of the ambush had been brought to a high state of perfection by the Gurkhas, but there were occasional lapses. After every devilish nicety has been arranged – the cross fire, the fallen tree round the bend of the road to stop the leading vehicle, the string of Hawkins grenades pulled across behind the rear one to prevent flight in that direction, the booby-traps and the fire-hardened *panjis* of sharpened bamboo planted away from the fire-positions on the 'safe' side of the road, where the experienced soldiers will dive for cover from the burst of crippling fire into the jungle – one essential act remains: the signal by the ambush commander to open fire. In the precise timing of this lies the whole secret of success. The ambush commander 'springs' the ambush when its victims are fairly inside the trap by firing the first shot. No one else, even under the severest provocation, may precede his signal.

Flushed with confidence from previous successes, Cane and Harper were standing carelessly on the open road while the young officer in charge explained his arrangements: 'There's a PIAT to stop even a light tank, there's a flame-thrower to make certain, and a Bren (light machine-gun) and I've laid some anti-tank mines . . .' when an unsuspicious and unobservant party of Japanese soldiers in a lorry drove serenely past them. The key man, whose finger should have been curled ready round his trigger, was to do a 'double-take' at the enemy passing within a few feet of him so the Gurkhas, who always followed their orders explicitly, remained motionless. The lorry passed the PIAT gunner, then the flame-thrower and then the Bren gunner unscathed. Unluckily for its passengers, a quarter of a mile further on their vehicle ran over a set of road mines prudently laid by the engineer platoon to cover them while they were working on a demolition, and blew up. The sole survivor, taking one look at the fierce Mongolian faces of the Gurkhas, dived into the forest. According to a later report, he emerged from it to steal a bicycle from a villager and pedalled off to his base, declaring to all who would listen that the *Chinese* Army had arrived. So even this slight misadventure served to confuse Japanese intelligence.

Morris Force at this stage was in command of the situation, full of the confidence that success breeds and what Cane called 'firebrand ideas'. Traffic on this supply artery of the 18th Division was already badly interrupted, and could be stopped altogether if a joint attack was mounted by both columns on the important staging post and road maintenance centre of Nalong, so the approaches to it were carefully reconnoitred. Herring was being pestered by the Japanese, but his patient work was soon to result in the creation of a guerrilla force which, though small, was to kill 300 of the enemy and tie up many more in chasing it. The two forces were poised for a big success, but there were breakers ahead. Friction was developing inside Morris Force and between Morris Force and Dah Force. There was also an additional difficulty. For some reason never explained, Herring was ordered by higher command to restrict his activities to the area north of the Taiping River, whereas his whole plan had been based on drawing his recruits from the villages full of old Burma Rifles to the south of it.[5] Special Force neglected both forces and kept Morris Force short of resupply and direct air support, in spite of clamorous signals demanding more explosives and pointing out the juicy targets at Nalong. Stilwell's headquarters was completely out of touch and had no idea what the two forces were doing, or had achieved. Later he was abruptly to order Morris Force into conventional operations against Japanese fixed defensive positions. All these gloomy developments, however, lay in the future. For the present, in the much-used cliché of those days, borrowed from fox-hunting, 'the tails of all the pack were up'.

Shortly after the sacking of Myothit, Captain Lazum Tang, Herring's Kachin second-in-command, appeared from the jungle to guide the columns to the Dah Force base and hide-out, and they went up to the rendez-vous with high hopes.[6]

It was now mid-April. As Lentaigne's plan began to unfold, Masters and the 111th Brigade went off to the north to establish the new blocking fortress at the northern end of the Railway Valley. The tracks of the re-deploying columns were criss-crossing across the map; some going to join Masters, others from Indaw going eastward to curl round and form a screen around the White City. At the White City itself there was much hard fighting, the Japanese being defeated with great slaughter. The First Chinese Army lay inert in front of Kamaing. The Marauders were licking their wounds and recuperating, having beaten off the Japanese at Nphum Gah. They were about to learn with dismay that Stilwell was planning a flank march to seize Myitkyina by *coup de main*, with themselves as a spearhead.

11

Thunder at the White City

AT THE BEGINNING of April all eyes, Japanese and British, were turned towards the White City, now a small but impregnable little fortress whose garrison dominated the southern entrance to the Railway Valley. The Japanese, that is to say General Kawabe of Burma Area Army, began to collect a counter-attack force powerful enough to eliminate it. Lentaigne's first positive action in command was to strengthen it.

Calvert, always the engineer, kept his troops hard at work on the defences. The whole area became a rabbit warren of slit trenches and burrows roofed over with logs proof against anything smaller than a direct hit from a heavy artillery shell. The perimeter wire was deepened into an obstacle sown with booby-traps and further protected by outlying minefields, and this was covered by the interlocking fire of machine-guns and mortars centrally controlled through an intricate web of buried telephone cables radiating from Calvert's command post. There was nothing static about Calvert's defence. The railway, physically blocked by the fortress and with three major bridges cut, was unusable, but the Japanese could still by-pass it with small convoys of supply vehicles and parties of reinforcements using the forest tracks. Accordingly, Chindit patrols roamed freely to the south mining the roads, ambushing the convoys and interfering with any repair work. To the north one of Calvert's Burma Rifle officers lived and moved impudently among the Japanese guard posts on the railway, organising a guerrilla and intelligence network among the Kachin villagers. Calvert now felt secure enough to entrust the defence of the White City to Lieutenant-Colonel Ron Degg and his redoubtable South Staffordshires and send off Skone and his Gurkhas and Christie's No. 50 Column, which had been 'floating' not very effectively around the White City, to beat up a Japanese position at Kadu, twenty miles up the railway.

Lentaigne's plan was to provide the White City with artillery and an addition to its striking force, so that Calvert would in effect have two brigades under command, one in the fortress and one in hand which could manoeuvre around it under cover of the artillery,

193

pinning any assailant of the White City between the two. By March 27th the admirable United States engineers had arrived in gliders to flatten a landing ground big enough to accept C-47 transports, a quarter of a mile outside the perimeter and west of the railway tracks, and into this there was flown between the 27th and 5th April six 40 mm Bofors anti-aircraft guns, four 25-pounder field-guns and four little 2-pounder anti-tank guns. From now on it was possible to maintain the White City direct, without recourse to parachute drops or ferrying via Broadway. This was all done without interference by the Japanese, but on April 4th they gave Calvert an unpleasant shock.

On that date a patrol of the South Staffordshires strolled rather too nonchalantly into Sepein village, from where the Japanese had been so brutally ejected on March 18th, to find it reoccupied and were pinned down by fire. It took a sharp little action, supported by Norman Durant with a mortar and a machine-gun, before it could be rescued. The Japanese were back and dug in too deeply to be driven out. They were a bare two miles from the new airstrip and if they showed the slightest initiative they could wreak havoc there. On the 5th the final sortie was to bring in the balance of the artillery, and Calvert wondered what his commission would be worth if twenty-five of General Old's precious C-47s were lost on his airstrip because he had failed to warn them off. To create a distraction he sent out a raiding party, accompanied by the irrepressible Colonel Peter Fleming with a mortar crew in a jeep. He, far from returning to his desk after the Aberdeen conference, had accepted an invitation from Calvert to taste the excitements of the White City. The night of April 6th was enlivened by a spectacular firework display of tracer, Verey lights, machine-gun fire and mortar bombs from the direction of Mawlu and Sepein, which alarmed the incoming pilots. They were reassured by Calvert, who strolled about the dispersal with his fingers crossed, lying cheerfully that the noise was normal and nothing to worry about. The guns were reassembled with great speed and efficiency, trundled off to their positions and emplaced. The field-guns were sited to cover Mawlu and the Bofors spread round the perimeter.

It was just in time. On the evening of the 6th the garrison was alerted by shells bursting in the air, followed by salvoes of horrid little high-velocity projectiles, so rapid in flight that they arrived before the bang of discharge or the whistle of their flight could warn the garrison to take cover. These were to be followed by the slow descent from the sky of huge mortar bombs whose splinters were enough to fell a good-sized tree. Fortunately they caused few casualties. The soldiers who may have cursed their brigadier for making them toil at their digging in the sweaty heat now had good cause to be grateful to him. A regular sequence now began of Japanese air raids by day and artillery bombardment by night. The Bofors guns of the 69th Regiment proved to be superbly manned, on one occasion shooting down five Japanese aircraft during a single raid, duly verified.[1] Counter-battery was more difficult, as the Japanese gunners, like their infantry, dug like moles and emplaced their guns singly, but Nicholls, commanding the 25-pounders, succeeded in fixing a number and either shot back, which temporarily silenced them or, more effectively, called in the Air Commando, who bombed the suspect areas. It was clear that the period of raiding and ambush was over, and that a hard, stand-up fight with a properly organised Japanese field force, was about to begin.

When General Kawabe, commanding Burma Area Army, realised the full weight and thrust of the Chindit offensive he was deeply perplexed and alarmed. He was without a single reserve formation – such as a division capable of sustained combat – and he had only a few battalions scattered along his line of communications. Mutaguchi had 100,000 of his best troops locked in battle west of the Chindwin. Tanaka and his élite but understrength 18th 'Chrysanthemum' Division was grappling with Stilwell's Chinese in the north, and badly needed reinforcement. He had only one weak division, the 56th,

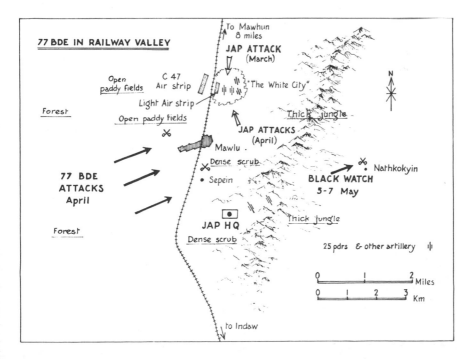

from which he had already borrowed a battalion for the attack on Broadway, watching the group of American trained Chinese sitting, fortunately for him, idle and inert east of the mighty Salween River in Yunnan, inside China. It took his staff a fortnight to estimate the nature of the Chindit descent and another to scratch up an *ad hoc* force to deal with it. (It must be said that the Japanese, like the Germans who taught them modern tactics, had a knack for rapidly creating task forces of this nature, as their officers and men were strongly disciplined and trained in a common doctrine.) As a first move he drew on second-rate battalions, regarded as suitable only for garrison duty, from points as far afield as Moulmein, Bassein and Saigon, and put them under a spare independent brigade headquarters commanded by General Hyashi. This was called Take Force, originally of three battalions and eventually made up from eight different ones. It numbered some 4,200 bayonets plus two obsolete light tanks, a few 75 mm guns and what the British called the 'Coalscuttle', because of the black cloud emitted by its bursting bomb. This was a huge, obsolete 150 mm mortar firing a 'bomb' weighing 200 pounds, some six inches in diameter (5.9 in) and five feet long. Where the Japanese found this antique piece is not known. It was originally designed for fixed emplacements in coastal fortresses for beach defence. Its bomb had poor fragmentation and poor lethality, but the noise it made tried the nerve of the most stout-hearted. Fergusson could hear the explosions clearly at Aberdeen, twenty-five miles away.

Hyashi, leaving detachments at Indaw to hold off the 16th Brigade, dug himself in solidly around Mawlu and prepared to soften up and assault the White City.[2]

Take Force was followed up by the headquarters and part of the 53rd Division, stationed at Kuala Lumpur in Malaya. This was not really a combat field formation, but rather a pool of reserves. It had no artillery and one of its regiments was still in Japan. It was reinforced, in the Japanese style, with guns drawn from here and there and formed into batteries: some light anti-aircraft guns, three 105 mm field howitzers and some of the little 70 mm battalion guns operated by the infantry. The divisional commander was sick, and exercised little operational control, so the fighting of the next phase was under General Hyashi himself. Later at Mawlu General Takeda took over and gradually Take Force was absorbed into his division. Its total strength, before it began to be worn down by fighting and disease, was never more than 6,500.

The various units of the 53rd (*Yasu* or 'Tranquil') Division were second-rate troops, largely of older or unfit men collected in battalions for internal security and occupation duties, and neither Hyashi nor Takeda were up to the standard of the best Japanese generals. (The élite 'Chrysanthemums', empty as their ranks were, strongly resented reinforcement from the 53rd: a British, rather than a Japanese reaction, it might be thought, but soldiers are remarkably similar, whatever their nation. It was as if the United States Marine Corps were asked to accept detachments of National Guard infantry.) Nevertheless, every Japanese soldier was prepared to sacrifice his life for the divine Emperor. In the defence, given a spade, a rifle and a bag of grenades he would frequently defy anything short of a combined assault by tanks and heavy artillery. The Japanese, lethal to the last, had to be extracted from their burrows by infantry, by hand as it were, and killed one by one. That was an expensive business. Meanwhile Lentaigne freed Calvert for a fully mobile, aggressive rôle. The West African Brigade was originally intended for use as the garrisons of strongholds. The 6th Battalion of the Nigeria Regiment had been landed at Broadway as the garrison for Aberdeen, but it had encountered Wakayuma's battalion in the Railway Valley when he was on his way to Broadway, and had come off the worst, being scattered and somewhat demoralised. The commanding officer was relieved and the brigade-major, Gordon Upjohn, put in command to reorganise them. In the meantime Wingate had ordered the 7th (Vaughan) and the 12th (Hughes) into Burma on the heels of the 14th Brigade as part of his plot to commit them before 'the rats got at them'. Hughes took over at Aberdeen until Upjohn was ready, and then both the 7th and the 12th, together with the brigade commander, A. H. Gillmore, moved to the White City. In addition Lentaigne sent Calvert the 45th Reconnaissance Regiment, now on its way to Broadway for evacuation.

The 12th arrived first and Calvert met them with a characteristic gesture. When Hughes reported on the radio that he was approaching the White City and needed guides, Calvert put on his red brigadier's cap, summoned his horse, his groom and his personal escort and rode out to meet him. In the British Army in peacetime the passage of a formed body of troops or its entry into a garrison was attended by no little formality. Guards turned out and presented arms, officers saluted and soldiers faced it and stood to attention. As Hughes' men emerged from the scrub in a long single file they were impressed to see their new commander on his horse saluting them. This good impression was followed up by his welcoming manner and vigorous orders. (It is also typical of Calvert that in his humorous, self-deprecating way he relates that he could not understand why he seemed allergic to his brigadier's 'red hat' – symbolic suppressed resentment of authority? Then he discovered that a colony of tiny ants had chosen it for a home, stinging his scalp every time he put it on.)

The West Africans were very different from Indian troops, whose

197

battalions were recruited from races martial by caste, tradition and temperament, had only a few white officers for superior direction and were led in battle largely by excellent Indian under-officers. The Nigerians, pagan, Muslim and Christian, outwardly so fierce-looking and the subject of fantasy by soldiers in British regiments, who suspected them of cannibalism and of cutting off the heads of their enemies, were in fact a grave, kindly, courteous and simple people. The African colonial battalions were raised for ceremonial purposes and 'imperial policing' as it used to be called, for keeping internal order and suppressing slavery and banditry. They had no experience of modern war and could not imagine its terrors. For them the soldier's trade was, by the standards of their poor country, well-paid as well as honourable and peaceful, spent at home where they could enjoy their calm and ordered military life in barracks with their wives. The British treated them with paternal affection, as children (and like children beat them on the bare bottom with rods as a lawful military punishment – 'six for arse'), and provided not only the officers, but a command level of white noncoms who supervised the technical work of their black colleagues. Few Africans understood why they had come to this strange country to fight the 'Japans', but they were all fatalists. The secret of commanding them was to speak their language, have sympathetic understanding of their religion and customs and win their trust as well as their obedience. In Gillmore, Hughes, Carfrae and Vaughan and Upjohn they had good officers. The two battalions fought well because they were led well.

Calvert wasted no time in bringing Hughes into the White City, where his men took the place of the 3rd/6th Gurkhas, who were up at Kadu. They settled down to guard the southern half of the perimeter, where they proved remarkably steady in their first battle.

'What did you think of the Japanese bombs?' Carfrae of No. 29 Column asked his young orderly.

He giggled like a girl; a shadow creeping up from his neck showed that he blushed. 'I was much afraid,' he answered, his eyes downcast. 'I covered my face with my hands lay still like one dead.'

'And now?'

'Now I feel better, Master. Allah has taken the fear away that was within me.'

Like all soldiers they soon learnt that if well dug into deep cover artillery fire is more noisy and frightening than lethal, but nonetheless their introduction to warfare was severe enough to test the nerves of the best and steadiest of troops.

The Japanese under Hyashi, fortunately for the garrison of the White City, knew nothing of sophisticated tactics which require carefully planned schedules of accurate fire and close coordination between the infantry and the guns. He simply battered away at the defences of the White City in the clumsiest and most unimaginative manner possible with his guns and mortars. He never attempted to surround it completely, nor to bring up his anti-aircraft guns to shoot down or harass the aircraft that kept it in food and ammunition. They were retained to protect his own base at Mawlu from the attentions of the Air Commando. Occasionally a few Japanese Zero fighter aircraft and light (Sally) bombers attacked the fortress, to be driven off with loss by the Bofors guns of the Royal Artillery. By night the usual Japanese routine was to bang away with their guns, which only had the effect of driving the garrison into their 'funk-holes', while Captain Nicholls, secure in a sand-bagged edifice on top of the appropriately named 'OP Hill', with his four guns tucked away in a deep draw behind him, shot back at them using the crude but effective method of taking bearings to the flashes and timing the interval between flash and the sound of the discharge arriving to obtain the range. This brisk but relatively feeble response was varied by day-time attacks by the Air Commando, Nicholls indicating the Japanese positions requiring treatment by firing smoke shell. Take Force was subjected to 500-pound bombs, cannon fire from P-51s, shells from the 75 mm gun carried by the B-26s and occasionally the thunderclaps of parachute bombs floating down to burst into hundreds of down-sweeping fragments. A British patrol found a despairing message from a Japanese officer that unless something was done about the Allied aircraft the whole operation was doomed: flesh and blood, he wrote, could not stand up to them.

Japanese bombardment and Chindit counter-bombardment was followed nightly by attempts by the Japanese to push 'Bangalore torpedoes' – long pipes filled with explosive – by hand through the wire to cut a gap for their assault troops, or even hopeless efforts by the attacking Japanese to climb over the wire and swamp the mines and booby-traps by sheer weight of numbers: all announced by the usual screams and shouts of 'Banzai'. Each of these attacks was met by a terrific, coordinated fire from every weapon in the garrison that could be brought to bear: rifles, Brens, machine-guns, mortars, and even by the anti-aircraft gunners close to the perimeter depressing their barrels and firing point-blank. One day they drove off a half-hearted attack by the light tanks. One of the gunners saved his crew when a grenade was tossed into the gunpit. He held a sandbag on top of it, to be blown into the air and injured, but he survived to be awarded the Military Medal. When one attack on these lines had been repulsed there was a pause and another was launched at exactly the same spot.

The sole result of these senseless assaults was a ghastly high-tide mark of Japanese corpses, added to every night, suspended on the wire or lying inaccessible in the minefield. It was impossible to remove them for burial and they rapidly putrefied in the tropical heat. Attempts to cremate them using flame-throwers where they lay was visually disgusting and merely substituted one revolting stench for another. The fortress was smothered by clouds of gorged flies. Towards the end of the siege the American light aircraft pilots who flew in regularly to take out the wounded declared that they had no need to navigate when making their final approach: they could smell the White City from a distance away.

The whole siege was an extraordinary affair. Hyashi made no attempt to hem the fortress in or interfere with the airstrips. The columns entered and left freely through the one sally-port remaining in the defences, and the bolder spirits in the garrison used by day to leave the stink and bathe or wash their clothes in one of the limpid streams outside the wire.

Calvert remained in command until Vaughan and his two Nigerian columns had reported, and Skone and Christie had found their way back from Kadu. He then left Gillmore in command with the South Staffordshires holding the north face, the 12th Nigeria the south and No. 20 Column of the Lancashire Fusiliers covering the light plane strip between the railway and the wire. His striking force now consisted of himself with his brigade-major and signals, radios, his élite assault company (Macpherson), No. 50 Column, Lancashire Fusiliers (Christie), 3rd/6th Gurkha Rifles, the two columns united (Skone) the 45th Reconnaissance (Astell), No. 29 Column (Carfrae), No. 35 Column (Vaughan), and 7th Nigeria. 'S' Troop, 25-pounders was in support and Nicholls accompanied the 3rd/6th with a portable radio to control its fire. In addition the Leicesters of the 16th Brigade were ordered to block the trail from Auktaw to Mawlu, to prevent any Japanese reinforcements from using it. (They might have been better employed at Mawlu itself, but Chindit belief, unjustified by results, of using columns to screen the battlefield, persisted. The Japanese often succeeded in simply walking round them.)

Calvert's first attack was put in overhastily, and with his columns in line abreast. He himself felt afterwards that he would have done better if he had spent some time probing Hyashi's positions and beginning with a heavy air attack, but he was under orders from Lentaigne to attack without delay. He flew over the Japanese positions in an L-5 to have a quick look at them and made a good, simple plan. The two Nigerian columns were to seize the village of Thayaung, dig in, establish a base for the attack and level an airstrip to take out casualties. (Casualties could not be left about, humanitarian or medical reasons apart. Christie had earlier been forced to leave a party of wounded hidden in a thicket as he had no immediate means of evacuating them. They were found by the Japanese and all murdered as they lay.) Skone and the Gurkhas were to go for Sepein, Astell to extend Skone's right, and Christie to Astell's right again, with orders to look out for the Japanese supply dump and transport park.

There was only one unforeseen difficulty. The villages were all surrounded by a dense growth of the tenacious lantana shrub, originally imported by Europeans for their gardens. It had now run wild and often covered hundreds of acres. The Japanese fire positions were just outside the village buildings in the lantana and invisible until the attackers stumbled on them. At first all went well, but Skone, having taken Sepein, found that the Japanese main position was further on and became entangled in the lantana. Unfortunately, Calvert had been sufficiently encouraged by his initial success to call on Vaughan to send a column to clear the enemy from Mawlu and so had no reserve to send to help the Gurkhas. Vaughan decided to go himself. He wrote afterwards in his diary:

13th April
    A terrific day!
    At 8.0 o'clock the Brigadier (Calvert) told me he wanted me to support the main attack by investing (attacking) the big place of Mawlu with one company.
    I thinned out the Thayaung perimeter defences, collecting a four-platoon company from 35 Column and at 9.0 a.m. led it off to carry this out.
    We swept through two villages without opposition, but on entering the outskirts of Mawlu at 11.0 a.m. fire and brimstone was suddenly let loose on us.
    I could write a whole book about today – the thirteenth of April! – but will just say that from 11.0 a.m. till 3.0 p.m. we fought an almost continuous battle, being subjected to rifle fire, LMG fire, Jap light mortar fire (the latter more noisy than effective) and finally even dive-bombing. The noise was terrific, the Africans on the whole took it extraordinarily well – for we were undoubtedly up against a very well prepared and dug-in Jap position – and there was so much to do all the time that one had absolutely no time to worry about danger.
    At 5.0 p.m. – after having previously sent a message to say that I could and would hold on to the part of Mawlu we had gained – I got an order to withdraw to the firm base.
    In the hope of concealing the direction and purpose of our move

I waited till dusk, put down a last 3-inch mortar bombardment on the centre of Mawlu in the hope of leading the enemy to suppose we were about to attack him again, and then withdrew.

Nobby Hall was magnificent in this attack.

Hall was awarded an immediate Military Cross.

It proved a hard day's fighting and finally Calvert had to consider whether he would dig in at close quarters, or break clear. He jumped on his horse and galloped across the entire front to see the situation for himself. His fire-power, he saw, was not enough. The 25-pounders were well-handled, but pitifully inadequate, and even the Air Commando's 500-pound bombs seemed insufficient to shift the Japanese from their bunkers in the lantana. Astell tried to work round behind them past Skone's flank, but he became equally entangled. The Gurkhas, Calvert noted, had lost the sharp edge of their appetite for combat; they were rather sullen and as the infantry say, a little 'sticky'. He took the whole brigade out of action, ordering them to close on No. 29 Column, bringing their wounded. The moment Christie began to withdraw the Japanese came out to attack him, which suited the Fusiliers, as they were able to see them at last and they shot a large number. The 'Second Battle of Mawlu' was therefore a draw, but at least Hyashi had been distracted from the White City.

The troops in reserve tried to follow the battle from that most anxious of view points, the rear edge of the battlefield, where bad rumours alternate with good, and the sound of firing moves into the distance only to break out again much nearer or, equally inexplicably, falls to a diminuendo of scattered shots only to rise to a sudden crescendo. Then came the dismal procession of walking wounded, shocked and silent. The Gurkhas, noted Carfrae, looked like puzzled children: many of the Gurkha riflemen were indeed very young. There followed seriously wounded on improvised stretchers. Carfrae's sharp but sensitive attention was caught by the reaction of his burly African company-sergeant-major to his first sight of the dead, not an African but two Japanese of a patrol that had bumped into the reserve position. Both were horribly maimed; the arm of one had been severed by a grenade and the guts of the other were trailing out of his belly. In peace the CSM was the ornament of the ceremonial parade; he roared like a bull on the barrack-square, and was the terror of the private soldiers. Here, confronted with the reality of war, 'he stood rigid, as motionless as the dead at whom he stared, unable to turn away his face, his lower lip trembled like a child's when tears are close and his large brown eyes were filled with revulsion, horror and fear'. He was never again the same man, said Carfrae. Such is the effect of that powerful reagent, battle, on the chemistry of the human personality. The flamboyant, often soft underneath, collapse morally, relationships within the fighting group change subtly, new leaders appear and old ones, bred up in the false values of peace, equally subtly, abdicate.

After his repulse Calvert decided to change to tactics better suited to the Chindit aptitude and organisation. Instead of battering at Hyashi's firm base he spread a net of ambushes to the south in the hope of starving him out. No. 29 Column scored a notable success. Carfrae set a large ambush on the main road with all his available fire-power lined up on one side. A solitary lorry drove into it, but before it could be picked off one of the white officers, over-excited, took a shot and missed. The Japanese tumbled out of the vehicle and fled unharmed into the forest. The column was a lorry in running order to the good, but the position was compromised. Carfrae, however, decided to stick to his orders and stay where he was. He was rewarded at dusk by the arrival of a whole convoy into his trap. This time the Verey light signal to open fire was given at exactly the correct moment when the whole target was inside it, and a fusillade of rifle, machine-gun and PIAT bombs tore into it at a few yards' range. The result was a massacre. At first light the next morning the Africans combed the jungle on the far side of the road and hunted out the surviving Japanese who had fled into it. The shattered lorries were searched for dead, and the wounded collected and given first aid. This puzzled the simple Nigerians. They were not cruel, simply logical. They could not understand why, while some of their comrades were searching for 'Japans' in the trees and shooting them, Carfrae should so sternly order them to desist from knocking on the head any Japanese whom they found to be still breathing. Their point was made for them by a Japanese sergeant. Carfrae heard a commotion and, turning round, saw an apparently dead man being lifted clear of a lorry, his uniform soaked with blood from top to toe, suddenly revive, seize a bayonet and, with a defiant yell, try to stab an African. For a moment of confusion this apparition stood erect, to go down once and for all, riddled with bullets from half a dozen rifles pressed against its body.

Vaughan and his company had come back from Mawlu carrying their thirty-odd wounded, but uplifted at having proved themselves against their formidable opponents. Carfrae found the whole affair of the ambush disgusting. At dawn after the long vigil he had said to one of his officers, 'Did it really happen?' to receive a puzzled look from his less imaginative platoon commander. He felt his few losses keenly, especially one of his best officers, who returned from the mopping up, his arm shattered and shrunk with pain, his faithful African orderly

fluttering around him with cries of dismay. He had no time to bury
the dead: he had to be off before the Japanese could find him. An
attempt to cremate the dead with petrol from the vehicle tanks only
resulted in charred corpses. In a chivalrous but futile gesture he left a
note for the Japanese fixed to a lorry, saying that the casualties were
dead before they had been set on fire, and that he had cared for the
wounded. No. 29 Column then faded into the jungle.

The fundamental weakness of Chindit tactics, as shown repeatedly,
was that it was impossible to build, as it were, an impenetrable fence
in the jungle. Lightly armed troops requiring only minimal supplies
could always sneak through using the jungle trails. Harassing could
produce results, but only slowly, and, as far as Take Force was
concerned, Calvert had not found the forward depots the Japanese
had built up around Mawlu. Hyashi intensified his efforts, un-
availingly, but persistently enough to alarm Gillmore, who feared
that his garrison was being worn down by exhaustion and lack of
sleep. He appealed to Calvert to intervene more directly, and Calvert
responded at once, leaving the Nigerians to continue to harry the
supply routes.

Analysing his mistakes, he decided this time to punch through on a
narrow front, keep a reserve in hand, and not ask too much of his
pride and joy, the Gurkhas of the 3rd/6th, now very tired. He formed
up the 45th in arrow-head formation to lead the attack, followed by
the 3rd/6th ready to swing right or left to exploit an advantage, with
his headquarters and assault company close behind, the whole closed
up so as to facilitate control, by shouting if the radios failed. Once
again the attack began well. A silent advance took the Japanese by
surprise, and a whole company, unprotected by sentries, was overrun
by the 45th while they were bathing and washing in a stream. The
first inkling of contact for Calvert's headquarters was the sight of a
stark-naked Japanese dashing through its ranks, with – close behind
and hunting absolutely mute – a huge, bearded trooper, his bayonet
point a few inches behind the bare posterior of his quarry. The pair
disappeared into the trees and the battle started. Once again,
however, the two sides became locked together in a close-range
shooting match in the damnable lantana.

Lieutenant Sealey of the Lancashire Fusiliers had a rotten day. As
he crossed a water-course his platoon came under fire and went to
ground. He went forward himself to scout the position and came
under heavy fire, and as he struggled back the prehensile lantana
entwined round his pistol and his kukri, removing both, and when he
dived back down the bank of the *chaung* to avoid the stream of bullets
whistling through the scrub he lost his rifle as well. He then found
that his platoon had bolted. It took him some time to locate them and

round them up, shame-faced and without a single casualty, except for a wounded mule.

The 45th were pinned. Trooper Aylen, now a veteran, could see no enemy and noted that the curtain of machine-gun bullets came no lower than about three feet. Accordingly he aligned his Bren in the general direction of the enemy, lay flat and proceeded to eat a belated breakfast. He noted his new commander, Astell, and the brigade commander strolling about with apparent unconcern amid the bullets, discussing their next move. The gallant Macpherson, the leader of the assault company, was ordered to find the enemy flank and attack, and did so with success, killing a large number of Japanese, but he himself was killed by a shot in the head. Brigade headquarters came under a close and hot fire – so close that Calvert's voice, as he personally called on the radio for the Air Commando to strike, drew a burst every time he spoke into the microphone; and so hot that, as he watched out of the corner of his eye, he saw a traversing Japanese machine-gun punch a level row of holes through the flanks of his vital mules, and they collapsed slowly, one by one, in succession as they were hit. Once again Calvert decided that he had to pull out, covered by the astonishingly close bombing of the Air Commando.

It was a desperate and costly throw, but as was discovered later, it had helped to draw Take Force's teeth. The bombing and strafing by the American pilots had taken a tremendous toll. The 'Third Battle of Mawlu' was on April 18th. On the morning of the 17th, by daylight for a change, Hyashi ordered a last desperate attempt to break into the White City under cover of an intense artillery bombardment which caused many casualties. Suicide groups with Bangalore torpedoes made a wide breach in the wire and, at last and triumphantly, the Japanese swarmed up the slopes of OP Hill. The gunners in the valley below elevated the muzzles of their 25-pounders, Durant's machine-gunners took a shot whenever they had a clear field of fire, and the rest of the garrison watched the fight from the neighbouring hill-tops. OP Hill was defended by a platoon of the South Staffords. Its commander was an interior decorator by trade, and regarded in that rugged unit as an aesthete, if not actually effeminate. But he was now able to confound all those who had chaffed him. He held on until he had only sixteen men out of his forty standing, and so gave time for Hughes' Nigerians to charge. Soon the whole feature was covered with Japanese and Africans fighting hand to hand in great confusion. The last Japanese to be killed was another wounded man who sprang to his feet seeking to take one opponent before he died, and as he ducked and twisted amid a dozen pointed rifles a huge African, arriving with a box of No. 36 grenades, swung it by its rope handle and smashed it on his head. Finally, the Japanese colonel leading the assault, achieved the *bushido* ideal in a more dignified manner, being killed on the horse he had ceremonially mounted for the occasion. That for a time ended all attempts to take the White City. Geneal Takeda took command, and he wisely decided to wait until the whole of his 53rd Division had been assembled and then mount a properly coordinated attack. He was a better commander than the crazy Hyashi, as he was to demonstrate against the 111th Brigade. However, as will be seen, by the time that he was ready, the White City garrison had slipped away.

In the meantime Lentaigne was occupied in analysing his position, making his plans, and obtaining the agreement to them of first Slim and then Stilwell, which was more difficult. In the meantime he left the three brigades west of the railway line to carry on with their harassing, except, as said, the 45th who were ordered to join Calvert. This may well have been at the urging of Tulloch who, as he confessed long afterwards, felt that he owed it to his dead friend and hero to defend his doctrine and his plans to the last, so a version of the defunct 'Plan B' continued until as late as April 26th, although Slim had stated on the 9th that all Chindit effort was to revert to the support of Stilwell. As a result a great chance was missed to smash Take Force outside the White City. Brodie had four good, fresh battalions and he could have been at Mawlu in three or four days. Instead he was told to go on pottering around, burning the scattered Japanese dumps, and when he did move came on slowly, pausing to inflict yet more demolitions on the railway. A chance was missed completely to alter the balance of forces in the Railway Valley by breaking up Take Force and the 53rd Division before it had completed its concentration.

Lentaigne's plan for the next phase of operations was dictated by four factors. First, he had to continue to block the Railway Valley. It was an unavoidable obligation the British and the Chindits owed to Stilwell. Second, he had to close down the strongholds. He was assured that no resources were available to convert their dirt strips to all-weather airfields. Third, he was convinced that Wingate was right and that ninety days was the limit of endurance for behind-the-lines operations. He knew that the only way out for his brigades was on foot northwards, after the final defeat of Tanaka, and where they were at present was too far south. Fourth, if his operations were to be successful he would have to change from milling around in scattered columns all over the jungles of Northern Burma in Chindit fashion, and concentrate his forces according to more orthodox tactics. (This is conjecture, but it is what he did, and there is sufficient evidence that he considered Wingate a charlatan and his military ideas nonsense.)

Lentaigne's new dispositions were simple enough in essence but would require a complicated set of moves whose detail will be given in Chapter 13. Briefly, part of the 16th Brigade was to be flown out from Aberdeen and part was to march to Broadway and be flown out from there. Then both strongholds would be closed down and their garrisons be made available for the next operation, which was to block the Railway Valley forty miles north of the White City in the area of Hopin. There Masters was to establish a block with battalions 'floating' round it. Calvert was to take his brigade to a position east of the railway and the Namyin River opposite Hopin, and prevent any attempt by the Japanese to interfere with Masters from that side.

The most delicate part of the operation would be the evacuation of the White City, with the Japanese dug in a bare two miles away and their artillery commanding both airstrips. To cover the move the whole of Brodie's brigade was to be used. One battalion was to relieve the South Staffords and the rest to encircle the White City and keep the Japanese occupied until all the wounded, heavy equipment and guns had been removed. The detailed plans for this had been worked out by Brigadier Gillmore, who would control the whole operation. Once clear the 14th and the 3rd West African Brigade with the 7th and 12th Battalions were also to march north, where Gillmore was to resume command of his 6th Battalion. Both brigades were then to take up positions in the mountains west of the railway corridor close to Hopin and near the Kyunsalai Pass through the Bumrawng Bum. The proper task of the three outlying brigades was not simply to protect Blackpool, but to come down like a hammer on any Japanese troops attacking it, and destroy them. Even allowing for the erosion of the Chindit columns by sickness their total force, excluding the garrison of the new block, was at that time 5,000 to 6,000 and a match for anything the Japanese could bring up in terms of numbers.

Lentaigne issued no long, detailed formal orders. His instructions were expressed in a pithy signal, expressing his intentions and telling the brigades where they were to go. This was the practice in the Force. The local commanders were left free to use their initiative and if their operations required coordination to arrange it between themselves. This was all very well in principle and for guerrilla operations, but Lentaigne's master plan, sound in itself and conforming to the classical maxims of war, was not a far-flung deep-penetration operation: it was a closely-knit conventional operation involving a direct defence and counter-attack against a resolute conventional enemy. The timings were all-important and all hopes of success depended on speed and punctuality, for the White City had to be firmly held until Masters was in position. Moreover the full fury of the monsoon rains could be expected in mid-May, after which all movement would be slowed to a crawl, and air supply and air support liable to long interruption. Close supervision by the commanding general was mandatory. The day of conclaves among tribal chieftains to arrange matters among themselves was over.

Stilwell, it need hardly be said, objected to the whole plan. He wished the Chindits to continue to hold the White City, without offering any solution to Lentaigne's problems. He averred that the northward move would simply draw the Japanese reserves into his sector. He, perhaps with the recollection of Lonkin, said that he did not wish to take the Chindits under his command, because they would not obey his orders. He only assented, sullenly and under protest, when Slim came up to Shaduzup with Lentaigne and gave Stilwell *his* orders. Stilwell was persuaded, because Lentaigne guaranteed that he would hold Blackpool until June 1st, by which time he could reasonably hope that the Chinese would have broken the deadlock at Kamaing and, if his secret plan succeeded, Galahad would be in Myitkyina.

12

The Strongholds Abandoned:
All March North

THE EVACUATION OF Aberdeen and Broadway presented no great problem to the staff once the aircraft had been made available. They were too remote to be exposed to Japanese interference, except from the air, and in any case General Takeda had enough to do in reopening the Railway Valley and pushing some badly needed reinforcements up to the 18th Division. Brigadier Gillmore, however, was faced with certain difficulties. There was the purely tactical one of slipping a large force away from the close presence of the enemy, which involved emerging from the White City in single file through the one narrow sally-port in the west face of the perimeter. If the Japanese were to prove alert and aggressive there would be a real danger of his becoming involved in a running rearguard action and even of part of his force being pinned half-in, half-out of the fortress. But this was not all. To add to his difficulties Lentaigne had ordered – for political and propaganda reasons – that all surplus gear, heavy radios, reserves of ammunition, even sick mules and above all, the artillery, must be extracted from all the strongholds and flown out to India. No impression must be given that the Chindits, only shortly before triumphantly ensconced in Japanese-occupied Burma, had been driven from their positions and had not, in the literal sense of the old phrase, stuck to their guns. Ambivalent as Lentaigne's feelings about the Chindits and the whole Chindit enterprise may have been, he knew only too well that in the battle for propaganda and publicity Special Force had more enemies in Comilla, Shaduzup and Delhi than it had in Tokyo.

Gillmore accordingly asked for help from the 14th Brigade and it was he who made the plan that was finally adopted. Brodie was ordered to move his brigade to cover the fortress. The outline of Gillmore's plan was for the Leicester columns to relieve the South Staffordshire in the White City garrison so that they could rejoin Calvert, send the Black Watch to block the tracks to the east of the White City, post the York and Lancaster columns to protect the main airstrip and for the Bedfordshire and Hertfordshire to remain in reserve. Inside this screen the C-47 transports would fly out all the equipment and guns; in one night, it was hoped. Then the garrison would steal out and all the columns melt into the forest in the usual Chindit style, to reappear forty miles to the north. At this moment Gillmore was abruptly relieved of his command by Lentaigne.

The dismissal of the commander in the White City when he was poised to execute a difficult operation planned by himself and, indeed, only fully understood by him, remains a mysterious trans-action. Gillmore may by temperament have been over-cautious and his difficulties bulked over-large in his mind, but he had done no more than what was sensible in calling for Calvert to resume his attacks on Mawlu, and he had held the White City against the strongest attack so far launched against it. Comparisons were made between his style of command and that of the flamboyant Calvert, but unfairly: Calvert was difficult to follow and impossible to imitate. When Colonel Kyte and Major Mead flew into the White City to plan the air side of the evacuation they found Gillmore in high spirits. He took them up to OP Hill to describe how the final Japanese assault had been broken. Then he seized the opportunity of having a senior staff officer from Force Headquarters present to discuss his own position. At that moment it looked as if he would shortly be without a command. Calvert was hoping to retain his 7th Battalion, Upjohn with the 6th was about to move north to cover Masters, and the 12th to come under Brodie's command after the evacuation. Gillmore had no headquarter column, for only he himself and his brigade-major had taken over in the White City, with the main part of the 77th Brigade headquarters to assist him. He hoped, he said, to command his own brigade, and he needed the staff and equipment to do it. If the plan did not permit of this and his battalions were to be shared out among the other brigadiers, then he might as well fly out. Kyte agreed to represent Gillmore's point of view, and to carry a personal letter from him to Lentaigne; a perfectly proper way of doing things. Lentaigne's reaction was to relieve Gillmore abruptly, by signal, and to send his deputy brigade commander, Colonel Ricketts, to the White City to take over.[1] It was given out that Gillmore's health was failing. This was not the proper way to do things. Lentaigne, quite apart from any question of Gillmore's competence, should have made it his business to visit the White City at this crucial stage of operations, if only to explain his future intentions to his brigadiers. It was one thing to give the Chindit brigadiers their head, but it was quite another not to visit them and take stock of the situation himself. From now on Lentaigne showed an inexplicable reluctance to leave his headquarters. He was to pay only one visit to the troops in the field. This was to Broadway, to reprimand Calvert. One cannot imagine Wingate not visiting Brodie, or the White City, or satisfying

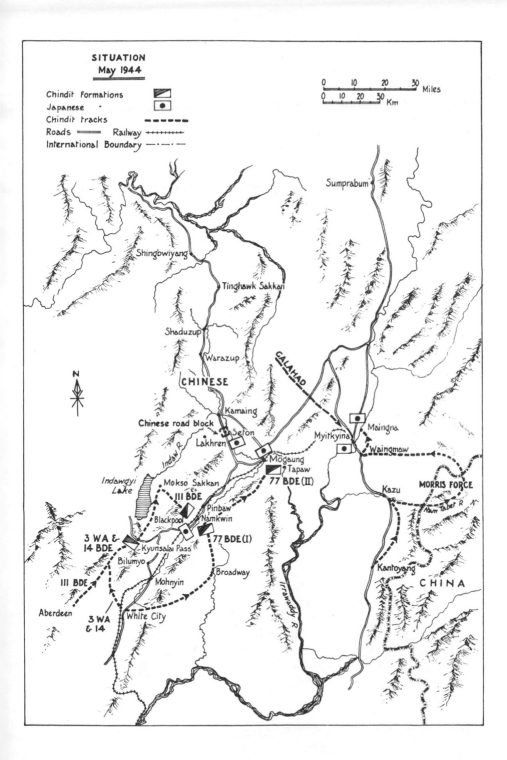

SITUATION
May 1944

Chindit Formations
Japanese
Chindit tracks
Roads ===== Railway ++++++
International Boundary —··—··—

0 10 20 30 Miles
0 10 20 30 Km

Sumprabum

Shingbwiyang

Tinghawk Sakkan

Shaduzup

Warazup

CHINESE

GALAHAD

Kamaing

Chinese road block

Lakhren   Seton

Myitkyina   Maingna

Waingmaw

Mogaung
Tapaw
77 BDE (II)

MORRIS FORCE

Kazu

Indaw R.

Indawgyi
Lake

Mokso Sakkan

III BDE

Blackpool   Pinbaw
Namkwin

Nam Tabet R.

3 WA &
14 BDE   Kyunsalai Pass   77 BDE (I)

Bilumyo

III BDE   Mohnyin   Broadway

Kantoyang   CHINA

Irrawaddy R.

Aberdeen

3 WA
& 14   White City

himself that the new block at Hopin was correctly sited. Furthermore, in the British Army it is customary for senior officers in command not only to see things for themselves, but also to confront anyone whom they decide to dismiss. Ironically, Lentaigne soon decided that Ricketts was to take all three battalions under his command eventually, and the 7th and 12th immediately. Ricketts knew nothing of the details of Gillmore's plan before he went in, nor, amazingly, did Brodie.

Brigadier Ricketts began his unexpected and exacting mission under certain handicaps. His connexion with West Africa had been only on the staff of the Command Headquarters; he had never commanded West African troops, and he did not speak the essential *lingua franca* – Hausa. He had at short notice been posted to India to succeed Gillmore as second-in-command of the brigade on that officer's promotion. He had no experience of Chindit fighting or training because his duties were to remain at base in India, supervising the supply of stores, ammunition and food to the columns in the field. His dealing with the Special Force staff had been almost entirely confined to the administrative branches. However, he had two valuable advantages. He was a professional infantryman, from a 'good' regiment, the Durham Light Infantry, and he was a trained staff officer. (It is worth remarking that he was outstanding in what was an outstanding command and staff echelon. He was one of eight ex-Chindits who were to reach the rank of major-general.) Also, fortunately, he had met Brodie before and the two men were on good terms.

Ricketts' first impressions of the White City and its garrison were unfavourable. The stink and lack of hygiene due to so many men being crowded into so small a space (the White City perimeter was no bigger than a fair-sized city park), the flies, the unburied Japanese dead and the constant shelling had depressed the morale of many otherwise stout-hearted men. There was some nervousness about the thought of evacuation. (Possibly the agoraphobia endemic in the garrisons of fortresses and strongpoints, the obsession that safety lies within and the enemy-haunted open spaces are dangerous, was beginning to manifest itself.) Intermittent shelling continued. Ricketts therefore made it his business to go around and speak to as many junior ranks as possible, explaining his plans and winning their confidence. He called for maximum air effort and artillery fire, so that all could see that the Japanese were being hit hard. On the day before the evacuation the troops were able to watch the Mitchell B-25s and the P-51 Mustangs pounding the enemy positions at Mawlu with parachute fragmentation bombs, and were awed and impressed when a lucky hit resulted in a gigantic blast and a pillar of smoke from an exploding ammunition dump. To make certain that there would be no interference from the Japanese, Ricketts decided to send the Bedfordshire and Hertfordshire as soon as he could lay hands on them to press on the Japanese positions without becoming inextricably committed, and be ready to make a noisy attack on the night of the evacuation. In the meantime he told Hughes to send out a company of his Nigerians to raid and shoot up the Japanese outposts, uttering their loudest and most terrifying war-cries. Soon, Ricketts observed with satisfaction, there was an air of confidence in the camp and some light had reappeared in the sunken eyes of the tired soldiers.

Next, Ricketts had to contact Brodie as quickly as possible and make verbal arrangements for a plan that in a conventional force would have occupied several staff officers writing a long operation order with numerous appendices and overlays. When he received a brief signal indicating that Brodie's headquarter column was approaching, he borrowed one of the ponies in the White City and rode out alone to look for him. A solitary horseman, he felt, would not excite the Japanese, and he galloped over the open space between Mawlu and the White City, moving too fast to be followed by a traversing machine-gun. Having scoured the scrub jungle to the west, he eventually met a very surprised Brodie who did not know that Ricketts was now in command at the White City, and was only too pleased to listen to and fall in with his detailed plans. Lieutenant-Colonel Eason of the Bedfordshire and Hertfordshire was equally cooperative, and led his columns off to reconnoitre the Mawlu position and harry it without demur or delay at the sudden request of a strange brigadier.[2]

The Japanese in fact had no suspicion that the Chindits had any intention of withdrawing: indeed Brodie's presence was soon detected and taken as evidence of reinforcement, as was the roar of aircraft arriving and departing on the night of May 9th. In any case they were not ready to attack the White City, as they were held up by command troubles. General Kawano was ill and had to be relieved by General Takeda, but this was not possible until May 14th. Meanwhile they had another and more important matter to attend to. As will be explained, the Japanese had already detected a task force – it was a combination of Galahad and a Chinese regiment, moving through the jungles north of the Mogaung River, clearly directed on Myitkyina and threatening to outflank Mutaguchi's blocking position at Kamaing. The first task given to Kawano was to push a whole regiment north, by-passing the White City through the jungles on its east, and reinforce the garrisons of Mogaung and Myitkyina. This, incidentally, shows that Stilwell's objection to any northward redeployment of the Chindits on the grounds that it would draw the

Japanese reserves in their wake and on to the First Chinese Army was groundless. The Japanese moves had already been decided.

Calvert had taken his columns, as ordered, up into the cool and peaceful heights of the Gangaw range; a welcome relief from the steamy heat and stink of the White City. There, the short daily marches became a pleasure, rations were plentiful, health improved and the spirits of the troops rose. He was, however, too restless to remain inactive. On May 1st he sent Vaughan and Carfrae to eradicate the Japanese post on the railway at Yawthit. The Nigerians in both the columns were now at the peak of their form. Carfrae's men fought their way through the village with great dash, only to find once more that the Japanese were dug in amid the horrible lantana scrub. Once again the combat became a murderous blind-man's-buff with both sides firing at a few yards' range whenever the sound of a shot or a voice calling out an order offered a target for a burst of fire or a grenade. The Africans gave the 'Japans' a good hammering, but complete success was denied them as the air support urgently called for never arrived. (May 1st was the date of the demise of the glorious No. 1 Air Commando, and possibly the new command and control channels were not yet working smoothly. At about this time Morris Force, far away on the Bhamo road, detected a particularly juicy target of about one hundred Japanese supply vehicles, and called for an air strike, also without any response.)

Vaughan was forced to withdraw. Carfrae and a Nigerian sergeant covered the leading sections, each firing a Bren, while the mortars laid down a smoke screen and the Nigerians, baffled but well pleased with themselves, broke clear. Remarkably, the Japanese made no attempt to follow them up, let alone meet attack with counter-attack. It was a faint but unmistakable sign that their famous élan was gradually being worn down.

The Black Watch scored a notable success on May 7th and 9th. The 2nd was a battalion of veterans, whose fighting edge was still keen after distinguishing itself in Somaliland against the Italians, against the German parachute troops in Crete and later in Tobruk. So far it had not been impressed with Chindit fighting or the conduct of affairs in Special Force. During the raiding operations west of Indaw it had seemed to the officers that most of their effort had been spent in aimless milling around, criss-crossing the tracks of other columns and marching long distance with very little to show for it all except a few brushes with the enemy and the destruction of one sizeable dump. The battalion was now to have all the action it desired. It left the Indaw area on April 23rd and, after doubling on its tracks to avoid the Japanese moving north along the line of the railway, arrived near the White City on May 3rd. By the 5th No. 73

Column had set an ambush of three platoons near Nathokyin. At eleven p.m. that night a long file of Japanese entered the killing area, and the Highlanders, holding their fire with their usual admirable discipline, waited until it was full and killed the majority of them. The Japanese column was led by an officer on a white horse who, when he had reached the far end of the trap, was shot down by Private McLuskie, whose duty it was to 'spring' the ambush at the exact moment. The tail of the Japanese column outside the trap, with typical Japanese courage, charged the long line of riflemen spread out along the track in the flank in an attempt to roll it up, but after some confused and desperate fighting in the dark, in which both sides fired on their own friends, the shattered Japanese drew off.

Colonel Green, like Colonel Wilkinson of the Leicesters, had organised his columns so that the administrative elements and most of the mules were grouped together and kept clear of the battle and the fighting elements combined. He left part of No. 42 Column to secure a base and the all-important light aircraft strip, and set another ambush, on the same track, with 200 men. On May 7th at about five a.m., having drawn a blank, he had decided to move and was on his way to rejoin No. 42 Column when a runner from his vanguard came back and reported excitedly, but quietly, that there was a party of Japanese approaching and was now about fifty yards ahead of the leading scouts. Colonel Green was one of those who had no doubts about the question whether Chindit tactical doctrine should be evasive or aggressive. He rapidly formed up his platoons in a diamond pattern, one leading, two on either side of the track and one in reserve following behind, and went straight into the attack. His initial charge shocked the Japanese and gave him the advantage. The Black Watch proved more than a match for the second-rate occupation battalions of the 53rd Division and Take Force. Its superior marksmanship and fire-control took a heavy toll, and the Japanese counter-attacks, launched in the usual suicidal way, merely presented the Black Watch with more targets.

Their din and repetition, however, showed that Green had bitten off more than he could chew. He had, in fact, intercepted a whole regiment, some 1,200 strong, on its way north. After five hours of fighting, with casualties mounting and his slender stock of ammunition running out, he broke off the action, calling his scattered platoons out of the battle by the simple but old-fashioned expedient of ordering his bugler to sound the 'Rally'. It took some time for the Black Watch strike force to reunite with the rest, but when Green was able to take stock he found that he could claim a notable success. Lying up the next night with part of his force near a track he saw a long procession

215

of Japanese in single file carrying the dead and wounded, which took four hours to pass.

His own losses had been severe: two officers killed, and two wounded. (One of them, standing not only upright but at attention amid the flying bullets when speaking to his commanding officer with the formality always expected in that regiment had been, as a result, shot through both ankles by the same bullet.) Twenty-four rank and file were killed and thirty-five wounded and some men were still missing. The two actions had cost the battalion seventy-eight casualties altogether, which was no small loss in Chindit fighting when there was little hope of trained replacements.[3]

These were all trifling actions – mere skirmishes – judged by the scale of the murderous encounters taking place west of the Chindwin, or even the cautious and ponderous moves of the First Chinese Army, but they were deadly and effective. The Chindits had turned the moral tables on the Japanese, whose earlier successes against the British had been due to various factors. One was their immense self-confidence and sheer spiritual force – a concept far transcending any Western notions of 'morale'. Another was the myopic arrogance which had led the British to believe that they could despise a coloured, Asiatic opponent. The Japanese on their side were afflicted by a similar vice: they had seen the backs of the British too often and too easily. Now it was their turn to be shocked by the reality that man for man, the despised British were obstinate and dangerous opponents and fully their equal. It may be too much to say that the assembling 53rd Division was cowed and submissive, but the fact is that between April 18th and May 11th they made not a single move against the White City. General Kawano's artillery alone could have frustrated Gillmore's whole plan if the field-guns had regularly shelled the main airstrip and if he had pushed his anti-aircraft guns forward instead of holding them back in a vain effort to shield his base at Mawlu from the terrible attacks of the American air force. These bloody little battles not only ensured that Kawano remained rooted to the ground while his quarry escaped without losing a man, but also that another three weeks or more would elapse before his successor, Takeda, could put a grip on Mogaung town or reinforce Tanaka's beleagured base in Myitkyina.

Another victory, but a bloodless one, can be credited to the staff of Special Force, not over any opponent, but over circumstances. The Chindit redeployment coincided with the crisis of the battle of Imphal-Kohima, when Imphal was completely cut off and being supplied only by air via fields on the Imphal plain. Any aircraft for evacuating the 16th Brigade and the gear from the strongholds over and above those detailed for normal resupply in the field had to be at the expense of the stocks in Imphal. The flight plans were complicated by the fact that different classes of cargo had to go to different airfields: the sick and wounded, for instance, to airfields where there were hospitals for immediate treatment before evacuation to India. The most economical use of aircraft required them to drop their passengers at Imphal and immediately fly back into Burma for a further load; these could not be the sick or wounded, as they had to wait in the open for aircraft returning empty from supplying the divisions fighting there. Many valuable mules had to be returned to India which required aircraft to be fitted out with temporary bamboo stalls and suitable arrangements for their stabling and care on arrival. Aircraft using the difficult Aberdeen strip could only take off with 3,000 pounds but the limit at Broadway was 5,000. This meant that five of Fergusson's columns had to march to Broadway from west of Indaw and only three could go from their own base at Aberdeen. A regular schedule of flights could be made, but it was subject to incessant alteration because of aircraft serviceability, the weather, or the Japanese air threat. Command and control had to be effected between the strongholds in Burma, Headquarters of General Old's Troop Carrier Command (in which was combined all RAF and USAAF troop transports), Headquarters, Special Force at Sylhet, and a number of different bases and airfields in India.

Neither the carriers nor the passengers were always cooperative or amenable. At Aberdeen nothing could convince the medical officers, naturally eager to do the best for their patients, that it was not in their best interests to put them on the first aircraft that arrived each night, as its destination was more important than its timing. It depended on the despatchers at the airfields in India whether the first sorties were tasked to return to Imphal.

As for mules, the air crews had an inordinate dislike of carrying them and would, if not detected, throw out the bamboo poles and matting in the hope of being given a more congenial load. Fortunately they had a passion for souvenirs, and the staff officers at the strongholds built up a stock of Japanese swords, currency, flags and other items as a system of rewards. Even so, Broadway was for a time overstocked with masterless mules. Broadway, its flare-path visible for miles, was spared air attack, but Aberdeen was raided severely at least once by twelve Zero fighters and three or four Sally light bombers. Fortunately they were misled into choosing the wrecks of the C-47s which had crashed on the evil Aberdeen strip as targets, and the anti-aircraft guns of the 69th Regiment knocked down no fewer than five, which was a remarkable tribute to their training. The main difficulty was constantly rearranging the various sorties and destinations over hundreds of miles, using a radio net crackling with static. The post-operation report from Broadway contained a specimen fragment of dialogue between Broadway ('LILO') and Headquarters, Special Force ('RED'):

LILO to RED: Can take 27 aircraft tonight all briefed for Sylhet.
RED to LILO: How many aircraft can you take tonight?
LILO to RED: Can take 27 aircraft tonight all briefed for Sylhet.
RED to LILO: In absence information am sending 5 aircraft tonight briefed proceed Chandina.
LILO to RED: Can take 27 aircraft tonight all briefed for Sylhet.
RED to LILO: Can produce 30 aircraft tonight.
LILO to RED: Well done, but can only produce loads for 27.
RED to LILO: Have you any PICKLES?
LILO to RED: If PICKLES PICKLES no. If PICKLES something else clarify.
RED to LILO: PICKLES code-word for Gliders.
LILO to RED: That code-word died two operations ago. Word now GIRLS. Have no GIRLS.

RED to ALL BRIGADES (in clear): Owing compromise code-word GIRLS word PICKLES will be substituted.

LILO to RED: How many aircraft are coming tonight?
RED to LILO: Pilots only wish to take essential stores.
LILO to RED: Very right of them. How many aircraft are coming tonight?
RED to LILO: How much artillery can you produce?
LILO to RED: All artillery evacuated two nights ago on your instructions.
RED to LILO: No aircraft arriving tonight.
(Fifteen aircraft arrive.)
Red (later, and crossly) to LILO: Pilots complain insufficient loads ready Chandina last night . . .

But then, staff work is more concerned with preventing order from becoming confusion or creating order from confusion than writing beautifully ordered plans.

The standard of flying was astonishing. Aberdeen would be condemned at sight for any air operation today by large aircraft, but 188 sorties were flown from it in the dark, carrying out 1,460 men, sixty-eight animals, fourteen guns and 200,000 pounds of stores for the loss of one aircraft. One Australian pilot with a vital mission arrived unexpectedly at Aberdeen just after the flare-path had been finally removed and landed by the light of the headlights of a jeep positioned at the beginning of the runway. Except for one aircraft which crashed shortly after take-off due to pilot error, not one aircraft and not one man was lost either at Aberdeen or at Broadway by accident or from enemy action. So ended a *tour de force* of airmanship and staff work, unnoticed, unsung and unrewarded, as such operations always are when perfectly executed.

It was now to be seen if the same trick could be played at the White City, where the C-47 strip was only 2,700 yards from the suspected position of the giant Japanese mortar and battery of field-guns at Mawlu. Everything now waited on Masters. On May 7th he reported that he had arrived in the vicinity of Hopin and was about to establish his blocking position. At two thirty p.m. on the 9th Ricketts received the code-word by radio from Force Headquarters that the evacuation of the White City would take place that night.

All the necessary preparations had been made and the orders given. Major Mead and his assistants had arrived from Aberdeen to supervise the loading of the aircraft and provide flying control. At five p.m. the American fighters and bombers arrived to work over all the suspected Japanese anti-aircraft gun positions. It looked alarmingly as if they had been reinforced, for the showers of hot splinters from the burst of their shells descending from the sky were dense enough to drive the Chindits, who had climbed the hill-tops to watch the spectacle, back to the cover of their trenches. Late in the afternoon Colonel Kyte called his lieutenant in the block and asked him laconically, 'Are you all set?' 'Yes,' replied Mead. 'Have you any questions?' 'No.' By ten p.m. Mead had to report if all was going well, using a single code-word. If anything went wrong the whole of the air side of the operation was to be called off, as the transport aircraft were too precious to be risked in what was, after all, a propaganda exercise.

At dusk the runway was marked with lights, the sick and wounded men assembled at the dispersal and a long file of tall Africans, carrying loads on their heads, emerged silently from the perimeter. The artillery came next. The heavy Bofors guns were remounted on their wheels and laboriously trundled to the airstrip and dismantled ready for emplaning, followed by three of the four 2-pounders. (The fourth had been inextricably trapped in its pit by a tree felled by the Japanese bombardment.) Three of the four 25-pounders were brought out, the fourth left in action to reply to any Japanese interference. The Bedfordshire and Hertfordshire columns, who had dug themselves in in front of Mawlu, began their feint attack to distract the Japanese. At seven forty-five p.m. the first C-47 was heard overhead and given the signal to land. Within the hour there were fourteen aircraft on the dispersal being loaded, the wounded first, and as they took off another stream came in steadily to take their place. Two nerve-racking hours passed, during which even the coolest and most confident expected the orderly sequence of events on the airstrip to be suddenly broken by a salvo of bursting shells. During the past few days some single rounds had landed on either side and finally on it, and it required no specialised knowledge to recognise that this was a careful preliminary registration by the Japanese guns. It seemed impossible that the intense air activity and the roar of aircraft taking off would go unpunished, whether the Bedfordshire and Hertfordshire columns were shooting up the infantry around Mawlu or not. Astonishingly all remained peaceful, and at ten p.m. Mead sent the single code-word, 'Slick', to Sylhet and Colonel Kyte was able to cease biting his nails and go to bed.

By midnight the whole operation was nearly complete, and Mead, a Royal Artillery officer, thought of the one 25-pounder left in the block. Ricketts had disapproved of the whole business of evacuating the stores and equipment at so great a risk, but he had had his orders. However, he knew the Royal Artillery's tradition of defending its guns to the last and its horror of losing them to the enemy, and he had said firmly to Mead: 'Now look here. I have every intention of abandoning this gun. It isn't going to make any difference to the war effort, so don't let's have anyone changing their mind and taking it out of action, and then finding the enemy artillery opening up and catching us with our trousers down.' Mead was not to be defeated so easily. He had telephones from the airstrip, where he presided, to garrison headquarters and to the artillery command post. He called Ricketts' brigade-major and, finding him alone, artfully demanded a decision as to whether the single gun was required any more, or not. Major Harrison gave the necessary permission and immediately Mead called for the gun. 'In an astonishingly short space of time the gun appeared out of the darkness, the sergeant who commanded its detachment (crew) thanking me in a voice broken with emotion for having arranged its rescue.'

Everything had gone smoothly, even the loading of the sick or superfluous mules. Those capricious animals, at times so unmoved by shelling or even wounds and so patient under their loads, and at others so ready to thumb their noses, so to speak, at the human race, had invariably one chosen time for disobedience; on being loaded into railway trucks or aircraft (dreading, perhaps, the dark interior). Not that night. They had perceived (and it was notable enough to record) that they were jostling each other and their drivers to board the waiting aircraft taking them to rest, peace and unlimited hay. With them went a foal, born to a pony mare in the fortress. A sentimental American was persuaded to accept it as an addition to his manifest.

The atmosphere relaxed. The loaders had been somewhat surprised, even annoyed, to discover that the incoming aircraft had brought in unnecessary boxes of rations which had to be taken off before loading could begin, but cheered to find that they were 'luxury' as opposed to the loathed 'K' ration, and there was even rum. (This, in fact had been the Chindit staff's disingenuous means of avoiding Eastern Air Command's dictum that only aircraft returning empty from supply runs would be available for the evacuation.) A Leicester officer emerged from the shadows to present Mead with a tin of plums, 'with the compliments of the garrison of the White City'. The big radio-set was closed down and loaded, Mead thanked the officers of the Leicesters and the Nigerians who had commanded the willing working parties, and emplaned. Operation HOLIDAY, as it had been code-named, was complete. Forty aircraft had flown in, thirty-seven loaded with stores, and three redirected to Broadway to assist the fly-out there. The cargoes from the White City had been one load of engineer stores, four of ammunition and one of heavy weapons, two of signal equipment, two aircraft full of wounded, three of sick men and mules, one jeep, one No. 33 Radio Station and thirteen pieces of artillery with their crews.

Ricketts was, of course, quite correct. The effort and risk far exceeded the material result but, negative as it may have been, it was an unrivalled piece of Chindit panache. They had the Japanese licked, and they flew in and out of Burma as they pleased. Mead, however, as he flew, tired but relieved and sipping his rum, was prescient enough to sense that the high adventure was over. The Wingate chapter had ended and the road the Chindits had henceforth to travel was to prove dolorous, rough and bloody.[4]

13

Profound in the Depths

IN THIS WAY the Chindit columns broke cleanly away from the much-battered and temporarily hypnotised Japanese and vanished into the forest. The problem now facing the three brigadiers was how, precisely, they were to put into effect the next and crucial stage of Lentaigne's plan. This had been sent out by radio in cipher in telegraphic form; concise, clear and pared of all except essential information. At its core was the establishment of a new block to take the place of the White City to deny the Japanese the use of the Railway Valley until June 1st. By that date, it was hoped, the Chinese would have broken through the front of the Japanese 18th Division at Kamaing thirty-five miles to the north, Chindits and Chinese would meet on the line Mogaung-Myitykina, and the Chindits' part in the campaign would be over.

To ensure that he could play his part Lentaigne brought all his resources to bear on the crucial point. Masters was to cease his marauding activities away in the south and, marching under the cover of the jungle, set up a block 'not north of Pinbaw and not south of Hopin'. (It was code-named CLYDESIDE, later altered to BLACKPOOL, as it will be called henceforth to avoid confusion.) He was to be in position by May 6th/7th, ready to receive by air the mass of stores and heavy weapons required to make Blackpool a fortress. As soon as the first of the strongholds to be abandoned, Aberdeen, was safely evacuated Lieutenant-Colonel Upjohn was to follow with its garrison, the 6th Nigeria, and 'float', i.e., provide a mobile protective force to the west of Blackpool. On may 3rd the 'floating' columns protecting Broadway, the King's No. 81 and No. 82, were to march direct to Blackpool and come under Masters' command, to be followed by the 3rd/9th Gurkha Rifles as soon as the evacuation of Broadway was complete, on May 13th. This would give Masters four and a half battalions and enough to hold his own against anything the Japanese could bring at him. Calvert, with what now remained of the 77th Brigade – the South Staffordshire, the Lancashire Fusiliers and the 3rd/6th Gurkha Rifles – was to sit opposite Blackpool in the Gangaw range east of the valley. The 14th and the 3rd West African

Brigades – the 7th and 12th Nigeria – were to do the same on the mountain massif overlooking Blackpool from the west. The 14th Brigade was to leave the Mawlu area on May 2nd. Redeployment was to be complete by May 23rd.[1]

This in essence was a very good plan and it marked a change in Chindit strategy. Gone for good was Wingate's quasi-guerrilla system of spreading a wide mesh of independent columns in which the Japanese would become entangled and reduced to impotence. Orthodox concentration of effort was to be the watchword for the future. A Chindit officer put it another way. 'Until then,' he said, 'we had been fighting like submarines, operating from distant safe harbours, emerging from the concealing sea – the jungle – to strike at targets in the open and then disappearing. Now we had to stay and fight in the open; a different sort of battle altogether.' (This, of course, was not quite correct, for in both the Indaw and White City phases Wingate had compromised his original theory, but it was a graphic simile, and serves.) The new strategy, it must be emphasised, was offensive: it offered far more than the prospect of passively holding Blackpool for three weeks. No fewer than ten battalions (at least 4,500-5,000 bayonets, allowing for wastage by battle casualties and sickness) were poised to trap the depleted Japanese 53rd Division and smash it against the anvil of the Blackpool defences; at least, in theory. It promised to be a complex operation from the point of view of command, control and communications, bearing in mind especially the peculiar nature of Special Force radio-communications with their intermittent nature and poor laterals. Lentaigne had sent out an 'instruction', as opposed to an 'order', a distinction clearly understood in the British Army as leaving the method of execution to the subordinate commanders on the spot. It was eminently suitable for typically Chindit tactics, but it was inadequate for the impending battle, when four separate brigades had to act in concert when compressed into a circle of ten mile radius.

The timings were critical, and the key date was the arrival of the monsoon rains, which could be expected with certainty around mid-May. After that all ground movement and air support would become difficult in the extreme. The choice of May 23rd as the date for completion of the manoeuvre is therefore hard to understand. Masters, as it turned out, was unavoidably late in arriving at Blackpool, so that the White City had to be held until the 10th. Brodie, by a change of plan, was retained to cover it and so eight whole days were lost that were to prove absolutely vital to the success of the plan, for this depended on having the 'floater' brigades in position on the right side of any natural obstacle likely to be rendered impassable by rain.

There was also another consideration. Stilwell had confided to no one (except to Slim, whom he swore to secrecy) his plan to break the stalemate at Kamaing. While all the Chindit redeployment was taking place, Galahad, with a Chinese regiment, was marching over the Kumon Bum with the mission of seizing Myitkyina by *coup de main*. The fortunes of the two forces were to be fatally linked.

None of these considerations were the concern of Brigadiers Brodie and Ricketts, nor would they have been unduly worried had they been aware of them. Their part was perfectly clear. It was to interpret Lentaigne's instruction in an intelligent manner, as they had done over the evacuation of the White City. The map revealed that Hopin could be reached by the road running from the southern part of the basin in which lay the great Indawgyi Lake, through a gap in the mountains, the Kyunsalai Pass. The large village of Nammun looked a possible site for a base. The two brigadiers agreed to march there on parallel routes through the jungle on the west side of the railway, the Nigerians on the left and the 14th Brigade on the right. Brodie's leading column, No. 74, commanded by the thrusting 'old Chindit' Geoffrey Lockett, was to make for the pass and secure it. That, they felt, was as far as they could plan. From then on they would be guided by circumstances.[2] By the 11th they had disappeared. The Japanese patrols, picking their way cautiously through the booby-traps, found the White City silent and deserted. One patrol was sent off west from the Railway Valley to try and discover where they had gone.

Calvert was by no means so cooperative or complaisant. He felt (as many of his young men felt, and feel to this day) that the White City could have been held indefinitely, and that it was disgraceful to surrender what had been captured with so much sacrifice. He had been contemptuous at what was, in his eyes, the passive, defensive policy which had accompanied the evacuation, and furious when he had been foiled in an attempt to borrow Lockett's column for an attack on the Japanese, concocted between the two 'old Chindits' in the old, independent, buccaneering Chindit style. Moreover his *amour-propre* was understandably bruised. Under Wingate he had always been consulted and the two had regularly discussed plans and tactics, and Wingate came to him, in the field. Now he was summarily given his orders by signal, and his two freshest battalions had been equally summarily removed from him, together with Vaughan's Nigerians, for whom he had formed a high regard. He was then invited to express an opinion on the state of his troops. By mid-May he had lost thirty-eight officers (the Gurkhas alone had ten British officers killed in action) and 592 rank and file killed, wounded or evacuated sick, and the drain of sick was increasing. All three commanding officers agreed that their columns badly needed rest.

Lined up, and awaiting action, Commando Platoon, 50 Column, near Sepein, to the south of the White City in April 1944.

Lancashire Fusiliers prepare to burn the Government Rest House at Mawhun, used as the Japanese Garrison HQ.

The railway bridge at Mawhun near Kadu – a six-man patrol of Lancashire Fusiliers destroyed the central span on the night of March 25th, 1944.

Brigadier Tulloch and on his left Wingate, at their Forward HQ.

Right, Major P. W. Mead, of the air operations section of Special Force HQ staff.

Kachin levies on the Naman air-strip.

Merrill, with pipe, and Stilwell, carbine on shoulder, with American pressmen at Myitkyina.

On the summit of Hill 60 just after its capture: Brigadier Ricketts gives orders to Captain MacFarlane of the 7th Nigeria Regiment.

"BARHAM"

"ARK ROYAL"

"REVENGE"

Three 'dreadnoughts' of the Royal Engineer 'Indawgyi Grand Fleet', used for transporting casualties.

Captain Frank Gerald Blaker, Highland Light Infantry, attached 3rd/9th Gurkha Rifles, awarded a posthumous VC for leading a successful attack.

Captain Michael Allmand, Indian Armoured Corps, attached 6th Gurkha Rifles, awarded a posthumous VC for repeatedly leading his company in attack against Japanese strongpoints at Mogaung.

The sole surviving Chindit VC, Rifleman Tulbahadur Pun, 6th Gurkha Rifles, who, as the last man standing in his platoon, cleared an MG post and gave covering fire for continued attack.

Lieut. George Albert Cairns, Somerset Light Infantry, attached South Staffords, who was mortally wounded in single combat with a Japanese officer, while repelling a counterattack in the White City and awarded a posthumous VC.

Brigadier Calvert gestures with characteristic force, watched by Lt-Col. Shaw
(*right*) in typical Chindit garb at Mogaung.

Wingate, whose death on March 24th,
1944, altered the course of the Chindit
campaign, as the Chindits remember
him.

There was first a half-promise of evacuation, but shortly after came an order to stay in. This did nothing to soothe Calvert's black mood.

As regards the new plan Calvert objected, and with some reason, that he was being given an unsound position – a 'death-trap' was the term he used, and he was not a nervous commander – wedged between the mountain wall and the Namyin River, facing Blackpool with the Japanese behind him. His signals to Lentaigne went from argumentative to abrasive to insubordinate. ('I was getting too big for my boots,' he admitted thirty-four years later.)

In one sense, all this was 'military friction', common enough in command relationships, and could have been avoided by earlier personal contact; but the root of the trouble lay rather deeper. Calvert was very tired, he had malaria and he was suffering from the depression which so often strikes after the moment of release from stress. He was accustomed to danger; that was not the trouble. Indeed he sought it, like a drug. He was at heart a romantic, like so many of the young men who volunteered for the commandoes, the airborne troops and the special forces. For them battle was a test of manhood, like sport, although a sport with a noble aim. Helping Stilwell was all very well, but how much more inspiring was Wingate's call to liberate Burma and restore it to the British Empire. To no one but Calvert would it have occurred to issue an order that all native craft plying on the Irrawaddy were to fly a Union Jack.

Commanding a brigade in hard-fought actions was starkly different from twisting the Japanese tail, guerrilla-fashion. Calvert found that he could no longer always lead men in battle: they had to be sent. Proud battalions began to wilt, yet were sent in to fight again. Friends were killed. When the gallant Ian Macpherson fell at Mawlu Calvert, distraught, turned back to look for his body, to be met by his own brigade-major's pistol rammed into his belly and the brutal reminder that his duty lay with his brigade. (An incident altogether in the old Chindit style, one cannot help feeling.)

The death of Wingate had been a shock to all the Chindits, but for Calvert it was a deep personal loss. Of the three men closest to Wingate, Tulloch was the unquestioning, devoted lieutenant; Fergusson, exceptionally able in his own right, was by no means unquestioning. But compared with those two there was a deeper relationship between Calvert and Wingate. They exchanged ideas. In the evolution of Wingate's military thought there is a lot of Calvert, and it was Calvert who could take one of Wingate's inspirations, like the 'stronghold', and make it a practical reality. By his own account Calvert had been a turbulent young officer with little respect for authority, who tended to lose his battles with the obstructive, the bureaucratic and the timid. Wingate had shown how they could be won. Now he was gone, and there was 'no one to look after them'. Calvert believed now that the whole Chindit adventure was going adrift, Wingate's plans were being discarded and his vision betrayed. It was an impossible mood for a subordinate commander, and Lentaigne, accustomed to the more orthodox and muted indiscipline of the regular army, was slow to recognise it. At last, however, overcoming his dislike of personal confrontation, he summoned Calvert to meet him at Broadway, on May 8th. There Lentaigne's natural kindliness came to the fore and he patiently explained to Calvert that the Fourteenth Army was engaged in a bitter struggle with the Japanese on which the whole campaign turned, that there were no troops at the moment available to relieve his brigade in-sufficient aircraft to lift it out, that they were under obligation to Stilwell to block the Railway Valley, and if it were a question of proving the worth of Wingate's ideas, then the best way of doing it would be to help Stilwell to secure the line Mogaung-Myitkyina. Lentaigne added that he did not want to lose Calvert, but if he had no faith in the plan and he continued to make objections he would have to go. His tact and firmness prevailed, Calvert came to his senses and the commander of Special Force was relieved that he had not been forced to dismiss his ablest and most aggressive brigadier.

Calvert recovered his balance and his sense of duty, although he continued to express his views with force and to draft signals in a style differing somewhat from the demure precision taught at the Staff College. One (May 26th) reads: 'No. 50 Column out of rations five days, No. 82 eight days. For God's sake tell air force to pull its fingers out. Weather is suitable. It is air force which is wet.' He and his staff held a lugubrious carousal on some rum Lentaigne had thoughtfully put in his aircraft, and then he led his battered and depleted columns back into the Railway Valley. As he re-crossed the Gangaw range ominous thunderstorms, the harbingers of the monsoon, flashed and reverberated in the mountains around them.

On May 13th the Japanese patrol sent to look for the Chindits on the other side of the valley had a stroke of luck. It surprised the Leicesters' No. 47 Column in its evening bivouac. Two officers, a sergeant-major and six privates were killed, thirteen men wounded and five were missing. It was a trivial although unpleasant incident, but its consequences were far-reaching. In the 14th Brigade the prevailing opinion was still that Chindit tactics were guerrilla and evasive ('tip-and-run', as Graves-Morris described them) and Brodie reacted as he had been trained. His columns were travelling in one long snake in single file, and he ordered their heads to wheel to the left some miles until they were deeper into the jungle, and then north again. This brought them into collision with the Nigerians, and the

African and British columns became sandwiched on the same track, resulting in confusion and inevitable delay.[3] Then it began to rain.

The terrain to the west of the Railway Valley is difficult enough in dry weather. Ridge and valley have no distinguishable pattern, or 'grain', the spot-heights on the map jump abruptly from 1,000 feet to 5,000 feet and the whorls of the contours are so close that at first glance the map presents a uniformly brown tinge. Every step of the way was up one impossible slope and down another, the only relief being when the route ran along the bed of a *chaung* (but even so Masters' headquarters column when traversing the same area recorded fording the Meza River sixteen times). When the monsoon downpour began, the hundreds of *chaungs* draining the area changed from clear rills or dry ravines to torrents of foaming water that could sweep away a man or a mule. The flanks of the hills became mud-slides. Steps had to be cut and revetted with bamboo, mules off-loaded and led to the top while the men carried up the weapons and heavy gear. A good day's march was five miles, a bad one a mile, but in that country horizontal distances meant nothing. The killer diseases like cerebral malaria and scrub typhus began to claim their victims – among them Eason, who had so skilfully contained the Japanese at Mawlu. The strength of those who continued to stagger along under the crushing weight of their packs and weapons was

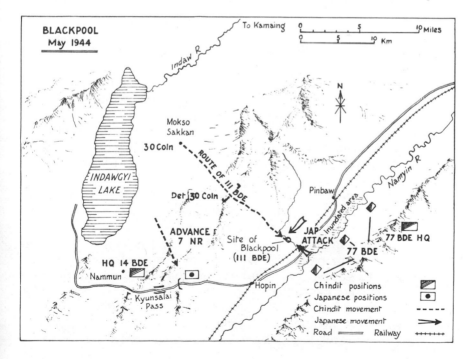

eroded as skin, rubbed raw by boots and shoulder straps, broke out into weeping ulcers that never had a chance to heal. Constant diarrhoea took its toll, as did low fevers and lack of food.[4] Supply dropping was often impossible. 'May 14th–May 19th. A killing march with no rations', is the terse record in the Leicesters' war diary. It took ten days to cover the thirty-five miles to Nammun. On the 20th Lockett, driving his column remorselessly on, secured the Kyunsalai Pass, beating the Japanese to it by twenty-four hours.

By that date Masters had been in position for a fortnight. He had chosen a possible site for the block in advance from maps and air photographs, which revealed a long spur thrusting out from the foot of the Bumrawng Bum towards the railway. This ended in a curious feature about 1,000 yards long and 500 deep which looked, for all the world, like an animal lying down with its four legs spread out at right angles; its nose pointing north-east and its tail south-west. As a possible approach route he considered the road from the Kyunsalai Pass to Hopin, and discarded it. It ran a long way through open country and the last thing he wanted was an encounter: the Japanese had to come to him after he had securely dug in and was ready for them. As an alternative his scouts discovered a surprisingly good if steep path over the Bumrawng massif which led from the little hamlet of Mokso Sakkan near the edge of the Indawgyi Lake and debouched where the jungle edge fringed the valley. There was no sign of the 6th Nigeria, so Masters left his trusted Gurkha No. 30 Column there to establish a base with orders to put a picket of a hundred men on the crest to guard the back entrance to the block. Then with his four remaining columns he went down into the valley where he and his Royal Air Force officer, disguised as Burmese, examined the terrain in detail. The back and legs of the 'animal' provided little knolls and ridges offering good fire positions, close observation of the railway a mile away, and a suitably angled re-entrant in which to conceal a 25-pounder battery. A clear stream on the side blind to the valley assured a supply of drinking water and there was a stretch of dry paddy fields right under the ridge on the open side which could be levelled to accept gliders and C-47s. The only disadvantage was that scrub and man-high grass obscured the fields of fire at the edge of the airstrip. This was to be Blackpool. It did not physically block the railway but, Masters considered, correctly as it turned out, with his guns and raiding parties he could effectively stop all railway traffic. The King's Own and the Cameronians took up their positions on May 8th, but no sooner had they thankfully cast off their terrible packs than they were attacked, before ever they had time to dig in or clear a space for the gliders bringing in the American engineers and plant to level the airstrip.

The collapse of the whole Blackpool plan must not be allowed to obscure the devotion of the 111th Brigade or its achievement in strangling the main Japanese supply route for a crucial fortnight. All the columns were below strength largely due to sickness. (The Cameronians had on the average twenty-five men in a platoon instead of forty.) The daylight hours were spent in back-breaking toil, digging shelters, weapon-slits, pits for the expected 25-pounders and levelling the glider strip. There was little rest for the fighting troops at night, for the commander of the Japanese post guarding the railway at Pinbaw had noted their arrival and with admirable tenacity attacked for five successive nights; and for five successive nights was beaten off. Admittedly the attacks were often by no more than a platoon and conducted without a vestige of skill, the Japanese, as usual, forming up after each repulse for one more suicidal attempt. The King's Own, a good, sturdy, north-country battalion, and the more mercurial Cameronians, fighting once more as infantry in the way they really understood, massacred the Japanese each time systematically with concentrated mortar fire and long bursts from their water-cooled Vickers machine-guns, but it was weary work. Red-eyed from lack of sleep, they then had to turn to all day as soon as the airstrip was open to unload aircraft and hump stores and reserve ammunition up on to the ridge.

The fly-in of stores was a horrific affair. The paddy fields descended in a series of steps marked by low water-retaining dykes which were never properly levelled, Japanese patrols skulked in the neighbouring scrub and the Pinbaw garrison had a single 75 mm gun which they used with good effect to harass the block and the airstrip. All the gliders bringing in the American engineers and plant were wrecked on landing; one, hit by machine-gun fire, plunged vertically into the ground for the loss of the engineers and the bulldozer. The grader and carry-all were hit by artillery fire when working on the strip. Three C-47s crash-landed, and one was set on fire by a Japanese patrol attacking with grenades while it was actually being unloaded. Yet the American pilots came in with unwavering determination and through their efforts Blackpool was stocked up and its batteries armed. Six Bofors and six Hispano guns were placed to guard the airfield, and on the 13th three 25-pounders were landed, followed later by a fourth, which were soon battering at the railway and shooting back at the troublesome Japanese guns.

Masters now had time to assess his situation. The Chindit brigade commanders were all outstanding officers and offer an interesting sample of the leaders the now well-tested British Army was throwing up from its diverse regiments. Fergusson, destined for high places in the future establishment; Rome, 'fiery' by some accounts, but a calming and long-headed adviser to the impulsive Calvert; the cautious Brodie; the dogged Morris; the thrusting Ricketts – all were professional soldiers of high quality. Like Calvert, Masters was at heart a maverick, seemingly the odd man out in the rigid, authoritarian society of the Gurkhas, but he had become a professional soldier by sheer application of a strong intelligence. Outsiders darkly regarded his sudden elevation as another example of the Gurkha fraternity looking after its own, but Lentaigne had chosen well. The commanders over whose heads he had been promoted gave him their respect as well as their loyalty – and not only was he respected; he was also liked.

'We were always made welcome at his headquarters,' said one officer, 'and came away feeling cheered up.' Another remembered attending a conference at Mokso Sakkan 'where Jack was sitting stripped to his shorts on a sort of bamboo throne his Gurkhas had made for him. We were rather solemn and depressed, until he began: "Well, chaps, lets get this next phase over and then we can go back to India for some proper peacetime soldiering."' His irreverence and occasional facetiousness were a tonic in bad times. Another Gurkha officer, by no means an uncritical admirer, recalls him as 'witty, flamboyant and amusing', adding: 'A very good leader, an excellent soldier, loved by the Gurkhas and . . . ruthless.'[5]

Masters was ambitious and knew that fame could be won by a successful defence at Blackpool but he was also a realist. His military perception was too detached and too clear to be blind to the weakness of his position if he was left unsupported. His columns had had a much longer march through the same mountains as the 14th Brigade and the men had been very tired on arrival. They had done their best, but there was no belt of wire at Blackpool ten or fifteen yards deep covered by mines, or the deep weapon-pits and shelters roofed with eight-inch tree-trunks able to defy a direct hit as at Broadway and the White City. He was short of men. Walter Scott had arrived from Broadway with his No. 81 Column, but No. 82 had dissolved in confusion after an encounter with the Japanese and some one hundred men had turned back. (They were found by 77th Brigade, where Calvert snapped them up and converted them into an extra rifle company for the Lancashire Fusiliers.) Scott was an outstanding officer, but experience at the White City had shown that a single column was not enough for the 'floating' rôle. There was no sign as yet of the 3rd/9th. There was no contact with the 14th Brigade, nor with the 77th which Masters believed to be 'resting' in the Gangaw range. Until the other brigades arrived, Blackpool was a fruit ripe for picking. He depended entirely on supplies dropped or landed on the airstrip for the ammunition which the hungry throats of his guns, mortars and machine-guns consumed by the ton. His one floater column would not even be able to keep the enemy anti-aircraft artillery at arm's length when it inevitably arrived. Masters' apprehensive ears were cocked for the first ominous *thump-thump-thump-thump* of the guns that could so easily be brought up into the scrub surrounding the air-strip. He summoned a light aircraft and went off to see the commander who, so unaccountably, had not come to see him.

It was not a satisfactory exchange of views. Masters' vehement demand that Lentaigne should urge on the 14th Brigade received the feeble reply that 'Tom Brodie was doing his best'. Lentaigne offered no suggestions on how the block should be held while he did. All that Masters got out of his visit was permission to abandon the block if in his opinion this brigade was in danger of destruction. He flew back to Blackpool grimly to await events.

The commander of 111th Brigade was not alone in his troubles. Masters' opponent, General Takeda, soon found out after assuming command of the 53rd Division that he was beset by difficulties. He had inherited a poor apology for a division, sadly below the standard and training and morale expected of Japanese Imperial troops. It was below strength, and the battalions of Take Force which was to augment his numbers had been badly mauled in the fighting of the past weeks. He had three conflicting missions: to operate the railway and protect it from attack; to seek out and destroy the Chindits; and to send reinforcements to the 18th Division, then hanging on only by its eyelids at Kamaing. He had little artillery and barely any air support, while he was exposed to the hammer blows of the Allied air forces throughout the length of the Railway Valley. True, the onset of bad weather would afford some protection from air attack, but it also slowed down his own movement. It took him five days to shift up his headquarters to Hopin and ten to redeploy his few guns. The railway had been cut into segments by ground and air attack (the Chindits alone had demolished six large bridges) and much of the rolling stock had been destroyed. The best his engineers could do was to run short trains pulled by motor lorries fitted with flanged wheels on each section and laboriously transship the supplies from one to the other round the breaks. The commander of the garrison at Pinbaw reported that a large force of Chindits had dug in opposite one of the transshipment points at Namkwin railway station and were being supplied by a stream of twin-engined aircraft. It had a battery of field-guns which shot accurately at any movement on the railway.

This was bad enough, but Takeda was also aware that the British 'airborne troops', as the Japanese believed them to be, were hovering in considerable strength on either side of the railway, ready to swoop down and cut it again at any point where it ran close to the jungle, and he had not the resources in numbers or jungle-trained troops to go chasing after them. The first and most important of his tasks, he saw, was to uproot the British block near Namkwin railway station, and in doing this he was not to repeat the errors of his predecessor at Mawlu, frittering his precious infantry away in a series of attacks made piecemeal in insufficient strength and without proper fire-support. The garrison commander at Pinbaw was told to continue protecting the railway operations and harassing the British as best he could while Takeda moved up his anti-aircraft guns to cut them off from air supply, deployed his field artillery and assembled his assault force. This was to be the 128th Infantry Regiment reinforced by a battalion from the 114th, which had to come up all the way from Rangoon, 2,000 bayonets in all. This took altogether eleven days from the time that the White City was found to be empty of British troops. In the meantime to cover his left he sent a battalion up to secure the Kyunsalai Pass. On May 22nd its leading company ran unsuspecting into Lockett's ambush and was shot to pieces, leaving fifty dead behind, but the rest took up a position astride the road to Hopin and held it against gradually increasing pressure from the British moving down from the pass. On the evening of the 23rd, after intense shelling, the 128th Regiment opened its attack on Blackpool.

Now was the moment for the 'floater' brigades to counter-attack in their turn, but the horrid fact, neither foreseen nor even now perceived by Lentaigne, was that all three were trapped on the wrong side of formidable obstacles; on the east a flooded river and on the west the monsoon-sodden jungles and the abrupt ridges of the Bumrawng Bum. The next column to arrive after Lockett had seized the jaws of the Kyunsalai Pass was Vaughan's, and in response to Lockett's appeal he immediately sent a platoon and a mortar detachment up to him, but there was never a chance of 14th Brigade exploiting this success and opening the Hopin road in time to help Masters at Blackpool. Brodie sent up No. 16 Column as soon as it arrived and gradually reinforced the pass area, but the Japanese astride the road could not be shifted by frontal attack and the obvious course of outflanking it through the jungle was immensely difficult. A column of the York and Lancaster spent all day struggling up a few hundred feet in the torrential rain in an attempt to find a route. Ricketts, with Vaughan's Nigerians, swung wide north of the pass up a track which climbed 2,000 feet in two miles and then slowly forced a route down the precipitous bed of a *chaung*, but by May 26th he had covered only five miles in horizontal distance and was still not down to the road to Hopin. Neither Brodie nor Ricketts had been informed of the existence of the track Masters had discovered leading from

Mokso Sakkan to Blackpool – 'a broad highway' compared to the Tagwin Chaung, as Ricketts commented long afterwards – but even had they known of it and moved towards it at once they would still have been too late.[6]

On his side of the valley Calvert had obediently spread his columns, now reorganised into three single battalions for lack of men, at the foot of the Gangaw range facing Blackpool; the position to which he had objected so strongly. In front of them was the Namyin Chaung, a fairish-sized river even in the dry season, with country boats, but these the Japanese had prudently removed. The Namyin drained the whole northern half of the valley into the Mogaung and now, fed by the water cascading down the mountain-sides, it had risen in boiling, coffee-coloured spate and spilt over its banks to flood the paddy fields to the width of a mile. Heroic, even fool-hardy, attempts were made to cross to assist the 111th Brigade, but except for a small patrol of the South Staffords who shot up a Japanese artillery position, and two brave officers who swam across alone to reconnoitre, all failed. (One returned so covered with leeches that he required a blood-transfusion to save his life.) So the 111th Brigade was left alone to fight for its life.

The most vivid, first-hand account of the fighting at Blackpool, is that accomplished writer, the brigade commander himself, in *The Road Past Mandalay*. But the most valuable as a factual framework is the log kept by an officer of 'U' Troop (four 25-pounders), 160th Field Regiment, Royal Artillery, who recorded the day, the exact time and the details of every event, including the missions fired, with range, bearing and ammunition expended, the supply drops, the enemy shelling, the casualties and the course of the final battle. The main observation post was on a prominent hill just inside the perimeter overlooking the airstrip, from where it was possible to observe a long stretch of the railway track, only a mile away at its nearest point to the block. The rôle of the guns was to prevent any movement on it by day, and in this it was highly effective, its biggest coup being the destruction of a complete train. 'Railway train engaged as pin point target by No. 1 gun. Destroyed. 55 high explosive (expended); is the laconic entry. By night patrols from the Cameronians went out to observe and ambush, accompanied by an artillery officer with a radio to call for fire support, and the log reveals that they were reaching out to over 4,000 yards from the perimeter.[7]

Another urgent task was to try to silence the Japanese guns which shelled the block and the airstrip every day. At first there was only one, the 75 mm near Pinbaw, but then a 105 mm, with a shell over double the weight, made its unwelcome appearance. It was not a formidable battery by the standards of the war but, firing continually into the crowded block in the daylight hours, it caused a steady drain of casualties and wore out the nerves of the defenders. The Japanese artillery was always difficult to locate, as it had a healthy respect for the Allied air force and its guns were dug in, usually singly, and carefully hidden in the jungle. Captain Young, commanding the 25-pounder troop, located the Pinbaw gun by the simple and daring method of going out to look for it with a patrol, and finding that that was too conspicuous, pushing on alone until he could see it and mark it on his map. Four 25-pounders, firing blind and without any instrumental aids, had only the remotest chance of the necessary direct hit. Young's own guns were, equally, never silenced, although the little valley in which they were hidden was searched every day by Japanese fire. The most effective counter was an air strike, and these were called down and the targets indicated by salvoes of smoke shell, but now that the weather had closed in the sorties found great difficulty in seeing the targets, and the Japanese fire continued unabated. Supply dropping also became difficult, and the guns did not receive any ammunition after May 18th. On the 19th Young took to the air in a light aircraft and made a close reconnaissance of the whole valley from Hopin to Pinbaw, being occasionally shot at by small arms but saw no sign of any Japanese activity. (The 19th was the day that Takeda moved his headquarters to Hopin and began the forward move of the 128th Regiment.)

On the 20th the garrison was greatly cheered by the arrival of the 3rd/9th Gurkha Rifles from Broadway. The 3rd/9th was an excellent battalion, at full strength, in good health and physical shape. (Its commanding officer put this down to the fact that it had joined Special Force as late as February 1944 and had escaped the over-arduous training of 1943 which, instead of strengthening the men, sent them into battle run-down and already tired.) Its young soldiers had been blooded in the successful defence of the stronghold and since then its training had not been neglected: an officer passing through Broadway noted with astonishment that the riflemen were parading for physical training neatly dressed in shorts as if they were in their depot in India, and not a hundred miles inside Japanese-held Burma. Illness had robbed it of its commanding officer while in Broadway, but his loss had been made good by transferring Major Harper, the volunteer for the Chindits from the Deccan Horse, who had been so active with the 4th/9th in setting ambushes on the Bhamo road, and brought to the more earnest Gurkha officers that blend of blasé efficiency peculiar to the best type of cavalryman. (He said long afterwards that he had never realised what hell he had been through in Blackpool until he read his brigade commander's book.) He had been delayed because of some unexplained failure in the transmission of orders, and reported to the 77th Brigade instead of going straight to Blackpool. Calvert told him that he was now attached to the 111th Brigade and then Harper wasted no time. He forded the Namyin Chaung just before it flooded and, preferring the direct to any stealthy approach, formed up his 900 men in open order ready to deploy for a fight and marched them across the open paddy fields to Blackpool in broad daylight, resisting a private impulse to blow up Namkwin railway station and the railway as he passed it.[8]

Masters was now able to thicken up his defences. The Cameronians closed up their defensive perimeter so that they and the King's Own shared the northern half of the block, and the 3rd/9th took over the whole southern sector. Masters now made an excusable misjudgment. The defences facing the railway had a steep natural glacis and a clear field of fire in the shape of the airstrip. If his Japanese opponent knew his business, he thought, he would avoid this and come at him from the other side, or from the south using the cover of the jungle along the ridge. Harper, in accordance with his orders, deployed his main strength to cover that sector of his perimeter and left only a company overlooking the airfield. Looking for a safe place for his headquarters defence platoon, and his Burma Rifles, who were too valuable as scouts to be wasted in combat, he put them on an outlying feature called 'Pimple'; the 'paw' of the 'right hind leg' of the 'animal'. This was to prove the Achilles heel of the whole defence of the block.[9]

During the 21st and the 22nd there was a lull in the Japanese shelling, but Masters was now becoming extremely anxious about his situation. Large numbers of enemy were seen in the villages nearby on the railway, on to which Young now turned the attention of his guns, engaging a pair of 105 mm howitzers towed by lorries, a convoy of thirty lorries carrying troops and the pagoda in Namkwin, reported by the Burma Rifles to be an artillery observation post. The weather was atrocious, Blackpool had no supply drops on either day, nor on the 23rd. Without any sign of so much as a patrol from the 14th Brigade Masters seized on another hope. Surely, he thought, the Chinese (who in fact were sitting in front of Kamaing doing nothing) must by now be on the move and somewhere near him. Accordingly Lieutenant Hart of the King's Own, one of the most enterprising of the reconnaissance platoon commanders, was sent off to find them.[10] Then, on the 23rd, Takeda struck his first blow. An intense bombardment opened at noon, judged by the British gunners as being from two 105 mm, four 70 mm infantry guns pushed up to short range and firing over open sights and a large number of mortars, the rate being estimated as 300 shells or bombs an hour. At four p.m. the Japanese rushed the Pimple whose garrison, shaken by the bombardment, did not wait for the shock but fled to the perimeter. The artillerymen manning the Bofors guns guarding the airstrip lowered their barrels and fired for as long as they dared at the Japanese infantry now swarming on to it, and then fled in their turn. This enabled the Japanese to mount machine-guns and a mortar observation post on the Pimple looking into the defences, and under their cover they assaulted the Cameronian's sector repeatedly, only to be shot down in large numbers and the perimeter remained intact. At nightfall the Japanese kept up their pressure on the King's Own sector.

The fate of the block was decided on May 24th. There was no major attack, but the artillery log recorded at seven a.m.: 'Very heavy mortar fire on OP Hill and incessant shelling of the whole block.' It was this that caused most of the casualties. The chaplains, working as a team, for no men could be spared for burial parties, had to resort to tipping the dead into empty trenches and pushing the parapet down to cover them. There was no hope of evacuation for seriously wounded. The chaplain of the King's Own saw a 'corpse' put out for burial suddenly move, and dashed back to the aid post, to receive the dreary answer that there was nothing that could be done except wait for the unfortunate man to die. Young, the artillery commander, was killed in his observation post, his gun-position officer who took over was soon wounded, the radio-set was smashed. The whole area was swept by intense machine-gun fire from the Pimple. The Cameronians attempted a counter-attack to recapture it. They succeeded in reaching it and killing some twenty-five Japanese and damaging two of the guns, but were forced back again. (Their gallant leader, Sergeant Donald, uttered the classic remark, 'I'm not trembling: I'm just shivering with excitement.')

During the day attempts were made to resupply the block and then Masters' worst fear was realised. The Japanese had hidden their anti-aircraft guns in the scrub surrounding the airstrip, and when the aircraft arrived the sky was filled with the black smoke of exploding shells and streams of tracer. The pilots flew with great courage and determination. Three, avoiding the usual approach down the valley, dropped down through the murk (for the storms were continuous) from the heights towering over the western side of the block and, flying wing-tip to wing-tip, tried to drop directly into it, but many of the parachutes fell outside. An American voice was heard on the radio saying: 'I'm sorry if this is falling wide, but most of my rudder surface is shot away.' Early in the afternoon two airstrikes were made, both on the railway, and two fighter-bomber sorties managed to find their way through the storms and were guided on to targets by the smoke shells of the artillery, who could see intense activity near the railway line, as if the Japanese were forming up for an attack. These seemed to have been effective, for no assault on the perimeter was made that day, and once again as the sun set the Japanese artillery fell silent.

Masters spent the night receiving reports and considering what he should do. His casualties had not so far been heavy, by the criterion of a desperate defence. (His first report gave the total as being 120 killed, sixty wounded and thirty missing, later amended to 130 wounded brought out by the columns.) He was short of rations, but that was not the crux of the matter: this was, that he was almost out of ammunition. Without outside assistance he would be overrun sooner than later. He could, of course, have given the heroic order to hold Blackpool 'to the last round and the last man, making a final effort with the bayonet', in the words of the old Field Service Regulations, and there was little doubt that had he called for such a sacrifice the three fine battalions in the block would have responded. But he certainly could not hold out for another whole week, until June 1st. There was no military sense in exchanging a day's more interruption of the railway traffic for a good brigade still able to fight. He could have hesitated, putting off the serious, and indeed, in the eyes of the Americans in Stilwell's headquarters, disgraceful, step of abandoning his mission, in the hope that help might yet appear from some quarter. That would have been equally fatal. The fact was that without strong external support Blackpool was simply a chopping block on which the Japanese artillery could cut his force to pieces. The continual monsoon storms as much as the Japanese anti-aircraft guns cut him off from air supply and from supporting airstrikes, not only because of the appalling flying conditions but because the targets and drop zones were often obscured by the driving rain.

Still Masters hesitated. But any doubts he felt were soon dispelled when the main perimeter was finally breached at five a.m. on May 25th. A strong attack drove the Gurkhas from their position overlooking the airstrip and the 25-pounder gun position, followed by another against the Cameronians. A further surge forward was only checked by Lieutenant Smyllie, who rallied his Gurkhas and charged, hurling grenades. In a forlorn hope the last reserves, two platoons led by two Lieutenant-Colonels, Scott of the King's and Thompson of the King's Own, counter-attacked. It stopped the Japanese but could not recover the lost ground.

At eight a.m. Masters decided that he must save his brigade to fight another day and wrote out a brief signal for Lentaigne to that effect. Naturally he had given no contingency orders for the withdrawal, as this would have depressed the spirits of the garrison, and it speaks volumes for his officers that they reacted so promptly and smoothly to what were some necessarily complicated instructions. The situation was very dangerous; in fact, by about eight a.m. it looked as if the brigade was trapped. The perimeter of the King's Own, round at the back of the block, was intact, but there were Japanese dug in there, and they had driven in a picket guarding the water-point, and so menaced the possible route for withdrawal. The 25-pounder position was now under small-arms fire. Lieutenant Large ordered his gunners to strip their pieces of sights and firing mechanisms, to set the command post on fire, and to withdraw to Brigade Headquarters.

Clearly the safest line of withdrawal for the brigade was back up over the Bumrawng Bum, where it could fall back on No. 30 Column, left with such foresight to guard the route. The problem was how to extricate the brigade, now at close grips with the Japanese. Masters had a mind well-stocked with expedients for every military emergency, and he remembered the tactics used to check an enemy pursuit in the tribal warfare of India's North-West Frontier, where he had cut his teeth as a soldier. He arranged for each battalion to drop off a rearguard at a suitable interval to hold a position astride the withdrawal route. He himself would follow at the tail of the brigade with his escort and pick up each one in succession as soon as the main body was safely past it. Here the fact that he had put the 3rd/9th into position back to front, facing what was now the rear of the block, was fortunate, as it meant that a whole rifle company was covering the exit from the perimeter and stood ready to act as the rearguard. For the same reason he had put two platoons of Scott's No. 81 Column as an outpost on the route up the hill he now intended to take. The Cameronians of No. 90 Column established the first of the lay-back positions, and the King's Own of No. 41 Column another behind that.

There was a good deal of confusion, but the Chindits were always remarkably quick and adaptable, seldom needing the long and elaborate orders such a manoeuvre would have demanded in an ordinary battalion. Hart arrived back from his mission to the Chinese, which had proved abortive, and was amazed to hear the hubbub in the normally quiet positions of his well-trained battalion, but he soon grasped what was happening, and took up a position to guard the rear of his column. (He had been eight miles to the north and met what his Burma Riflemen assured him was a party of Chinese, but on making the recognition signal they shot at him: not that this disproved that they were Chinese.) The withdrawal of brigade headquarters at first went badly wrong. All the stretcher cases and walking wounded requiring help were grouped with it and all the spare men, including the artillerymen, who had fourteen wounded of their own with only one unwounded officer, were detailed to carry or help, and this pilgrimage of pain, moving at snail's pace in single file, came under a hail of mortar bombs. It then divided and in error some took a path to the right which brought them under a hot rifle- and machine-gun fire from the Japanese dug in opposite the King's Own. For a short time it was all very unpleasant. Richard Rhodes-James, the cipher officer, was suddenly confronted with a freshly severed head whose open eyes looked up at him from the track, and in the next minute a shell hit a stretcher and blew the wounded man and the bearers up into the air. A pony carrying a wounded man was hit, reared over backwards and momentarily blocked the route, to curses and cries of dismay. Worse than the dead (who on a battlefield seem somehow not shocking but infinitely remote) was the sight and sound of the wounded, some of whom were screaming with agony as they were hauled along by men desperate to escape from the beaten zone of the mortars, and others who, freshly hit, came crying out as they recoiled from the firing on the right-hand path. One man crawled by the side of the column begging for help, but it could not be halted, and the least check brought shouts from the men behind calling for it to move on.

Some men panicked and threw down their stretchers and though others, of a more generous spirit, took them up, the horrible question was asked: what was the use of carrying those already terribly injured on a trek over a 3,000-foot mountain which they could not hope to survive? Morphia was reserved for those who could be kept alive. Some of the others were given the merciful release of a bullet from a comrade's rifle. Rhodes-James' Scottish corporal, until then always the most cheerful man in his section, reappeared, deeply shocked, from the fatal right-hand route. The two sergeants, he said, had been hit and killed, and he had had to shoot two terribly injured Gurkha orderlies. Then, in almost dreamlike contrast to this ghastly scene, the men in the shuffling column saw Colonel Scott of the King's whose column was guarding the route, sitting unmoved and oblivious to the shelling by the side of the track – 'as if he were resting during a stroll in the country'. It was a steadying sight, and soon the ordeal was over. They were out of the barrage, the trail entered the forest and suddenly there was silence and peace.[11]

The main body also lost its way, through being misdirected by a staff officer from Brigade Headquarters, although the route was obvious on the ground, and it took a detour which might have had disastrous results. Masters and Harper had a bad half hour as they moved up the track, to find no one on it, but luckily the mistake was noticed and the column looped back on to the correct route.[12] The retreat of the three battalions was conducted in good order. Every man who was not badly wounded carried his personal weapon, and some carried or assisted the wounded. ('Rifleman Jagar Bahadur carried Moti Bahadur three miles on his back,' says the war diary of the 3rd/9th.) Only the mortars and Vickers guns had to be left for lack of mules, which had either been sent back out of the block to Mokso Sakkan or killed in the bombardment. By mid-day the whole brigade was clear. The evacuation had taken some time. Orders did not even reach Harper until ten fifty a.m., and it took the rest of the day to cover six miles, climbing steeply up hill.

No one could understand why the Japanese did not close the half-shut trap they had placed round Blackpool, or why they failed to pursue. Rhodes-James, conscious of almost brushing the Japanese at the water-point with his right shoulder as the column of wounded came out of the block, ascribed it to Divine Providence. That cannot be discounted, but the military fact is that the 53rd Division were not of the same stuff as the troops who had overrun Malaya and Burma, humiliated the British in the Arakan or were still grappling with the Fourteenth Army on the road from Kohima to Imphal. They were just capable of holding ground or making a frontal attack if herded on by their officers, they were all rotten with untreated malaria, and half-starved. Those who had burst into the perimeter that morning were seen to forage in the trenches for food and stop to eat packets of 'K' rations. The basic cause, however, can perhaps be found in the Chinese proverb, 'If your enemy takes refuge in the mountains, leave him alone.' Takeda must have been only too happy to see his dangerous opponent disappearing into the forest without having to endure the sort of bloodbath experienced by Take Force at Mawlu.

It took the brigade three days to reach Mokso Sakkan. The columns sorted themselves out as they marched, the missing rejoined and the combined doctors and chaplains set up a staging post for the wounded, where their dressings could be attended to and, by making a levy on rations, they could be given some food and tea. Masters came striding up the track from the rear to rejoin his headquarters; a martial figure, armed with carbine, kukri, pistol – and a Japanese officer's sword.[13] On the downhill side of the mountain the head-quarter column, to its relief and joy, was met by Upjohn's Nigerians, who were busy cutting and revetting steps in the precipitous trail to help them down, and who tenderly took over the work of carrying the wounded. On the 28th Masters signalled to Special Force Head-quarters that he had with him 130 wounded, and 2,000 men properly organised and under arms.[14]

14

Lack of Amity

THE CRISIS AT Blackpool could not have overtaken Lentaigne at a more unfortunate moment. In May two important changes took place in the structure of South-East Asia Command. Stilwell's odd position as Deputy to the Supreme Allied Commander and subordinate to Slim and the British Fourteenth Army had been a political expedient. It had long been agreed that once the First Chinese Army reached Kamaing it would be ended. After some wrangling it was also agreed, at Stilwell's insistence, that he would be responsible, in his guise of a field commander, directly to Mountbatten. At the same time, and much against his will, he agreed to accept Special Force under his operational command. Accordingly on May 19th Lentaigne with a small staff flew to Shaduzup in the Mogaung Valley to establish a forward headquarters close to Headquarters, Chinese Army in India/'Northern Combat Area Command', from where Stilwell personally directed the Chinese First Army. It was a pleasant enough site, although it was on the former battlefield and there was still a strong whiff of dead Japanese in the air, and the huts the Chinese soldiers had built for it leaked copiously in the unending rain. Lentaigne hopefully code-named it AMITY.

On the very day that Masters was disengaging at Blackpool, the two generals were discussing the next moves of the Chindit brigades. With great secrecy Stilwell had adopted the plan, concocted by Hunter and Merrill, for a flank march by-passing the whole Japanese defence system in the Hukawng valley and making directly for Myitkyina, the key point in Stilwell's strategy, through the jungles of the Kumon Bum. On the 17th he received the splendid news that Galahad had captured Myitkyina West airfield, and this altered his whole view of the utility of the Chindits in the Railway Valley. He no longer wished them to stay as far from him as possible, but desired them, while still blocking the railway, to divert their main effort against the town of Mogaung, which was in fact, because of its situation, equal in significance to Myitkyina. The prospects of 'amity' between the two men had never been bright, but when Stilwell learnt that without any reference to him the British had withdrawn from

Blackpool, and that in consequence a force of some 4,500 to 5,000 Japanese with artillery was free to move towards the two key towns, whatever chances there had been of it were wrecked beyond repair. Here, felt Stilwell, was justification for his twin beliefs that the Chindits could not fight and that they would not obey his orders. He immediately complained in writing to the Supreme Allied Commander, and Mountbatten, who was not blind to the true circumstances, was nonetheless forced to institute an enquiry which wasted everyone's time and caused much resentment on both sides.

The Chindits, both in the field and at Shaduzup, complained that Stilwell's desk-bound staff were culpably ignorant of the conditions in which they fought, but Lentaigne's position was not a strong one. He also was in the dark, partly through circumstances and partly because of his own omission to go and see things for himself. From the point of view of communications his new headquarters suffered from the same disadvantage as the columns and Brigade Headquarters in the field: it relied on the central retransmitting station at his main headquarters far away at Sylhet. He does not seem aware, from the context of his signals, of the weakness of the lateral communications, and of the fact that brigade commanders and column commanders could speak to each other directly only with difficulty, if at all. To make matters worse, the cipher officer on his little staff could not cope with the flood of messages coming in. The backlog was at first about 150 and there was a twenty-four hour lag before they were all read. Lentaigne's perception of the battle at that juncture was limited to the routine 'sitrep' telegraphed each evening for presentation at his next morning's conference, augmented by scraps of information from the debriefing of the pilots of the various supply and strike missions, which also had to be retransmitted from Sylhet.

The last signal from Masters received at Amity was his sitrep of May 24th. The one announcing his evacuation of the block, handed in to his brigade signal centre on the morning of the 25th, was never transmitted. This seems to have been because the radio operators, in the 'flap' resulting from the unexpected orders to prepare to leave the block, dismantled the station, although another version says that the set was damaged by shell fire.[1] On May 25th Lentaigne sent out a flurry of signals which had no relation to the realities of the situation. 'Ammunition and ration situation at Blackpool grave owing to AA interference with supply drops. Orders to hold until June 1st.' (To Brodie.) 'Attack enemy area with maximum columns and destroy AA guns.' (To Calvert.) 'You will give maximum assistance to minimum of four columns.' He ignored Ricketts and Upjohn altogether.

Upjohn's position on the 21st was that he was ahead of the other two brigades. Vaughan saw one of his columns taking a supply drop

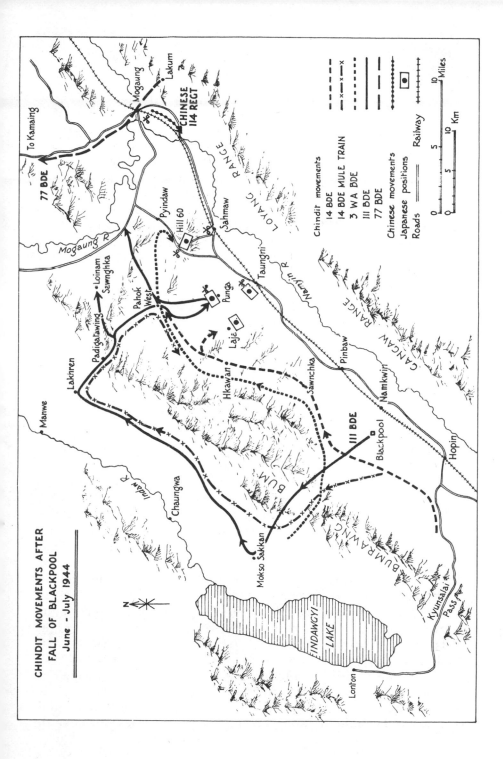

CHINDIT MOVEMENTS AFTER
FALL OF BLACKPOOL
June – July 1944

N

Key / Legend:

Chindit movements
- 14 BDE
- 14 BDE MULE TRAIN
- 3 WA BDE
- 111 BDE
- 77 BDE

Chinese movements
Japanese positions
Roads
Railway

Miles 10 / 5 / 0
Km 10 / 5 / 0

Place names and features:

To Kamaing
Mogaung
Lakum
CHINESE 114 REGT
77 BDE
Pyindaw
Hill 60
Sahmaw
LOYANG RANGE
Mogaung R.
Loinam
Sawnghka
Padigatawing
Pahok West
Punga
Taungni
Namyin R.
Lakhren
Laje
Hkawan
Sawnchka
Pinbaw
GANGAW RANGE
Namkwin
Manwe
Indaw R.
Chaungwa
BUM
Blackpool
111 BDE
Hopin
Mokso Sakkan
BUMRAWNG
INDAWGYI LAKE
Lonton
Kyunsalai Pass

on that day near Nammun. He still had to traverse the edge of the now flooded marsh which lay on the eastern shore of the lake, after which he faced a two or three day trek to Masters from Mokso Sakkan.

Brodie responded with an accurate report of the progress of his columns, adding, '. . . hill route very difficult. At present cannot give' an estimate of time of arrival at Blackpool but realise urgency.' Calvert as a last desperate measure sent his brigade assault company to try to cross the Namyin, but this, without assault boats, proved impossible. Then Lentaigne signalled to Masters: 'If you decide to abandon coordinate plan with 14 and 77 Brigades. 14 and 77 Brigades to continue [sic] to stop movement along the road and railway.'

This was the height of unreality. Flying conditions were admittedly very bad, but even if the brigades could not have been visited, a sortie by a staff officer in an L-5, which could brave all but the worst conditions, might have revealed the floods in the Railway Valley and the state of the Namyin Chaung. There was nothing at this point Lentaigne could do to redeem a situation he should have gripped much earlier – and whose dangers he should have foreseen, for surely the monsoon was not an unknown phenomenon – but he should at least have understood the circumstances even if he could not cure them.

During the day a fighter-bomber sortie was sent to look over Blackpool to see if it could help, but it made no radio contact, saw no movement of any kind and was not even greeted by Japanese anti-aircraft fire. The pilot of the one supply aircraft able to get through the weather found the same but, while questing about, saw through a break in the rain-clouds a long column of men wearing the unmistakable Chindit slouch hats filing westwards up the slope of the Bumrawng Bum. On the 26th No. 30 Column signalled confirmation and on 28th Masters reported his arrival at Mokso Sakkan. He followed this up with a depressed private letter to Lentaigne, describing the action in detail and regretting that he had let him down, to which Lentaigne signalled in reply: 'Well done. Would have ordered evacuation earlier if information available.' In the subsequent recriminations he assumed full responsibility, which was correct and British. But this did not mollify Stilwell: on the contrary.

The next problem to bear heavily down on Lentaigne was the state of the Chindits in the field. By Wingate's reckoning the 77th and 111th Brigades and Morris Force were due for relief at the beginning of June, and the 14th Brigade and the Nigerians three weeks later, but Stilwell had rejected the 'ninety-day contract' for Galahad as quite contrary to any military usage he understood and refused to concede it to the Chindits. He was determined that every man should be kept in as long as he was fit enough to lift a weapon. Indeed, his own staff were already combing the American hospital at Margharita, near Ledo, for Galahads fit enough to rejoin their unit. Lentaigne felt that it was his duty in the circumstances to call for one, grand final effort from the Chindits. The question was how long this could be sustained without the total destruction of the Force. This was a real prospect. By June 4th Galahad had lost from its original strength of 3,000 only 394 killed, wounded and missing, but 2,000 from disease, although the British did not know these figures at the time.

The true state of the morale of the Force was subsequently proved by the fact that the Chindits continued to fight in terrible conditions and with men dropping daily from disease, and after terrible travail succeeded in their objectives. These included Mogaung, captured against the most dogged resistance of the Japanese who, though also sick and worn out, defended each last weapon-slit and bunker to the bitter end. The survivors attribute this to the way their spiritual batteries had been charged in the first place by their legendary commander Wingate, and to their strong Chindit sense of being unique and an élite. Nevertheless, morale – motivation, courage, esprit de corps, loyalty to the group and to comrades-in-arms – is expendable. Lentaigne had to make some assessment.

This in modern armies is not a matter for subjective judgment. 'Spiritual' factors are not to be scorned (the Japanese placed them at the head of the list), but there are more tangible forms of evidence. Morale can be measured empirically by the reaction the general obtains when he visits the soldiers and talks to them. Such visiting was difficult (but not impossible) in the dispersed conditions of Special Force. It can be gauged even more reliably, in conventionally placed armies at least, by the incidence of self-inflicted wounds, psychoneurosis, absenteeism and desertion and the general state of discipline. Self-inflicted wounds among the Chindits seem to have been very rare, and psychoneurosis the same; or rather, it was not diagnosed, as the symptoms were soon overlaid by those of disease and malnutrition. (The artillery records simply mention one or two men being treated for 'shock' after shelling.) Desertion and absenteeism were hardly options for those who wished to escape, since they carried with them an almost certain prospect of an unpleasant death at the hands of the Japanese. In such a force as the Chindits discipline had ultimately to be based on indoctrination, the weeding out of weak material, the example of the leaders and the consent of the led. Nevertheless, the problem remained of how to deal with those who slipped through the net, or whose weaknesses betrayed them in the field. The 'skiver', to use the soldier's word, might have found a spell in the relatively mild conditions of a British Second World War detention or field punishment centre infinitely preferable to sweating under a seventy-pound pack and Bren gun on half rations through a Japanese-infested tropical jungle. But any such dodge was out of the question. It would, moreover, have been quite impossible to satisfy the strongly legalistic British Army's requirements, which for serious offences demanded the presence of accused, escort and witnesses, possibly for weeks, at permanently sitting court-martials in India.

Wingate, a violent man by temperament, devised, instead, a violent code. For serious offences, such as stealing rations or sleeping on sentry duty, the offender would be flogged; for repeated offences or more serious ones, banished from the column with a rifle and five rounds of ammunition to take his chance; for cowardice in the face of the enemy, he would be shot. This code was propagated by word of mouth during the training period in 1943, with the false information that it had been legitimised by a secret order of the Commander-in-Chief in India. (Who, of course, had no power to do any such thing.)

Both the wisdom and the logic of the policy were doubtful. There is a point at which a starving man cannot refrain from cramming a handful of food into his mouth, cost what it may, or a tired one from falling asleep. And if the policy was sound, it would be applicable to all severe operations, airborne operations and sieges in particular. Conditions at Kohima, for instance, were fully as unpleasant as anything faced even by the Chindits. But as penology, it was *not* sound. Experience had shown that the death penalty did not check cowardice or desertion: the reverse was the case.[2] It was also impolitic. Flogging had been abolished more than eighty years before in Britain, and the death penalty for military offences,[3] together with 'field punishments' such as being trussed up to a gun-wheel, had been suspended after the First World War by Act of Parliament. In 1939–45, public opinion was extremely sensitive on the subject of harsh military discipline in any form. However, when the new code was made known to all ranks, the soldiers were not shocked. They saw the point and, as soldiers often do in such matters, took a perverse pride in this unique condition of their service as Chindits.

In fact, the discipline of the Chindits was such that officers seldom resorted to a code so repugnant to their previous training and attitude towards their men, which by British Army tradition was deeply paternalistic, and when they did so it was with much heart-searching. Lieutenant Patterson, Royal Engineers, for instance, when he found two Lancashire Fusiliers asleep on sentry duty, simply reprimanded them.[4] The death penalty was never imposed, as far as is known. The only candidate was a white non-commissioned officer in the 7th Nigeria whose nerve had gone and who refused a second chance to make good on a dangerous patrol. Lieutenant-Colonel Vaughan weighed up the consequences on the morale of his black soldiers, who were easily upset, if one of their trusted white 'sargy's' was shown to be in disgrace in so drastic and horrifying a manner. So he was flown out, as good riddance.[5] This would certainly have been Calvert's solution. He had, perhaps as a result of his experiences at the Royal Military Academy, a strong dislike of military punishment and bullying of any sort, and expressed his standpoint in the lines, 'He who has no stomach for this fight, let him depart . . .'[6] (although he was very strict about the degree of severity of illness which qualified for evacuation). As regards expulsion from the column, he had experimented with it during the LONGCLOTH operation in 1943 when he commanded a column of Gurkhas. The banished riflemen simply followed pathetically in his wake, living on little scraps of food left for them by their comrades, so he eventually relented and allowed them to rejoin after a severe scolding. Nor did he beat. Vaughan was much stricter. He awarded the customary 'six for arse' to ration thieves, as he was permitted to do by the regulations of the West African Frontier Force, and was indignant when the 3rd/6th were allowed to get away with such pilfering 'when there is so much good bamboo growing in the jungle'. The only verifiable case of expulsion is of two men in the King's Own, already punished by beating for the disgraceful offence of rifling a comrade's pack for rations saved during a period when there had been no supply drop and now found guilty of a new offence. (One of them successfully made his way to safety from the Indawgyi area.)[7]

The authenticated cases of 'flogging' – in fact beating with a bamboo – are few: two in the Royal Artillery column in the 16th Brigade,[8] mentioned earlier in this book; a Gurkha in headquarters of 111th Brigade;[9] the two men in the King's Own punished for stealing rations;[10] two in a York and Lancaster column for sleeping while on sentry duty,[11] and two Cameronians who were seized and beaten by the fiery Captain Macgillicuddy himself when he detected them helping themselves to rations while collecting supplies from a drop.[12] The only case ever judicially investigated was that involving the two men in the York and Lancaster column; in 1946 the commanding officer who had authorised the action (of his other column commander) was tried by court-martial, and acquitted. The defence pleaded that the evidence had been scrupulously weighed, that the men had consented to be punished, and that the punishment itself was no more severe than would be inflicted by a schoolmaster, which somewhat discounted the alternative defence that in conditions so horrific only Draconian punishments would be of use.[13] Brigadier Brodie did not resort to such punishments in the only known case of a more serious offence, when a number of his brigade defence platoon ran away when attacked by the Japanese. After they had been rounded up they were disgraced by being made to do more than their share of fatigues and be the first to go without rations if there was a shortfall in supplies. (Many of the guilty were indifferent soldiers, happily discarded by battalions when the platoon was formed, who felt inferior and unwanted. Unlike their equivalent in 77th Brigade, they were not an élite expected to fight, but largely used as fatigue-men, orderlies and for guard duty.)[14] There is ample evidence that Wingate's code was resorted to only exceptionally, and that the discipline of the force was good.

As for morale, no blanket assessment is possible, because it manifests itself in different ways in different units. The Lancashire Fusiliers, rated by Calvert as his weakest unit, persisted in the fighting at their own level, but nonetheless they fought. No. 82 Column never distinguished itself, but the hundred fugitives who were taken into the Lancashire Fusiliers did well at the bitter end of the campaign. The Cameronians repulsed every attack on their perimeter at Blackpool and had had great success in raiding opera-tions, but they burnt themselves out.[15] Some good units were informal, but the unsurpassed Black Watch, as seen by the doctor, Lieutenant Bower, shaved, stood to attention when spoken to, saluted their officers and, what struck him most, treated him, a greenhorn, completely at sea among the Chindits, with unending kindness and courtesy.[16]

Three post-operational assessments of morale survive, but they must be treated with reserve because they were made by a junior medical officer whose psychiatric knowledge and military experience is not specified. The questions he asked might equally have occurred to experienced regimental officers and possibly been better evaluated by them. All the samples were British. The object of the enquiry was to assess the morale of each brigade as a whole. One reasonable complaint was that many of the men who broke down during the training period were replaced by those who had been originally rejected for being over-age or of inferior physique, but who then, at short notice, had been taken into the field without any hardening training and who suffered accordingly. The only reference to flogging was in the 111th Brigade, and the complaint was that, although it was agreed that it was justified, it should not have been inflicted publicly in front of the 'natives'. The psychiatrist reported that the morale of the 77th Brigade, which had had by far the largest share of fighting and suffered the largest number of battle casualties, was excellent; the 14th Brigade very good and the 111th Brigade very bad. (An assessment, it must be added, later firmly rejected by the brigade commander and also by officers of the King's Own. The report does not appear to have been seen by them at the time.)[17]

The true state of affairs was that the spirit of the 111th Brigade had been depressed by the failure at Blackpool, but the men of the other brigades were not far from the end of their tether either, morale being an expendable asset. As will be told, even the indomitable Calvert perceived that his brigade had almost reached the point of breakdown and took it out of action in defiance of orders. Nevertheless, during the last agonising weeks of the campaign, all four brigades, including the 111th, continued to march and fight with astonishing tenacity, aware that their only hope of rest was to clear out the last of the Japanese between them and Stilwell's Chinese. But at that stage their real enemy was not the Japanese, but exhaustion, malnutrition and disease.

The total number of sick flown out and admitted to hospital was 5,412 but many were treated inside Burma and remained in the ranks. When the force was at last relieved almost every man required rest and a special diet and one in two was admitted to hospital. At Lentaigne's request his senior medical officer reported on the condition of a large sample on July 7th. 'Of 1,208 men examined 625 fit for active service, 258 fit for base duties only, 225 require immediate hospitalisation or to be sent to a convalescent depot. The number of fit men is decreasing as incidence of sickness hits them (malaria, sores and diarrhoea). Mepacrin suppression now at three tablets per day. *All* have had one attack of malaria, some up to fourteen. Condition and ability to recover due to fatigue and malnutrition low.' As Colonel Graves-Morris, CO of the 2nd Battalion of the York and Lancasters, was to say later, of 900 of his men who had landed at Aberdeen, '380, the wrecks of their former selves', marched out in July, 1944.

After the monsoon had broken the sick had to walk long distances to the few airstrips still operating, only the most severe cases being given rides on ponies, or on pad elephants impressed by the Burma Rifles from the friendly Kachin tribesmen. Lieutenant Bower, keeping himself going by will-power (he soon had ulcers on the balls of his unhardened feet and was in agony much of the time), noted that at some point the sick lost all wish to live, and some died on the way. The going was dreadful, liquid mud lubricating the rocks and fallen timber on the trails, with the added hazards of holes poached by the feet of the elephants moving with the party; so deep that the diminutive Gurkhas were in danger of drowning when they stumbled into them and had to be hauled out by main force. Bower noted one group of sick, who seemed almost catatonic, expressionless, and sprawling in grotesque attitudes like puppets thrown into a box, riding in the wicker howdah of an elephant. Only the efforts of the medical orderlies and the fitter men coopted to help them, who brutally drove on the column, prevented men from apathetically lying down by the trail to seek release in death. If the morale of the whole Force was to be sustained it was essential that every man knew that he had at least a good chance of survival and evacuation to India. In June and July this was achieved by the combined inspiration of the Royal Air Force and the Royal Engineers.

By the end of May there was a large accumulation of sick and wounded awaiting evacuation from the three brigades in the area of the Indawgyi Lake, for whom the only outlets were the short airstrips at Nammun and Mokso Sakkan suitable only for the few L-1s in the light plane squadrons.* The light planes were still operating, but after the disbandment of No. 1 Air Commando, Special Force no longer had the exclusive or even the first call on their services, and they had to be tasked through the sluggish staff machinery of Stilwell's field headquarters on a priority basis, the Chindits having to stand in the queue like everyone else. Someone had the happy inspiration to use flying boats operating from the lake, a suggestion to which the Royal Air Force responded with remarkable speed. Two four-engined Sunderland flying boats, normally used for long-range maritime reconnaissance and anti-submarine work, were first flown to a perilous landing-place on the Brahmaputra River at Dibrugarh. The Japanese Air Force was by that time almost completely subdued, but the big, slow aircraft were very vulnerable to a single prowling fighter, and there was a track along the west side of the lake used by patrols of the Japanese at Kamaing, only thirty-five miles away. These were, however, minor dangers compared with those of a 180-mile flight over the intervening 5,000-foot Patkai Bum, now shrouded in storm clouds, while the lake itself was frequently whipped into 'monstrous and foam-crested' waves by squalls from the surrounding mountains and was full of half-submerged trees uprooted by the storms. Then there was the problem of embarking the casualties from a shore-line with no natural landing-places and consisting of forest or marsh or a combination of the two. The combined Royal Engineers of the brigades, with African detachments to help, set to work and with great speed built camps where the wounded could be assembled: the Nigerians having an aptitude for building primitive huts with only their *pangas* (cutlasses) for tools. They made jetties and bamboo rafts driven by outboard motors dropped from the air, and surveyed and cleared the landing-places. The Sunderlands brought in cargoes of food, medical supplies, more

* The L-1s had the shortest take-off and landing distances of all the aircraft in the No. 1 Air Commando.

engineer stores, outboard motors and rubber assault boats, and took out forty casualties at a time. The first set of sorties cleared 240. Even so the casualties mounted faster than the numbers flown out. By mid-June another 400 were collected at Mokso Sakkan, but by then one of the flying boats had been wrecked by a storm at its moorings on the Brahmaputra and the other had been withdrawn. The engineers thereupon conceived another bold improvisation. The Chinese had at last broken the Japanese front, so might it not be possible to float the casualties on rafts down the unexplored Indaw Chaung which drained the waters of the lake into the Mogaung River at Kamaing?

Reconnaissance showed that the waterway was choked with weed and logs and was moreover infested with parties of Japanese withdrawing from Kamaing in the area. A patrol from No. 61 Column assigned to protect the route was in a country boat when it met a Japanese officer on a raft. He refused to surrender and was pursued by the platoon commander, who boarded the raft to seize him – live Japanese prisoners were a prize – but in the ensuing struggle the raft overturned and Captain Turner had to stab him to death in the water before he could swim to safety. Barring such interruptions it seemed a feasible route, and the engineers designed super-rafts capable of forcing their way back up the strong current to the lake after delivering their quota of sick. They consisted of five rubber assault boats with a strong bamboo raft wrapped in a huge tarpaulin to improve bouyancy lashed port and starboard, the whole being thirty-seven feet overall and twelve in the beam, fitted with a timber cutwater in front and propelled by a team of up to four outboard motors. Each had a proper 'head', or latrine, a canopy to provide shade, racks of bunks for lying cases, a radio and a mast to fly the largest Union Jack the ordnance services in India could provide. This was not so much for patriotic reasons as in the hope that it might deter the trigger-happy bandits of the Chinese First Army from shooting at them. Each craft could carry up to thirty-five men. Ten of these made up the 'Indawgyi Grand Fleet': the Royal Engineer craft *Ark Royal, Vindictive, Valiant, Vanguard, Revenge, Renown, Resolution, Barham, Benbow* and *Blenheim*. They provided a regular casualty evacuation route until the end of the campaign and saved many lives, in spite of the difficulties of navigation, which occasionally made it necessary for the patients themselves to set to and cut weed, 'hacking away madly with knives, machetes, and bayonets', or plunge into the water to move log-jams. There was little rest for a Chindit invalid until he was finally loaded into an aircraft.[18]

All this, together with the considerable logistic feat of keeping the columns supplied in the field, was achieved by the energy of the

Chindits' own staff, led by Brigadier Tulloch, with the cooperation of half a dozen different agencies, ranging from the ordnance and medical services back in India to Eastern Air Command. This effectively disposes of the lingering belief that the 'staff' were united in their obstruction of Special Force. The only difficulty the Chindits were to encounter was in their dealings with Stilwell's own head-quarters.

As regards Stilwell himself, it is impossible not to admire him for his qualities as a soldier, and not to enter into his feelings in that third week of May. As he sat in his austere camp at Shaduzup – he never allowed himself the comfort or convenience of a well-built office, operations room or mess – and pored over his map, three places stood out and riveted their names on his clear and prehensile mind: Kamaing, Mogaung and Myitkyina. Tanaka and his 18th Division had since April been immovably wedged in the gullet of the Mogaung Valley, blocking the way in front of Kamaing, and for nearly a month Stilwell's two Chinese divisional commanders, restrained by the private messages of Chiang Kai-shek, had procrastinated over every forward move he ordered. The Japanese had to be shifted from Kamaing before any more progress could be made by Brigadier-General Pick and his army of road-building engineers. Mogaung commanded the routes connecting Kamaing and Myitkyina and the exit from the Railway Valley. Myitkyina was vital for its airfields, its position on the air route over the 'hump' to China and as the crossing place over the Irrawaddy for the new road. Of these three Stilwell had fixed his highest hopes on the capture of Myitkyina, but it was really Mogaung that mattered. With that in his hands the Japanese at Kamaing would be cut off from their base and Myitkyina isolated so that it could be reduced at leisure.

The moment when Hunter signalled that he had captured the airfield at Myitkyina was a dramatic one, and Stilwell was overjoyed, but the climacteric event of his whole campaign was on May 20th. That morning Major-General Sun Li-jen, commanding the 38th Division, turned to the American liaison officer attached to him and said: 'I think we go on to take Kamaing now.' Stilwell's operational plan as usual was based on encirclement, in the hope of trapping and destroying the 18th Division and not merely driving it back to yet another defensive position, and this time the Chinese did not hesitate or hold back. One of Sun's regiments swung wide round Tanaka's right flank and cut the road behind him at the little village of Seton on May 26th. There they hung on grimly, beating off one desperate counter-attack after another, while their comrades battered against the Japanese positions in front of Kamaing. The 18th Division was now in terrible danger and if Mogaung could be captured its fate was sealed. At Myitkyina things were not going so well, but it was invested on three sides and if the ferry sites on the far bank of the Irrawaddy could be captured its isolation would be complete. Across the Salween in China the American equipped and directed Chinese Expeditionary Force with fifteen divisions had at last been permitted by Chiang Kai-shek to advance. Its ponderous offensive had rolled across the Salween River and would soon, Stilwell hoped, drive back the single Japanese division facing it and begin to clear the Chinese end of the Ledo road.[19]

Stilwell sometimes quoted Foch. Perhaps at that moment he remembered his service in France in 1918 and the Marshal's great rallying cry echoed in his mind. *'Tout le monde à la bataille!'* Forgetting all that he had said or thought about the Chindits, he saw that they were ideally placed to close the trap, so he directed Morris Force on to the villages on the east bank of the Irrawaddy opposite Myitkyina and the other four brigades to converge on Mogaung. He was right, and there was one man who, had he still been alive, would have backed him: Wingate. The Chindits responded. They gave him Mogaung, and as late as August those who were left still mopping up pockets of Japanese on the roads to the south, but without any encouragement beyond the belief that sooner or later they would be released from their ordeal. Fortunately, they were stoics to a man, and were in any case unaware of their American taskmaster's ignorance of their plight or the depth of his callousness. They consoled themselves by humming rude or sarcastic doggerels to lift their weary feet – 'Hear the angel voices calling, good old Joe' and 'Chindit, Chindit, don't be blue/Dextrose Joe will see you through'.

It was Stilwell's misfortune that he had only to think of the hated Limeys for his wits to fly out of his head. His trouble was that he could not talk to ordinary men, let alone the British. It would be unfair to blame him for lacking the touch of a Montgomery or the flamboyance of a Patton, and it is sentimental in any case to believe that successful generals must be lovable or charismatic: the reverse is usually the case. But it is part of the ordinary technique of command to show oneself, to inspect, to chat and even to explain. Stilwell visited Myitkyina frequently; why not Mogaung? He could have seen for himself, and however determined he was that those Chindits capable of bearing arms should continue to fight, he could at least have matched his demands to their abilities. He cannot, however, be condemned for this blank spot. It may well have been due to some old and deep-seated injury to his personality: it is unnatural to hate so much. What is less excusable is that while he could analyse a situation with the utmost clarity and formulate excellent plans his contempt for formal staff work infected his staff, and led to his plans being bungled in their execution.

At his curious composite headquarters he had a number of able officers, but this was hardly reflected in the quality of their staff work. Merrill (still commanding Galahad, but from Stilwell's headquarters), Easterbrook (Stilwell's son-in-law), Joseph Stilwell, junior (head of G2 or intelligence staff section) and Haydon C. Boatner (simultaneously chief-of-staff of Chih Hui Pu and commanding general of Northern Combat Area Command), all satisfied the exacting standards of the United States Army to become major-generals in due course, and has been said, and the others seem to have known their business. Yet none ever took the trouble to visit the Chindits in the field. What caused the bitterest complaints inside Amity was that none seemed to understand the limitations of the Chindit column or battalion when it was used in the conventional infantry rôle, its lack of artillery and its absolute dependence on direct air support. Nor had thought been given to the possibility of Japanese resistance or to the nature of the country over which the Chindits had to fight. Brigadier Morris had to point out on one occasion that the route he had been ordered to use was flooded to a depth exceeding the average height of a Gurkha soldier. Stilwell's system of command was to choose a point of tactical significance from the map and measure its distance from the position of the column designated to capture it. This was divided by the standard speed of a marching infantryman – two and a half miles per hour – and by this artless calculation Stilwell's staff arrived at the day and hour by which the objective should be captured. When it was not, a request was made to Amity, in writing, for an explanation for Lentaigne's failure to obey his orders, in writing. 'How our hearts sank,' recalled one of the Amity staff, 'when yet another of those awful long sealed envelopes was brought over by a rather shamefaced American officer.'[20] The explanations were seldom accepted and Stilwell followed them up by complaints to the Supreme Allied Commander, who at the end of June was forced to descend to the level of bothering himself with battalion-size operations and fly to Shaduzup to resolve the differences between his deputy and a relatively junior general officer. The British were first shocked and indignant at this extraordinary way of conducting military operations having so far only dealt with the supremely cooperative and warlike American airmen and engineers. Then they became contemptuous, and finally treated the staff's behaviour with derision. It was not, as will be seen, as if they were shrinking from casualties or failing after desperate struggles to carry the strongpoints they were ordered to assault.

On the working level the staff at Amity were frustrated by the fact that Stilwell's field headquarters was not in a strict sense geared to operations. His orders and directives went out in writing, on parchment-like paper with a printed heading, each authenticated by the commanding general or his chief-of-staff. Incoming documents were dealt with in strict rotation of arrival in the 'in'-tray by a staff who worked a daily routine suitable for administrative duties in peace, and who left the office at mealtimes and all night with only a roster duty officer, who logged requests or telephone calls without being able to take any executive action.[21] The British staff, led by a young live wire with combat experience in the person of Henry Alexander, were trained to accept a general policy and then take full responsibility at the level of major for the details of its execution. (They spoke for their commanding general and in his name without having constantly to refer back. An error might earn a rebuke, but failure to act earned dismissal.) The Americans had to refer every-thing upwards, however trivial.

Where this difference in procedure led to frustration was over the question of air strikes. These now had to be provided by the 10th United States Air Force whose forward squadrons were based only a short distance away at Tinghawk Sakkan airfield, but each request had to be processed through Stilwell's staff. It was found that they understood nothing of the proper technique of air support: the process of briefing pilots, informing the unit in the field of which of their requests had been agreed, if any, and monitoring the operation. They actually ordered the Chindit army/air liaison officer to be withdrawn from Tinghawk. Nor did they understand the elaborate and flexible method of controlling the aircraft over the target devised for the Chindits by Squadron-Leader Thompson. This was all gradually put right, because the young officers on both sides took each other's measure and began to cooperate, and things improved immensely when a United States Army Air Force officer, Major van Deusen joined Stilwell's headquarters.[22] He was a pilot with operational experience and a sense of urgency, who frequently flew fighter-bomber missions himself so as to study the operational problem on the spot. Nevertheless, relations between the two headquarters, and also between the much tried Brigadier Morris when he was placed directly under the equally inept Myitkyina Task Force headquarters, continued to be fraught with recriminations and misunderstandings. This bore heavily on Lentaigne, whose natural inclination was to give a loose rein to his fiery temper, but whose duty it was to suffer in silence in the name of cooperation. He was mistaken in this: the only way to deal with Stilwell was to go for him.

15

The Chindits' Last Battle

WE LEFT BRIGADIER Morris and Colonel Herring far away on the border of China developing their operations against the Bhamo road. Guerrilla warfare is always beset by misadventures and misunderstandings, and there was no shortage of these, what with poor communications, incomprehensible orders from headquarters, erratic orders from Morris and lack of information and frustration over air support. Nevertheless, by mid-May both Morris Force and Dah Force had had considerable success.

Dah Force from first to last killed rather more than its own numbers of Japanese. The three Gurkha columns between them (No. 40 eventually joined Morris on May 3rd) had demolished eight large bridges, including two iron ones, two ferry installations and numerous small bridges, and had blown a long section of the road from a cliff face into the gorge below. The Gurkhas had come down from their mountain fastnesses to hit the road in six different places, and the two forces between them, by means of patrols, ambushes and attacks on the road engineers, prevented the repair of the breaks. Supplies to Myitkyina were never completely cut off, but they were substantially reduced. Units the Japanese could ill spare were deflected to guarding the road and chasing the Kachins and Gurkhas back into the jungle; all supply convoys were liable to ambush and the movement of all but large bodies of troops made hazardous. For a battalion and a half and Herring's little mission it was a handsome dividend, and a vindication of Wingate's purer, earlier doctrine.

The price was the same as elsewhere in Special Force. Morris, himself suffering from repeated bouts of malaria, saw that even his sturdy Gurkhas were reaching the end of their endurance and his thoughts were turning to the prospects of relief. Then came splendid news. On May 17th his observers reported extraordinary air activity over Myitkyina. Streams of aircraft were coming over the mountains, and the town was being bombed. The news on the radio that Myitkyina had fallen was received with great joy. The mission was complete and now, surely, Morris Force could march out. This hope was soon dashed. There was still fighting to be done. On May 25th

Morris Force was ordered to pack up, march north forthwith and come directly under the Myitkyina Task Force Commander. Morris made haste to comply, but at that moment he was in a most awkward position. He and No. 40 Column were up in the mountains four miles from the Chinese frontier. The other two columns were fourteen miles away blocking the crossings of the Nam Tabet River. While they were in contact with a sizeable Japanese force the Nam Tabet rose in its monsoon spate, cutting off the troops on the north bank from those on the south. Only some notable fighting by a Gurkha sergeant, who held up 200 Japanese, enabled them to break clear. It took No. 49 and No. 94 Columns some time to collect themselves, but they were still separated from their mule trains and momentarily out of touch with Morris. The only remaining bridge over the flooded river was up stream, in China, so when Morris Force was finally assembled it had to make a killing detour of fifty miles through the mountains, which it completed at the remarkable speed of ten miles a day. (It was in any case hardly feasible to use the direct route up the road, now full of reinforcements from the Japanese 56th Division hurrying to Myitkyina. It arrived on May 30th.) Back at Shaduzup the first of the series of letters of complaint, headed 'Apparent Disobedience of Orders', was handed to Lentaigne on May 26th, asking why Morris was not at Myitkyina. This was doubly perverse, as Stilwell's headquarters was in walking distance and a verbal explanation could have been obtained in ten minutes, and his staff had no excuse for not informing themselves in the first place about Morris's situation.

The trouble, Limey-baiting apart, was that the Myitkyina operation had gone badly wrong. Stilwell's premature announcement, broadcast to all the world, that he had captured it had rebounded on him, and as a result he was at his most bilious and looking for victims to savage. The American official historians, departing from their usual scrupulous objectivity, say at this juncture that 'the brilliant seizure of the Myitkyina airstrip was the height of Stilwell's career and the climax of the North Burma Campaign'. This verdict must be weighed against the actual events.[1]

Operation END RUN – the code-word, from American football, has a flavour both of outflanking and scoring a decisive goal – was certainly a bold and imaginative manoeuvre. For it Stilwell authorised the creation of a special Task Force organised in three columns, two of a Galahad battalion and a Chinese infantry regiment and a third of a Galahad battalion and 300 Kachin levies. Colonel Hunter was relegated to the command of one of the columns, made up of the 1st Battalion and the 150th Regiment.[2] The Myitkyina Task Force command was given to Stilwell's favourite, Brigadier-General Merrill, who after his heart attack had been retained at Shaduzup as the nominal commander of Galahad. He alone was entrusted with planning and preparation, for Stilwell, following his old practice of playing off one of his team against another, had slightingly excluded his chief-of-staff, Brigadier-General Haydon C. Boatner, from the whole enterprise.[3] (Boatner was to become the target of much bitter criticism, not all of it fair, for he was a trained staff officer and incapable of committing the blunders of which Merrill was guilty.)

Merrill's first objective was Myitkyina South airfield, which was to be approached by a secret route over the jungle-clad Kumon Bum, as formidable a mountain obstacle as any met by the Chindits. It took nineteen days to cover the fifty miles from the assembly area to the airfield.

Two of the columns became entangled in the Japanese outposts, but the redoubtable Hunter threaded his way between them and on May 17th informed Stilwell that the airfield was in his hands, and in working order. Stilwell was beside himself with joy, as well he might be, for he had pulled off – *almost* – what many believed to be the impossible. Then there was a hiatus.

What Merrill had failed to grasp was that the capture of the airfield was only the first step to the grand goal of Myitkyina. All he had gained was the jumping-off point for the attack on the town. The operation was similar to any other air-supported operation, whose elaborate techniques had long since been perfected; it was, after all, the year 1944. The roots of the fiasco go back to the basic estimates on which all planning was based. No comparison was made of the balance of forces. It was believed that the town was held by some 350 Japanese: the correct figure was 3,500, rising later to over 4,000.[4] The Chinese regiments were incapable of the simplest manoeuvre; the one with Hunter had only 800 men with weapons. The physical condition of Galahad was ignored. (One battalion was so afflicted with dysentery that the men had cut out the seats of their trousers to avoid fouling themselves when suddenly griped.) It was believed that the town could be carried by a single rush by unsupported infantry, and the sole artillery provided for the assault on its formidable bunker systems was two 75 mm howitzers. These were elementary errors.

Even more serious was the failure to have a flight plan made jointly with the air force by which all the essential equipment and the massive supplies of ammunition required for the attack were flown in according to a schedule of priorities, beginning with Merrill and his headquarters and radio communications, ready to grip the situation from the outset and seize the prize Hunter had put within his reach. All the technical arrangements for the attack (start-lines, axes of advance, targets for artillery, air strikes and so on) should have been made in advance on a contingency basis from air photographs.

Hunter had pressed Merrill for details of the plan, only to be brushed aside. The moment he arrived at the airfield, Merrill told him, he would fly in and take over himself. He agreed to send in five days' supply of ammunition and food as first priority.

In response to his success signal there arrived on the 17th, much to Hunter's fury and chagrin, a company of airfield construction engineers, for whom there was no immediate task, Brigadier-General Old of Troop Carrier Command, very properly coming in ahead of his precious transport aircraft to check the condition of the airfield, some Chinese anti-aircraft machine gunners, and part of another Chinese regiment without commander or staff. Of Merrill and the ammunition there was no sign; nor was there on the 18th. Most of the space on that day was taken up with twelve British Bofors anti-aircraft guns with their crews. (This unexpected addition to the task force reveals much about the lack of planning. When General Stratemeyer, Eastern Air Command, heard, apparently at the last minute, what was afoot, he peremptorily demanded adequate airfield defence. This sudden request went ricochetting down the command chain until it fell in the lap of Special Force, who with great speed organised two light anti-aircraft artillery troops from the guns just pulled out of the strongholds, only to find that Old's headquarters new nothing about either END RUN or anti-aircraft guns. They refused to provide any aircraft without the personal authority of General Old, but were out of touch with him and did not know where he was. He was at Shaduzup, of course, a stone's throw from Amity. Major Mead has described in his best and most sarcastic style how the radio channels echoed all night with voices with British accents speaking in the cryptic lingo of Special Force: 'Where is the ancient?' 'Do you mean the *old one*?' 'Old one not here.' 'Well, no *ancient*, no *tubes*', and so on until the missing general was located at five a.m. and gave a sleepy affirmative.) On the 18th Stilwell himself appeared at Myitkyina, dizzy with euphoria and with thirteen American war correspondents. He gave Hunter no guidance (Hunter was not a favourite), did not notice anything was amiss, and flew away again. Merrill finally looked in on the 19th, gave no orders to Hunter, returned to Shaduzup, had another severe heart attack, and relinquished command. Hunter, left with the initiative and responsibility, twice sent the Chinese 150th Regiment to try the defences of Myitkyina. On the first occasion it lost its way in crossing an open plain in daylight with the town in full sight. On the second the Japanese allowed it to enter the defences, but in the counter-attack that followed the Chinese became confused, fought each other and, in the words of the official history, 'drove themselves right back out of the town', adding, 'there was much confusion in the first few days at

Myitkyina'. Inevitably: no task force commander to replace Merrill was appointed until the 22nd. The choice fell on an unfortunate full colonel. But, put in to command a force of now divisional size (twelve battalions), he was relieved within the week. Stilwell then put in Brigadier-General Boatner.

Stilwell dismissed the idea of calling for the excellent all-British 36th Infantry Division, already earmarked for him and waiting to come in, as he was adamant that Myitkyina must be captured only by his American-Chinese troops.[5] Galahad, the old Chindit-trained Galahad, had virtually ceased to exist as a fighting force and in pursuit of his aim Stilwell filled the gaps in its ranks by misappropriating United States Army engineers from the road construction force, totally untrained, who more than once broke and fled under Japanese counter-attack. Stilwell flew more than once into Myitkyina to verify Boatner's gloomy but accurate situation reports. He deluded himself that the men of Galahad still 'looked good' and failed, apparently, to perceive that the deployment favoured neither a policy of starving out the garrison nor a concentrated punch. He resorted to the barren expedient of relieving Boatner in his turn. At that juncture he still believed that the Japanese garrison was only 500, and a good heave would throw it out. Such was the inane direction under which the Chindits were to suffer for the next two months.

Morris Force was its earliest victim. His mission, Morris found, was to secure, without delay, two straggling villages – Waingmaw and Maingna, on the east bank of the Irrawaddy opposite Myitkyina – which commanded the ferry points by which supplies and reinforcements entered the town. Morris, still under the impression that the town had fallen and all that remained was a mopping-up operation, hustled his troops into action as soon as they arrived. Waingmaw, he had been told, was only lightly held, if at all. In fact, inside the dense belt of lantana scrub surrounding the village was a system of strongpoints held by a garrison somewhat larger than Morris Force.

The Gurkhas assaulted Waingmaw three times, and three times they penetrated its defences. On the second occasion two Gurkha corporals crawled in on their bellies to stalk the bunkers and stuff grenades through the loop-holes. They killed some 130 Japanese when they obliged by counter-attacking with their usual ferocity, but it was in vain. Morris had insufficient strength to hold his gains and he continually ran out of ammunition. He pulled back to rest and evacuate his wounded, and flew into Myitkyina to explain his situation to Boatner.

It was not exactly a meeting of like minds. Boatner was at heart a good man. He had been friendly with Wingate and admired him, he had been of great help to Fergusson and the 16th Brigade, and it is worth noting that after the war was over Mountbatten sent him a personal copy of his Despatches. A fair share of the credit for the creation of the First Chinese Army must go to him.

He was not, however, a natural field commander. He was rigidly authoritarian in the fashion of American generals, demanding unquestioning obedience to orders. He was ill, and he was under considerable pressure from his intransigent and by this time purblind commander. 'Jumbo' Morris was equally a blunt and abrasive Indian Army officer of the old school, who made his impatience with anyone who could not see his point of view only too clear. He explained the strength of the defences, the unsuitability of Chindit columns for normal infantry work, his lack of men and his crying need for an abundant supply of ammunition and massive air and artillery support if he was to make any impression. Told to emulate the Chinese, who had just lost thirty-two out of thirty-six men committed without artillery support to an attack on a strong-point, Morris' reply was: 'Well, general, that is what I have been telling you for the past hour I will not do.'[6] He, mistakenly perhaps, construed Boatner's constant references to 'maximum force and effort' as a reflection on the courage of the 9th Gurkha Rifles; an impression which unfortunately percolated through to his officers. Boatner's successor did give him the fire support he needed to attack Maingna, but there was a blight on the whole Myitkyina affair. The artillery support proved to be two Chinese-manned guns firing blind over the town. This was understandably refused, with thanks. The air attack, usually so efficient, went sadly astray. The P-51s dropped their first bombs on the infantry start-line, fortunately killing no one but halting the whole attack. The B-25s dropped half their bombs in the Irrawaddy. The other half, landing on target, unaccountably did not explode. An urgent signal from Myitkyina Task Force called off the attack: the air force had forgotten to mention that they were using a new device, long-delay action bombs, which went off at intervals for the next twelve hours; it would be as well that the Gurkhas did not try to enter the village.

The best results were obtained in the accustomed Chindit manner by sudden blows delivered from the jungle. One evening Colonel Cane's Burma Rifles officer, scouting a village in the moonlight, was startled by a touch on his arm when what seemed to be a Burman materialised out of the shadows. He was in fact a sixty-year old Gurkha long domiciled in the country, and he said he had a particularly juicy target. This 'elderly fire-brand' led Lieutenant-Colonel Cane himself into his own village, striding down the main road to within fifty yards of some large huts in which 150 Japanese soldiers were harbouring for the night, with a mass of pack animals with supplies for the garrison tethered outside. No sentries were posted and a great chatter arose from the huts. Cane sent back for every man he had, four platoons, briefed them carefully and filed them up in the waning moon to form a long firing line at close range, shoulder to shoulder. On a given signal every man blazed away at point blank range for ninety seconds and on another they promptly disengaged and withdrew to the jungle. Old Udai Bahadur coolly remained to observe the results. There had been a great slaughter. The next day Cane went back to mop up, determined to make a bayonet charge, an affair he recorded with bloodthirsty relish:

> One [Japanese] ran straight into the river . . . the second dived into a dug-out . . . we sent a grenade to share it with him . . . [it] decided there was no room for him in one piece and splattered him over the walls. Another set off for the jungle screaming at the top of his voice pursued by a party of Gurkhas who were trying to skewer him . . . we burnt all the huts and stores in a grand blaze . . . having had a very amusing little action.

But, he added,

> the men were all tired and worn out. Had they been on a good run they would have been fit for a bit more, but being pitch-forked into actions they knew would be failures was far from good for morale and it speaks volumes that they went on slogging the enemy with grim determination. They proved again and again the wonderful quality of the Khas Gurkha.

The proof was costly. When after a prolonged and wearing altercation with Stilwell Lentaigne secured the order for Morris to come out of action on July 17th his force numbered himself, very ill, eight British officers and seven rifle sections, perhaps fifty men in all out of the 1,350 who had marched north from Chowringhee.

While Morris was prowling round the back entrance to Myitkyina the three Chindit brigades grouped round the Indawgyi Lake began yet another horrific march through the monsoon-drenched mountains to redeploy in front of their new objectives, dying as they went. In the meantime Calvert readied himself to pull out the keystone of the Japanese defensive arch at Mogaung. He knew that a Chindit attack on Mogaung was planned and, acting on Lentaigne's warning order, had already on May 27th detached Rome and the 3rd/6th Gurkha Rifles to make a fighting reconnaissance of its approaches, but the latter was by no means willing. Lentaigne may well have been perplexed by Calvert's signals, for on May 19th, his spirits rising, this indomitable officer was arguing for a more offensive policy: 'It is essential to prove that LRPG can conquer and hold and not just harass and this can only be done by fighting,' he said. But on the 29th he was off on a different tack. In a long signal to Lentaigne he argued in favour of remaining in his hide-out in the Gangaw range and for a reversion to guerrilla tactics, using boats to cross the floods. He wanted to exploit and not abandon the Kachin organisation so carefully built up for him by Musgrave-Wood. He was prepared to make a good effort, he said, but 'Mogaung might prove too tough a nut to crack'. He concluded: 'Therefore suggest we do *not* repeat *not* make flat-out attack against Mogaung in which we risk everything. Can this be given earnest consideration? Only way we can be defeated is by hammering our heads against a brick wall.'

These rapidly fluctuating opinions were not a sign of irresolution. Calvert liked to 'think aloud', and when he was denied the opportunity for a personal dialogue was to turn, too readily perhaps, to the signal pad. In fact, he and Rome had already had long and detailed discussions on how they would tackle Mogaung. They would first, they concluded, have to secure a 'firm base', proof against Japanese counter-attack and protected by a warning screen of Kachin scouts. In this would be established the light plane strip, a drop zone for supplies, a hospital and dumps of ammunition. (The brigade was to expend 60,000 rounds of mortar bombs alone.) They would need guns or some heavy mortars, but everything would depend on air support and to ensure its accuracy they would have to secure a commanding position from which his airforce officers could observe and control each strike. Mogaung was strongly held and surrounded by water obstacles and there would be no question of storming it: it would have to be a battle of attrition and a bloody business, but it would have to be faced. Calvert, seeing that it was fruitless to persist in his operations along the flooded Namyin River, sent the South Staffordshire off to join Rome, and awaited his final instructions.

Lentaigne's reply to Calvert's protests and counter-suggestions was laconic. The 'information paragraph' consisted of a single sentence telling him that the Chinese had put a block on the road at Seton behind the 18th Division: no further explanation or embroidery was required to bring home its significance to a soldier of Calvert's perception. The rest read: 'You will take Mogaung with 77th Brigade, less 81 and 82 Columns and levies. Plan at your discretion. Ensure adequate ammunition. Give timings.' Calvert described this as a perfect example of a directive from one commander to another. He set off at once with the Lancashire Fusiliers, fighting his way as he went, for the Japanese were already alerted. Lieutenant Sealy of No. 50 Column recalled:

'An hour or so after dawn my platoon had to be on the track for another day's progress towards Mogaung . . . We had just formed up when there was an outburst of firing a short way ahead of us . . . I could see that we were going to be in action before breakfast (except that we had nothing on which to breakfast). The Company Commander came along to say that the track forked about two hundred yards ahead and an unknown number of Japs were in the "V" of two tracks. I was to clear them out. I decided to have two sections in front of me and the other two behind. We would run along the right-hand side of the "V", all turn left on a whistle signal and sweep through the wood with bayonets fixed and grenades handy. This hurried manoeuvre went like clockwork and we soon came out on the left-hand side of the "V". We had killed a few and suffered no casualties at all in my platoon.

'My fellows had been cheered up by the activity and we were soon leading the column in earnest along quite a well defined track along the top of a broad ridge. The jungle had opened out a lot at this point; scattered clumps of bamboo, some light undergrowth and some tall teak. We had reached the middle of a shallow depression possibly two hundred yards across when we came under fire from our immediate front. My platoon was behind the crest in just no time at all. Unfortunately, all four sections had gone to my right so platoon HQ – myself, runner, batman and Pl. Sgt. – were isolated on the extreme left.

'Behind the crest we were safe from all but the grenades being lobbed over. Looking to my right I could see Corporal Butcher's section, the second section on my right, was several yards ahead of us busily pumping grenades from their discharger cups. Seeing this, I ordered an immediate advance up the slope, as the Japs were only thirty or forty yards ahead, and started forward with my platoon HQ. Jack, my batman, was within arm's length of me on my left. He was hit immediately and it looked, as he fell, as if a bullet had entered the point of his right elbow. I called out to Wheeler to put a dressing on and turned to see how the rest of the platoon was getting on. Corporal Butcher and his section had made excellent progress. He had, in effect, from his position near the centre taken over command of the platoon by coordinating short advances by the sections in turn with the liberal use of grenades to keep the Japs' heads well down. This action was typical of Butcher. On several occasions he had quite naturally taken charge of affairs when he was in a better position to do so than anyone else. In the endless discussions I and my NCOs had had, working out courses of action to suit all sorts of situations, Butcher never had much to say but he seemed to have a natural flair for giving the orders at the right time.

'I saw him reach the summit, almost alone, he stood for a second or so firing a Bren from his hip, and then silence, it was all over. As I joined him one of the men handed me a Jap battle flag, which had obviously been around a great deal, with the remark that it was probably lousy with typhus. I took the chance and stuffed it in my shirt. There were no Jap wounded and I looked at the dead to make sure they were dead.

'The only casualty in my platoon was, to my great sorrow, Jack, my batman. A bullet had entered his chest, killing him instantly.

'We were then ordered to continue the march. It was now about 2 p.m. and we had had no food. I, at least, was beginning to feel exhausted. We had been marching along for no more than half an hour when it started to happen all over again, but this one was worse. My platoon was at the bottom of a steep slope with a little clearing in it; opposite rose a steep bare track some ten feet wide with really dense bamboo on either side. The firing was coming from immediately in front of us at the top of the track. Fortunately it was going way above our heads – no doubt the Japs could see some of our column up the track behind us. I was ordered to attack straight up the track immediately and was told that our 3-inch mortars would be in action to assist. We were so close to the Japs and expected to be a deal closer in no time at all that I had grave doubts about the mortars. I remember saying to myself – Right, this is it. There's no way out of this one – so here goes. I just told my section commanders that it could only be a free for all to the top and the quicker we got there the better. The Japs were still not firing *at* us so I thought if we got up the forty yards to the summit really fast we could surprise them a little. We did our best and Corporal Butcher and I arrived almost at the top together. We were stopped by several logs strewn anyhow across the track. The Jap fire had stopped and I thought they must have withdrawn to another position further along the track. They had, but not very far – over came a shower of hand grenades. I could see them in the air and was down behind a log before any of them landed. I heard Corporal Butcher scream and saw him rolling over and over into the jungle on our right. When I met him again nine months later in India he told me that his one thought at the time was just to roll off the summit of the hill. Good soldier that he was he realised that to get *up* and attempt to run could have been fatal. My men were all spaced out in the track below me but nobody was moving forward. The first shower of grenades had not been followed by any further offensive action so I started to run down to where the bulk of my platoon were. I was strongly encouraged to leave the top by the sudden arrival of what sounded like heavy mortar bombs.

'As I ran I was suddenly sent sprawling by an almighty knock on my left leg. I lay where I was, making myself as small as possible and praying that the mortar fire would lift a little. After what was, I suppose, a few seconds but seemed much longer, the mortar fire was pushed forward. I shouted to my runner to tell my platoon sergeant to take over the assault and get to the top behind the mortar barrage. Within a few minutes he was dead – shot between the eyes as he reached the summit. I felt for him, as I had felt for myself in the first attempt, that he didn't have a chance. Going straight up a narrow track with no cover with the enemy just waiting for your head to come into view, you have to be lucky – I was.

'The fighting, or more properly skirmishing, rolled on all day, dealing with three more pockets of resistance, until night fell when [the head of] our column reached the (small) village of Lamin, four miles from Mogaung, but it was to be many a weary and painful hour before I reached it.

'The fighting for that day (it was D-day in Europe) was over for my platoon. Corporal Butcher had been found unconscious, his back and shoulders looked terrible but the MO reckoned that if he was flown out fairly soon he'd have nothing to worry about – and so it proved. We had done our job successfully but I had lost my batman, who was a real friend and looked after me almost like a father, my platoon sergeant, the ideal type of fighting NCO was dead, I was wounded and took no further part in the campaign, and my best Section commander likewise.

'All that evening, night and the early hours of next morning the wounded were being dragged and hauled into the village. No bones had been broken in my leg and I was able to stagger along a bit with the liberal use of morphia helped by relays of two helpers. Some hours before dawn I and the men helping me could go no further. It was pitch black and raining. We got off the track and the three of us sat under one gas cape. We had one cigarette between us. After sharing this I was helped ten or so yards into the jungle where I was to stay until morning when we were told that proper stretcher parties would be sent out. When I awoke it was light and I could see a very tall, powerful fellow whom I knew as Jock, from the South Staffords. I called him over and it appeared he had been sent to find me. He gave me a pig-a-back to the village.'

Calvert in his reply to give his timings had optimistically given June 6th as D-day for his main attack, but he had underestimated the difficulties of the ground and the persistence of the Japanese outposts. (This did not prevent Stilwell's staff from demanding in their usual fashion an explanation of why it had taken the 77th Brigade a week to

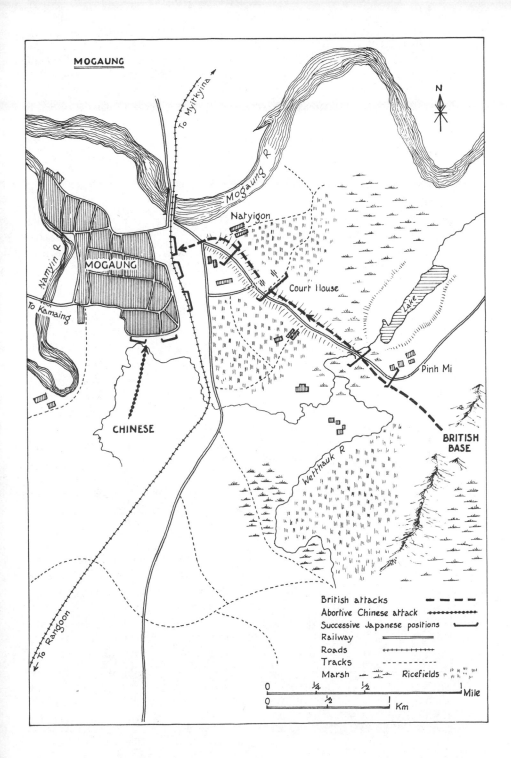

MOGAUNG

N

To Myitkyina

Mogaung R.

Natyigon

MOGAUNG

Namyin R.

To Kamaing

Court House

Lake

Pinh Mi

CHINESE

BRITISH
BASE

Wetthauk R.

To Rangoon

British attacks   ▬ ▬ ▬ ▬
Abortive Chinese attack   ••••••••••
Successive Japanese positions   ⌐_⌐
Railway   ─────
Roads   +++++++
Tracks   - - - - -
Marsh   Ricefields

0   ¼   ½   Mile
0   ½   Km

cover a map distance of twenty miles; an enquiry Lentaigne tactfully did not repeat to Calvert.)

The fact was that Mogaung was the very devil of a place to get at. The west side of the town was washed by the Namyin and the north by the Mogaung River, running at six knots. The only approach was from the south-east along a narrow road built up on a causeway, with flooded ground, lakes and marshes right and left and a deep *chaung*, bridged only where the road crossed it, barring any flanking movement. From the ridge Calvert had chosen as his base of attack to the town lay two miles of open country studded with villages, all fortified in the Japanese fashion with bunkers cut underneath them and all able to bring interlocking fire to bear over the front. The Japanese garrison at the lowest computation was some 3,500: a regiment of the 53rd Division, later reinforced by another battalion, and the service troops looking after the ammunition dumps and the hospital, where the very patients in the beds were armed with grenades.

There was only one option open: a concentrated, narrow thrust and a battle of attrition. Each position had to be carefully and closely reconnoitred, a dangerous business in itself, then bombed, and the assault troops had to go in immediately the P-51s had finished their work behind a barrage of mortar and machine-gun fire. As each position was captured it was consolidated and used as a jumping off point for an attack on the next. Such were the mechanics. For the soldiers their world, as ever, was bounded by the two or three hundred yards they could see to shoot a rifle in the eternity of rain, shell-fire, mud and sleeplessness, relieved only by a few hours in reserve, the mail or some luxury rations. Heaven was a letter from home, dry feet and a tin of British steak and kidney pie.

Said Durant in his memoir: 'I have purposely left out all the descriptions of rotting bodies and dangling guts, because that is a constant factor in war the world over.' He was right. His own muted, matter-of-fact prose conveys the flavour of combat better:

'We heard firing break out on the right and after some time a runner came up to say that they had run into a number of Jap snipers whom they couldn't see and from whom they were suffering heavy casualties. A Platoon commander who had been flown in as reinforcement the day before had been killed and the company second-in-command had been hit in the leg, besides which there were several casualties, they could make no headway and to save casualties were withdrawing. This left us in a very nasty salient. Archie (Major A. Wavell, son of the Viceroy) had one platoon on the right facing out towards these reported snipers, one platoon 400 yards away on the left facing the village which was our objective and one platoon in the centre facing the river, and we knew it was only a question of time before the snipers turned their attention to us. The first we knew was when Archie's second-in-command (a motherly married and family character who should never have been in) was shot through the head and killed instantly as he fussed about getting people under cover. At the same time everything opened up on the left as the Jap tried to push out the platoon facing the village and things got so serious there that the centre platoon had to be moved over to give support. The sniping on the right became heavier and still it was impossible to see where the firing was coming from. I had a Vickers mounted as if for AA and sprayed all the large trees, but it was entirely blind shooting. A platoon came up to reinforce us and was sent round to the right to clear what they could, but they hadn't gone fifteen yards before four men were down and the rest pinned down. The Jap then began, quite successfully, to grenade the wounded and when we tried to bring them in two more men were hit. Archie Wavell, trying a new line, set off with a section but within a few seconds was back holding his left hand which was hanging by a shred of muscle, having been hit by a sniper at twenty yards' range. He was astonishingly calm, gave out orders and then walked back unassisted to the RAP. Meanwhile on the left casualties were equally heavy and as it was getting dusk we were none of us feeling too happy, and even when the order came for us to withdraw we knew that somehow we had to get the wounded in. They seemed to be covered by two snipers so David Wilcox stationed himself where he might be able to get a shot and someone else began rustling the bushes nearby. The Jap moved and standing up David shot him at the same time getting a graze under his chin from the second sniper's bullet. But he saw him as well and, having a carbine, was able to fire quickly enough to get him; it was a very courageous action.'

Major Wavell's wound got Calvert into another, undeserved scrape with Lentaigne. Orders came for him to be flown out at once, and were duly passed on, but the wounded were piling up at the airstrip, and Wavell refused to emplane until every soldier who, in his own opinion, was more severely wounded than he had been taken out. Once more some abrasive signals were exchanged, as Lentaigne suspected that Calvert was once more having a fit of disobedience, but this time he had other and more serious matters to occupy his attention than even the evacuation of the Viceroy's son.

His brigade was fighting with tremendous determination. The American pilots excelled themselves, and their rapport with Thompson and his controllers was complete. They came in through the vilest of weather to deliver their strikes with unfailing accuracy in response to their guidance. Nothing could have been done without them, for there was no room for manoeuvre: the weary troops plodded forward after each strike until they were close enough – those who were still standing – to shoot their tommy-guns or stuff grenades or squirt flame-throwers through the embrasures of the Japanese bunkers. Monteith, of the Fusiliers, was killed because he was simply too tired to crawl when in the front line.

Michael Allmand, like Montieth, was a cavalry officer who had joined the infantry, in his case the 3rd/6th Gurkha Rifles, and, still only a lieutenant, was an acting captain in a rifle company which was halted by fierce, close-range fire in front of the Pinh Mi bridge. In the first of three single-handed attacks this quiet and rather retiring young officer drove out the Japanese with a shower of grenades hurled at close-range and, in a feat unusual if not unique for a British-born Gurkha officer, killed three of the defenders with a kukri. Inspired, the tired riflemen cleared the bridge and the village and, wading chest deep across the stream, established a foothold on the far side. The Fusiliers took over and captured the Court House and a three-gun battery dug in around it. Then in their turn the South Staffordshires and the Gurkhas took over until they were pressing against the little suburb of Natyigon.

Calvert's problem was that his brigade was bleeding to death. His bayonet strength at the beginning of the advance to Mogaung was 2,355; when the town fell it was down to 806 effectives. At mid-point in the battle it may have been 1,200, but this included many sick and wounded who were still fighting in the ranks, and this figure was dropping at an alarming rate. The loss of leaders was all but crippling, and the wounded collected in his field hospital had reached 250. Morale was holding up, but under the incessant Japanese shelling everyone was becoming very tired and jumpy. The one sustaining thought was to get in to Mogaung and end the agony.

Calvert knew that the Chinese had broken through at Kamaing and that there was a regiment on its way to him. But where was it? He sent one of his Burma Rifle officers to look for it, and asked Colonel Rome to make a direct appeal to Stilwell himself for it to hurry up.[7] (At this stage a South Staffordshire poet composed the variation to the Negro spiritual: 'I'm coming, I'm coming, but my pace is awful slow/I hear the Chindit voices calling, *jillho*, Joe': 'Jillho' being bazaar Hindustani for 'get a move on'.)

To the great relief of everyone Colonel Li and the 114th Regiment arrived on the 18th. The town could now be sealed off against further Japanese reinforcement, and his guns could reply to the Japanese artillery sited away to the west. A final attack was planned for the 24th. The South Staffordshire and the Gurkhas were ordered to take the last outer bastion, Natyigon, while Li rolled up the final Japanese line of defence dug in along the railway embankment in a drive from the south side of the town. A whole day's fighting was required to clear Natyigon and it claimed, among other lives, that of Michael Allmand. Two days after the fight for the Pinh Mi bridge he had once again led an attack, thirty yards ahead of the company he was now commanding, but now the pitcher was to go to the well for last time. At the right-hand end of the railway embankment nearest the bridge over the Mogaung River, his company was once again stopped by a Japanese machine-gun post. Allmand could no longer run, his feet were rotten with endless soaking, but he splashed slowly through the mud and shell holes to silence it, to fall mortally wounded at the moment of success.

In the same action 'B' Company of the 3rd/6th were attacking the bridge itself. Both the leading platoons were pinned, and the leading section was reduced to the section commander (a *naik*, or corporal) and two men. The *naik* ordered the two men to follow him in a charge, but fell, as did one of the riflemen, leaving only Riflemen Tulbahadur Pun on his feet. Tulbahadur went on alone, firing his Bren gun from the hip, cleared out the crew of the strongpoint opposing them, killing three and putting the rest to flight. Then, from their own position, he gave supporting fire to his comrades as they fought their way up to take the objective.

Allmand was awarded a posthumous Victoria Cross. Tulbahadur, happily, survived to receive his.

At the end of the day the Chindits were halted along the line of the still-impregnable railway embankment. The Chinese had failed them: nothing would persuade them to attack fixed defences, whatever they might have agreed to: it was simply not their style. Durant recorded:

'No one was particularly keen about the attack, the first fine, careless rapture being replaced by a resigned fatalism. I slept fully dressed that night and only woke up when our mortars began their uproar at 03.45. I hurriedly collected up my equipment and carbine and moved up to the start-line to walk into the most unpleasant situation of the whole campaign; for the Japs had opened up in reply with field-guns, whizz bangs and mortars and had our area taped. Although there was a moon it was fairly dark and there was the inevitable confusion caused by platoons sorting themselves out into open order and getting into correct positions. There was no cover, and for forty-five minutes I was more frightened than ever before or since, and it was with the most indescribable sense of relief that I heard the Jap firing stop at 04.30. Quarter of an hour later I moved forward with the second company just as it was getting light.

271

'The ground in front was marshy with knee-high grass and occasional banks and hollows, whilst a few large trees gave additional cover. Beyond this was a large group of stone and wooden buildings, all badly knocked about by bombing and on our right was the raised embankment of the road.

'We had only moved forward about 500 yards when we bumped the rear of the leading company and found that they were pegged down by two strongpoints. One platoon had reached and lined the railway embankment in the dark but at first light had been enfiladed by a Jap MG from a red brick house on their left and were now for all practical purposes non-existent. David Wilcox's platoon had run up against a Jap strongpoint, cleared it and then come under MG fired from a battered wooden building ahead, under which the Japs were dug in. His platoon was reduced to one weak section. Whilst orders were given out in the wreckage of what had been a house, the Jap began shelling again, still very accurately, and at the same time a sniper (whom we eventually found and silenced up a tree 300 yards away) began picking off people at a disturbingly quick rate.

'The flame-throwers were now summoned from the rear and as they moved past where I was lying, a shell burst and, puncturing one of the weapons, set it on fire. The wretched man who was carrying it was a mass of flame but managed to get it off and all we could do was to roll him into some water in a near-by ditch. The others went forward and got to work on the positions under the house but even so it was a long time before the Japs there were finished off. Only one broke out, all his clothes on fire, and was shot down, but the remainder preferred to stay where they were and get burnt to death, and we found that the officer had committed suicide by shooting himself through the head with his revolver. When this point was cleared we moved on and brought all we could to bear on the red house and after half an hour had the satisfaction of seeing about twenty Japs leave it, some of whom we killed with the MGs as they tried to get away. The Gurkhas meanwhile, meeting little opposition, had reached the end of the railway bridge and we now moved up on the line and began to dig in. By then the Brigadier was on the scene and when he heard of our casualties he decided to send the LFs forward with one company of Gurkhas whilst the Chinese advanced from the south. Our battalion was taken out and sent right back to rest, but the MMGs were left under command of the Gurkhas, and so I stayed on the railway line.

'Every man had fought magnificently under very unpleasant conditions, and although our casualties had been heavy we had achieved our objective and killed a lot of Japs on the way. The Chinese were full of admiration but thought we were quite mad, for with oriental patience they would have taken a week to do the same attack and probably suffered five per cent of our casualties.'

Calvert pulled out was left of the South Staffordshires, sent up a company of the Fusiliers to hold his gains and braced himself for a forlorn hope with the remnants of his brigade assault company. He was saved the trouble. As he sat on the morning of the 26th in a shell crater giving his final orders, away on the left there could be seen a swarm of Chinese advancing, without drawing any fire, laughing and chattering as they went. Their patrols, always inquisitive, had smelt an air of emptiness in the town, but they had been forestalled by the Gurkhas.

'I went forward straight away with the Gurkhas commanding officer to see about setting gun positions in case of a counter attack, and so I had the good fortune to see the town before the Chinese poured over it. In days of peace it must have been a very pleasant place with wide tree-lined streets, some lovely pagodas and priest's living-quarters, some large, stone buildings – the bank, certain shops, police station, etc. – and very solid and well-built wooden buildings raised on props in the Burmese fashion; it was the market centre for all the natives for miles around and the centre of the north Burma sugar industry.

'When we went in the whole place was deserted, and the only living creatures were unkempt dogs and wildly unfriendly cats.

'Not one building had been left untouched by bombing, all windows were broken, roofs removed, walls cracked, and the golden pagodas were chipped or blasted to the ground. Every road was cratered and the whole town was overgrown with rank weeds and waist-high grass, whilst all around lay the usual symbols of disorder – dead mules and ponies, fallen signal cables, boxes of ammunition, twisted bicycles, abandoned lorries, petrol cans, rations, equipment and lakes of paper, letters, orders and books.

'When we got to the river we found the rafts made of oil-drums and planks on which the Jap had made his way out, and all that day stray bodies came drifting down the stream and were promptly engaged by every available Chinaman in the vain hope that some at least had a breath of air still in them. As I put the last gun into position on the edge of the town a few half-hearted shots were fired at me from the thick reeds by the river banks, and a Gurkha patrol which was sent out found three Jap officers and six men in hiding there – probably non-swimmers.'[8]

So fell Mogaung, a strong place not inferior to Myitkyina, after sixteen days of continual assault by three battalions of British and Gurkha infantry. In the history of infantry fighting the feat of the 77th

Brigade is unsurpassed, not only as a tactical model, or as an example of the real face of combat undisguised by the cosmetics of regimental pride, false stoicism or patriotism, but also as an illustration of the extraordinary capacity of ordinary men – the Japanese, suffering under the terrible pounding of the P-51s must not be forgotten – for courage and self-sacrifice.

It was a victory marred by those necessary lice on the military body, the public relations staff. The release from Stilwell's head-quarters was that the Chinese had captured Mogaung, assisted by the Chindits. When the news broadcast was picked up, Calvert, irrepres-sible even in his post-battle depression, signalled, 'The Chinese having taken Mogaung 77 Brigade is proceeding to take Umbrage.' Legend has it that Stilwell's staff earnestly queried this and asked for verification of the map reference.

Calvert's next demarche was less frivolous. While he collected his troops and began to fly out his sick and wounded there was an exchange of signals enquiring how many men the brigade could provide, assembled into a single composite unit if necessary, to keep up the pressure on the Japanese, and instructions to move to Myitkyina. Calvert baulked at asking any more of his men, closed down his radio link to Amity and virtually disappeared for fourteen days while he marched his survivors out to Kamaing. The dis-obedient brigadier was summoned to Shaduzup to explain himself to Stilwell. It was an unusual form of carpeting. Calvert was accom-panied by Lentaigne, who had urged him to control his unruly tongue, while Alexander, in Chindit style, genially advised the opposite, telling Caivert 'to give him hell'. Stilwell was flanked by Boatner and his son Colonel Stilwell.

'Well, Calvert,' he said, 'I have been wanting to meet you for some time.'

'I have been wanting to meet you too, sir,' replied Calvert, not to be outdone in politeness, whether or not a court-martial resulted.

'You sent some very strong signals.'

'You should have seen the ones my brigade-major wouldn't let me send.'

This struck exactly the right note. Calvert followed this up with a flat, factual recital of the operations of his brigade and their casualty figures; Stilwell interrupting only to ask Boatner or his son for verification and ask, 'Why wasn't I told?'[9] He ended by asking Calvert to write five citations for Silver Stars he proposed to award in token of the brigade's achievements. He gave one to Calvert himself. This was to be the only award or acknowledgment he was to receive for the capture of Mogaung.

It would be pleasant to record that after this Stilwell changed his attitude to the Chindit forces remaining in the field, but this was not to be so. The wrangles between Lentaigne and Stilwell continued; first on the usual grounds that the Chindit commanders were not displaying 'maximum force and effort' and then over the question of evacuation. Neither Stilwell nor Boatner (now back in Shaduzup once more) could understand that a fighting unit is not only a technical but a social entity, at once a team of specialists and a complex of family-like groups, and that after a certain point, when casualties have eaten away the skilled fighters and the junior leaders, it ceases to be a *unit*. Stilwell was obsessed with arithmetic: as long as there were a hundred fit men in a brigade they should be given a task and expected to complete it. Boatner was obsessed with geometry; measuring distances on the map.

Although they had before them the example of Galahad and a whole division of Chinese who could make no headway in Myitkyina even with the aid of lavish artillery and air support, they expected the Chindits to take Japanese strongpoints, often without either. While Stilwell and Boatner were constantly urging Lentaigne on and upbraiding him because the Chindits were slow, they were apparently blind to the fact that Colonel Li and his 114th Regiment had reverted to their usual form and were dawdling at Mogaung within ten miles of the same objectives. Generals often have to make harsh or agonising decisions to push troops to their uttermost, and there was nothing between Lentaigne and Stilwell that could not have been settled by goodwill and common sense. As it was there had to be two interventions by the Supreme Allied Commander himself. On June 30th Mountbatten paid a visit to Shaduzup to see Stilwell and left under the impression that all was settled, but nothing was ever settled with Stilwell. On July 25th Mountbatten had to send his own American Deputy Chief-of-Staff, Major-General A. C. Wedemeyer, in what was more a diplomatic than a military mission, to discuss such matters as the take-over of Chindit mules by the incoming British 36th Division, and the difficulties of grouping Gurkhas and West Africans as individuals in other units whose officers could not speak their language. (Boatner's contribution at this conference was, once more, to ask Wedemeyer to ask Lentaigne the distance on the map from the forward Chindit positions, and his estimate of the Japanese strength; the innuendo being obvious.)

Lentaigne from start to finish acquitted himself honourably in these dismal and unmilitary transactions. The pressures on him were great. In the long transcript of the conference of July 25th there is not a single word from the American side expressing understanding of the British difficulties, let alone a word of praise or commendation.[10] Lentaigne had to deal with a man incapable of generosity, but also a dangerous one, who was as much, indeed more, a political than a military figure. A false move or a flash of his Irish temper could, in his understanding, compromise the British position with the Americans as a whole. With exemplary patience he restricted himself to reiterating the limitations of the Chindits when used as assault infantry, the lack of air support due to the weather and the difficulty of movement. He made his points, went to the limit in agreeing what was possible, and stuck to his agreement. Any shortcomings he may have had as a commander were more than made good by him in this last phase. His emaciated columns responded to his demands, and their by no means uncomplaining but unremitting valour enabled him to keep his bargain.

After the fall in succession of Kamaing and Mogaung the wrecks of the 18th and 53rd Divisions (the latter had lost the 128th Regiment complete at Mogaung) fell back and dug themselves in so as to control the roads leading south, around Taungni and Sahmaw. These two small towns were the final objectives given to Special Force and the fighting was for possession of two centres of resistance, Point 2171 and 'Hill 60', nicknamed after that ill-omened height of the Western Front of the First World War. In the worst marching conditions they had yet encountered the three brigades set off, making two or three miles a day.

After his withdrawal from Blackpool Masters had spent his time energetically re-equipping and reorganising his brigade, and evacuating his sick and wounded. The British troops were conscious of the fact that they had completed more than the promised ninety days' service behind the enemy lines and were earnestly hoping that they might be relieved. (Rhodes-James records how the headquarters personnel haunted his cipher office for the welcome signal, only to be disappointed day after day.) But when Lentaigne's new orders arrived they grimly and resolutely shouldered their packs and weapons and set off once more. Masters' route led first north through the swamps on the east shore of the lake, then over the mountainridge to Lakhren, where he set up his operational base, and then south-west towards Point 2171, the brigade's designated objective.

The West Africans, now united under Ricketts, took Masters' old route over the Bumrawng Bum, skirted close to the site of Blackpool and so up the west side of the Railway Valley. Brodie finally cleared the Japanese from the Kyunsalai Pass and followed behind the West Africans. Between them they could muster some eleven weak companies of riflemen and their heavy-weapon platoons. The Cameronians were no longer capable of attacking, and were relegated to holding the brigade base. The King's Own were hardly better off, with only 120 men remaining on July 12th. The York and Lancaster

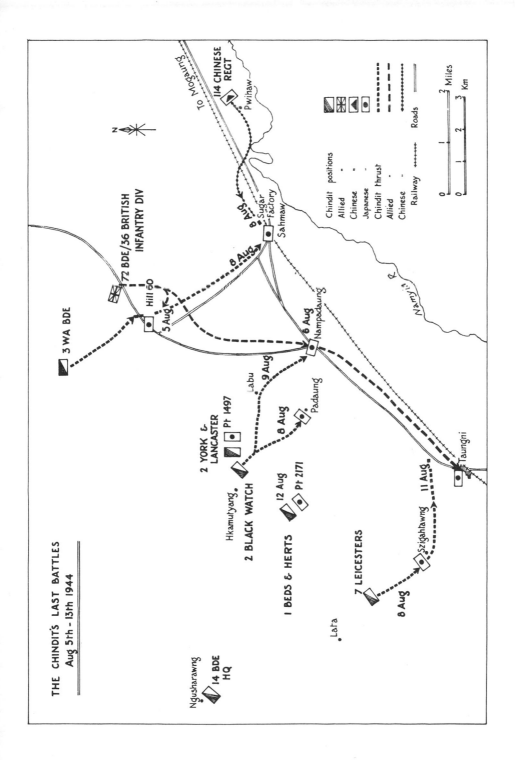

THE CHINDIT'S LAST BATTLES
Aug 5th - 13th 1944

3 WA BDE

72 BDE/36 BRITISH
INFANTRY DIV

Hill 60

5 Aug

8 Aug

8 Aug

Sugar
Factory

Sahmaw

To Mogaung

114 CHINESE
REGT

Pwihaw

Namyin R.

6 Aug
Nampadaung

9 Aug

Labu

2 YORK &
LANCASTER

Pt 1497

Hkamutyang.

8 Aug

Padaung

2 BLACK WATCH

12 Aug

Pt 2171

1 BEDS & HERTS

11 Aug

Szigahtawng

Taungni

7 LEICESTERS

8 Aug

Lara

Ngusharawng

14 BDE
HQ

N

Chindit positions
Allied   "
Chinese   "
Japanese "
Chindit thrust
Allied   "
Chinese   "
Railway
Roads

2 Miles
3 Km

lost no fewer than fifty-eight men dead from disease in the field. The Black Watch could at the end muster some fifty men capable of attacking. It was in fact a march in two directions simultaneously, one set of columns going north and east, while another smaller one, composed of the sick who dropped out piteously as they went, strove to make its way westwards to Lakhren and so to the lake and the Royal Engineer's 'navy'. The east-bound columns applied themselves to the slow and murderous business of driving through the Japanese outposts hidden in the jungle. MacGullicuddy, the hero of No. 30 Column, was killed on patrol, plunging it into deep gloom. Losses among the leaders hit the Africans, dependent on their white sergeants, particularly hard. 'It was now a painfully small group of white scarecrows who gathered round for the evening conference,' wrote Sergeant Shaw of the 12th Nigeria. 'Only nine of the White City Europeans were left.' It fell to Ricketts to attempt Hill 60, an intricate warren of earthworks with bottle-shaped fire-positions each holding a Japanese with just sufficient space for head or a weapon to be poked out to meet an attack. Inside these burrows they lived, ate, slept, defecated and fought without emerging, and in them they died. At the end of the battle Hill 60 looked like its original: a mound of churned earth with bare tree-trunks standing up like poles and cratered like the moon. It fell at last on August 5th, to two Nigerian columns and two battalions of the British 36th Division. Ricketts took Samaw on the 8th. Li, stirred into action, eventually arrived there on the same day.

Major Mead flew in to assess the value of the air support with a bottle of rum (the passport for staff visitors) which he gave to Ricketts, who, he noted, had grown a huge black beard like a Greek orthodox priest. Ricketts was lucky to be alive, for he was always up at the forward positions and had been peppered by fragments of a grenade thrown at him by an apparently dead Japanese. Mead, who could speak 'Coast-Pidgin', chatted with the Nigerians, and invited their opinion. '"Dey planes done come – dey go boom-boom-boom, de Japans, dey die plenty." I said I was glad to hear it. One asked. "Sah, you-self, you done send planes?"' Mead admitted his rôle. There was a hurried confabulation, and the spokesman had a whip-round for 'K' ration cigarettes which were formally presented, and formally accepted: '"For sen' na planes, sah."'

The three Gurkha columns of 111th Brigade closed up on Point 2171. It took four days to drive in the outer Japanese posts and clear a start-line. On the 9th the 3rd/9th attacked, and paid the usual price. The preliminary airstrike never arrived but the Gurkhas actually took the position by 'storm', a rare event in modern war at any time and rarer still in the war against Japan. There being nothing else for it, one company led by two Gurkha officers, charged. Thirty men went down in the first rush, the British company commander was wounded in two places and his Gurkha lieutenant Yembahadur had his thigh smashed by a burst of machine-gun fire. On his way down hill Yembahadur saw his commanding officer. 'He shouted to the stretcher-bearers to halt,' said Colonel Harper, 'gave me a full report on the situation and finished by practically ordering me to continue the attack.' The plan called for this frontal attack to coincide with another on the rear of the Japanese. This was delayed by the usual difficulties of the ground, and its commander was not in position when he heard the yells and shots on the other side of the hill. Hurrying on, he ran into machine-gun fire and the Gurkha riflemen went to ground. Major Blaker, calling on them to follow, dashed at the gun firing his carbine and went down riddled with bullet wounds, but his men got up and followed him and the two companies, amazingly, swept the hillsides and met triumphant on the crest. Blaker was the third Chindit officer to be awarded a posthumous Victoria Cross. Harper proceeded to hold Point 2171 against counter-attack for several days, but then the Japanese got round behind him and Masters was forced to order him to withdraw.

It was at this stage of the final battles that Stilwell complained that the Chindits were abandoning their objectives, or not pressing on towards them with sufficient resolution, and Lentaigne took the step of invoking the aid of the Supreme Allied Commander and so brought about the conference of July 25th. The record gives the clear impression that the Chindits were finished, fit only to hold ground until the 36th Division could take over. This was proved false by the 14th Brigade. Brodie's columns finished in a burst of sustained, offensive action, unrecorded and unsung, whose details can only be found in privately produced regimental histories or the yellowing pages of the war diaries. The 7th Leicesters fought their way into Taungni, and so cut the road on August 11th. On the 12th the Bedfordshire and Hertfordshire recaptured Point 2171. The York and Lancaster drove the Japanese off the heights barring the route to the junction of the Mogaung and Kamaing roads; the Black Watch went through, and the two battalions met the oncoming troops of the 36th Division on the road on the 9th.

The last action of the Black Watch, carried out even at that dreadful stage with their traditional panache, was at the village of Labu one and a half miles from the road. It took three days to close up to the last line of Japanese dug-outs. There was no air support and the mortars could not shift the Japanese. At the last air drop a set of pipes had been received, and with these Piper Lark, an Englishman serving in the battalion, played in the last charge, ordered as a forlorn hope, and the position was carried.

The fighting was over.[11] The Chindits had faithfully met the demands of the remorseless and ungrateful Stilwell, and also fulfilled the prophecy of their equally remorseless dead leader that many of them would leave their bones in jungle graves but that they would win undying fame, not that they were much concerned at that moment with their place in history. All they wanted was to throw off their packs for the last time, rest and sleep. Pride in what they had achieved was to dawn later.

The siege of Myitkyina had dragged on through June and July. Major-General Mizukami held off attacks of varying ineptitude made by a Task Force which had grown to two Chinese Divisions, the wreck of 'old' Galahad, and a 'new' Galahad made up of raw replacements from the United States; both these last under command of Colonel Hunter. The trouble was that the Chinese were incapable of a coordinated attack, and thought little of any attempt to storm the defences. Their response to orders to attack was to sit in their trenches and pour volumes of small-arms fire into the air. The one major effort to make a coordinated assault was further frustrated by a misdirected air attack in which forty per cent of the bombs dropped on Galahad. The Task Force commander then reverted to the old-fashioned method of heavy bombardment and a methodical series of small advances, each carefully consolidated, which gradually tightened the noose round the town and wore down the garrison by attrition. This was eventually successful. Estimates of the strength of the Japanese defenders vary, but it may have been 2,757 of all ranks. By mid-July Mizukami had lost 790 killed and had 1,180 wounded, most of whom remained in their fire-positions. His second-in-command, Maruyama (the colonel who had fought Galahad at Nphum Ga), suggested that a further sacrifice was militarily useless, and he agreed.

During the first days of August air reconnaissance revealed rafts moored under the near bank of the Irrawaddy and encouraged by this and a general slackening of resistance the Chinese decided to infiltrate the defences on the night of the 3rd, but they were just too late. Maruyama had slipped away with 600 men, and only 187, wounded and unable to move, were left in the defences. Major-General Mizukami, who had held up ten times his own numbers, backed by the most powerful air force in the world, for two months and sixteen days, followed the Bushido code, asking the Emperor's forgiveness for his failure and committing ritual suicide. Stilwell, who had correctly discerned by the end of July that he had as good as reached his objective, left Shaduzup and the direction of the siege which had cost him so much anxiety and went to meet his own doom.

16

Epilogue

THE FALL OF Myitkyina at the time seemed to be the climax of a mighty endeavour, planned on the grandest scale, logical in its concept and resting on the American belief (now, alas, somewhat battered) that there was no obstacle so great that it could not be surmounted by American ingenuity, American wealth, American skills and American drive. The reasoning on which this belief was based was stark and simple: American military philosophy rejected any subtle or refined approach, and the term 'intellectual' was not then in its vocabulary. The American system was to analyse the situation so as to perceive the correct goal, and thus arrive at the 'mission', calculate all the necessary resources of men and material required, formulate a plan leading as directly as possible to the goal, and then attack remorselessly, expending men and material as necessary until it was reached. There are worse systems for waging war, if wage war you must.

The American strategists who planned the war against Japan concluded that the mobilisation of resources must include the equipping and reorganising on American lines of the ramshackle Chinese armies. This in turn demanded the fabulous land route of road and pipe-line from India to China. The key-point on this route was Myitkyina. China was therefore the goal and the capture of Myitkyina the *mission*. 'Forget anything', ran the old United States Army Staff School precept, 'but never forget your mission.'

The British Staff College taught an exactly similar process to its students ('the appreciation of the situation') but it was not always apparent in their thinking. There was, and still is, in the ranks of the Chindit veterans considerable confusion about the nature of their rôle and mission, due entirely to Wingate's imaginative, intuitive shifts of mood and purpose: to 'liberate our territory of Burma'; to assist Stilwell; to pull the Fourteenth Army's chestnuts out of the fire. No such obscuring of the sacred mission was possible under the American system. In their deeply authoritarian military hierarchy once the mission was laid down it was almost impious to question it. To the Americans the British way of conducting war was incomprehensible.

The British did indeed define their goals, but they were politically more sophisticated and subtle than the Americans, more pragmatic, more elastic in their plans, attempting to reconcile large strategies with a famine in resources, and always seeking an alternative, indirect route round a difficulty or a hard pocket of resistance. The Americans mistook this for lack of resolution. Stilwell can be pardoned for his exasperation with the apparent disciples of Fabius Maximus and Sun-Tzu who obstructed him in Delhi on one side and Chunking on the other. *His* mission was clear.

Stilwell was indeed a complex man, and the chariot of his mind was drawn by fractious horses pulling against each other. Certainly he wished to distinguish himself as a general in the field in his country's service, this was an honourable ambition. Certainly he wished to revenge the humiliating defeat in Burma in 1942, and this did not make him any the worse a soldier. Certainly he wished to score off and show up the pusillanimous Limeys; a less respectable aim but only human. It must also be remembered that he was already, in spite of himself, a political figure, forced to take account of political realities and with a need to reinforce his position in Washington, where he was faced with double difficulties. He could not persuade his President to take a firm line with Chiang Kai-shek, and his own air force commander inside China, Chennault, was lobbying for an air-predominant strategy exactly the opposite of Stilwell's own. All these factors counted, but the lead horse of his chariot was the *mission*. Everything fed through his tunnel vision to his diamond-sharp little mind always added up to one word: *Myitkina*. It was no idle self-indulgence which made him step down from his other great responsibilities to take command in the field.

The long and bitter journey of the soldiers of five nations whom Stilwell drove along the road to his Pisgah was therefore justified by military logic, or so it might be thought, but the flawless chain stemmed from a false assumption. The American vision of China was a total delusion. How this delusion was born, how it grew and how it obtained such a grip on the American imagination is a large and complex subject, but that it was indeed a delusion was already becoming clear to the hard-headed American planners as early as 1944. It seemed even by then that their Pacific strategy might defeat Japan before ever a China policy would pay off. The effort on the road was accordingly scaled down to a simple improvement of the Bhamo road along which Morris and Herring had been skirmishing, and a pipe-line. What was plain to many observers and too long ignored by all except a few Americans was that it was beyond their power to modernise China. Chiang Kai-shek was determined on only one thing – not to fight. His officials were ineffective and corrupt and his generals men of straw.* The resumed Chinese offensive in Burma was to peter out near Lashio. All the great effort and sacrifice was wasted. The 'Stilwell Highway', where it has not been washed away by monsoon floods or reconquered by the encroaching jungle, remains a road from nowhere to nowhere; a monument to a monumental misjudgment.

The most distinguished casualty of the China delusion was Stilwell himself. He alone of the Americans saw Chiang Kai-shek with clear eyes, and once his first mission was completèd he, with his characteristic single-mindedness, set himself the next one. The new Chinese armies in China, he decided, must be made to fight, or allowed to fight. The only way to ensure that the vast flow of American aid was not wasted was, he felt, to make each successive instalment a reward for positive action. On September 19th he had the pleasure of handing the Generalissimo a note from Roosevelt expressing his hardening attitude. The manner of delivery he adopted was undiplomatic. 'It harpooned the little bugger in the guts,' he confided to his diary. But it also harpooned his own position and a month later, as a result of Chiang Kai-shek's insistent demand, he was recalled to the United States. His career had ended.

There remains the question of how the great Chindit adventure related to the operation's central aim. The arguments revolve around rival theories of warfare. Orthodox strategists take the view that resources squandered could have been better used elsewhere. Had, for instance, the 70th Division not been plundered to make up Special Force it would have been available to reinforce Imphal, which was momentarily in jeopardy while a division was flown up from the Arakan. Others, while recognising Operation THURSDAY as the prototype of air mobile warfare, argue that it would have been better to have used it concentrated on one decisive spot. In complete contrast, some of Wingate's followers see Long-Range Penetration as an extreme variant of the 'indirect approach', which would infallibly have succeeded had not Wingate's original plans been abandoned and perverted by Lentaigne and Stilwell.[1]

Such formal, all-embracing theoretical models of warfare are suspect. It is the mechanics that count and the Chindit effort must be judged on such practical grounds. What emerges so strikingly from the record is how far and how long the Chindit columns marched and

---

* Chiang Kai-shek's attitude and political problems cannot be simply or briefly explained, but it might be fair to say that the dictator could not afford to have any strong or able generals in command in the army, which was the only basis of his power. As for fighting the enemy, he could see, perhaps as clearly as anyone, that the Japanese were already doomed and that any exertion on his part was superfluous. He needed his army in being for the forthcoming struggle with the Communists.

how infrequently they engaged the enemy. The great trek of the 16th Brigade resulted in only two battalion actions of any consequence. The 111th Brigade exerted its full force on the enemy for only three weeks in May. Sergeant Shaw never heard a shot fired between leaving the White City in mid-May and the fighting round Hill 60 at the end of July. Brodie did almost all he was asked to do, but the track of his columns resembles the wanderings of a nomadic tribe punctuated by skirmishes. The reason was that, though the Chindits could vault by air over a mountainrange, once down on the ground their columns were hobbled to the pace of a man leading a mule. They were not in the least analagous to the aircraft or submarines to which they had been compared. They had great strategic but little tactical mobility. Wingate had had a prophetic vision of 'three-dimensional' war, but it had to wait for the perfection of the helicopter a quarter of a century later before it could be realised.

All this said and all special pleading heard, one important fact remains to be stated. What the Chindits and Galahad did between them was to prise loose the blocks in Tanaka's defensive wall and finally sever his jugular vein where it ran through the Railway Valley to Mogaung. Without them there can be no doubt that the Chinese would have stuck in the Hukawng Valley all the summer. It was all in vain, but that does not detract from their achievement; a triumph of stoicism over appalling adversity.

Triumph apart, the campaign ended, as campaigns often do, in anti-climax. In history the curtain seldom comes down at the end of the third act with the story completed, although it is tempting to write as if it sometimes did.

Galahad's story ended on a sour note. The treatment of the sick and wounded, many of whom Stilwell's staff had attempted to hustle back into action half-healed or half-cured, became a scandal. The administration and the welfare of the men was a disgrace and conditions at the convalescent depot so bad that the men rioted. This gave rise to a rumour that the unit had mutinied, which was far from the case. 'Old' Galahad had virtually ceased to exist after END RUN and 'new' Galahad, a mixture of engineer troops filched from the road-building task force and a detachment of half-trained recruits from the United States (one met a British officer on his way up to Myitkyina and asked him if he could explain how his carbine worked),[2] was hammered into shape by the indomitable Hunter, and it was still gnawing into the town's defences when the Japanese stole away. The scandal of Galahad's treatment was hushed up, conditions improved, medals were distributed; and the ill-used 5307 Composite Unit (Provisional) was accepted into the United States Infantry as the 475th Regiment, complete with colours and the hard-earned battle-honour *Myitkyina*, but few real Galahads remained to enjoy this belated recognition of their prowess. Stilwell before he left offered Hunter the official command, but Hunter had had enough of him and his cronies and rebelled at last, so he was sent home.

The fit, pink-cheeked soldiers of the 36th Division were astonished at the sight of the gaunt, bearded scarecrows called 'Chindits' who emerged from the jungle, but the apparitions were British infantry, always protected by their sacred amulet, the cap-badge; emblem of regimental pride. Normality was soon to resume its rule. As soon as he had camped, Colonel Green ordered a formal drill parade for his Black Watch and delivered a lecture, on *discipline*. The wreck of the Leicesters when it deplaned in India marched into the rest camp with arms sloped and at attention, and the men remained after they were dismissed to criticise the other columns as they arrived and to see if their smartness and bearing could compare with their own.

Back in India the sadly depleted Chindit ranks were fleshed out with reinforcements, and Gurkhas and British once more began to train with, incredibly, enthusiasm for another and better THURSDAY. But in February 1945 the commanding officers were assembled to hear with chagrin that Special Force had ceased to exist.

It took the 36th Division three months to fight its way back to Indaw, a goal abandoned by the Chindits in April, but by then all eyes were on Slim's army as it drove across the Chindwin into central and southern Burma. That brilliant feat was eclipsed in turn by Hiroshima. Then the Americans, the British, the Chinese and the Japanese all went away. The Burmans, the Shans, the Karens and the Kachins whose country they had used as a battlefield were left to piece their lives together, rebuild the towns and cities shattered by the foreigners who had come to liberate them and, free at last, to govern themselves as best they could.

Sources

War Diaries
The Chindit war diaries (Public Record Office, listed by units under 3rd Indian Infantry Division) are incomplete and in some cases mutilated. There is no war diary of field HQ of 14th Brigade, a number of unit war diaries are missing (some, possibly not kept at all, e.g. The Cameronians; some, e.g. 1st King's, were kept, but have disappeared), the maps from the 16th Brigade diary have been removed, and the files for the controversial month of March are missing from both the 16th Brigade diary and from the Operations Branch diary of HQ, Special Force. The diaries of the 3rd West African Brigade are sketchy and uninformative, but fortunately Carfrae's account, Vaughan's private diary, Shaw's book and the recollections of Major-General Ricketts enabled the gap to be filled. The diaries of the HQs 77th and 111th Brigades were admirably kept, as were many of the surviving unit diaries, which is greatly to their credit, considering the conditions in which adjutants and staff officers worked.

Unpublished or privately printed sources
The belief that they were engaged in a memorable enterprise led a number of Chindits to keep notes and diaries or write accounts while memory was fresh:
Anon. (In fact by Lieutenant-Colonel the Revd. P. Cane, column commander in 4th/9th Gurkha Rifles), *Chinese Chindits* Morris Force. (Privately printed)
N. P. Aylen (Trooper, 45th Recce Regt), *A B.O.R. in Burma*
R. J. Bower (Medical officer), *My Experiences in the Chindit Campaign in Burma 1944*
C. C. Carfrae, (No. 29 Column, 7th Nigeria Regt.), *Dark Company*
N. Durant (Machine-gun platoon commander, South Staffords), *Narrative*, written as a long letter to his family
P. H. Graves Morris (Commanded 2nd Bn York and Lancaster Regt.), *84 and 65 Chindit Columns in Burma 1944*

SOURCES

A. Harper (4/9th Gurkha Rifles, later commanded the 3rd/9th), *Joining the Chindits* (Fragment)
D. C. Herring, Report on the operations of Dah Force
D. S. McCutcheon, *Writings Pertaining to the 3rd Bn 4th Prince of Wales Own Gurkha Rifles* (Detailed history of Nos. 30 and 40 Columns)
—— Copy of *Use and Employment of L.R.P. Forces* (100 pp. by G(Trg) branch, HQ, Special Force)
P. W. Mead, *Chindit HQ*
W. H. Miller (2nd King's Own), *A Chaplain with the Chindits*
R. Needham (No. 51 Column) *The 51st Field Regiment R.A. Sept 1943 to October 1944*
S. R. Nicholls, 'Notes on services of 'R', 'S' and 'U' troops of 160th Fd Reg R.A. 25 pdrs. Original log of 'U' Tp at Blackpool.'
H. N. F. Patterson (Royal Engineer officer with No. 50 Column), *Nine Weeks in Burma*
R. E. Prather (Pilot of light aircraft, USAAF), (Privately printed), *Easy into Burma*
R. Rhodes-James (HQ 111th Brigade), *Flying Column*
J. R. Sealy (platoon commander in No. 50 Column), Narratives
I. L. Simpson (No. 40 Column), Pocket diary, with original maps
G. W. Symes, Extracts from Diary
C. P. Vaughan, *Record of Operations of 7th Bn the Nigeria Regiment* (Private diary, with full notes on column organisation)

* * *

P. W. Mead and R. Thompson, Memorandum on S. Woodburn Kirby's 'assessment of Wingate (War Against Japan III pp 217–223)' IWM document No 78/12/L, 1978, based on the Tulloch papers.

Verbal Testimony
Even allowing for the lapse of time this proved in almost all cases accurate as regards fact when it could be checked against war diaries, especially when witnesses could refresh their memories from contemporary map sheets. The depth and colour of subjective or anecdotal evidence and opinions on personalities revealed how deeply events were impressed on the memory of witnesses.

Maps
Many witnesses had retained the map sheets they had used in the field, of ¼, ½ and 1 inch to one mile scale. Colonels McCutcheon and Simpson had complete sets marked with the route and daily stages of their marches.

288

*Japanese Interrogations**
Post-war interrogation by British Intelligence, undated:
Some views of the Wingate Expeditions of 1943 and 1944 from the Japanese standpoint.
Payagyi Interrogation Report No. 1: A Short History of the 18th Japanese Division.
Payagyi Interrogation Report No. 2: A Short History of the 53rd Japanese Division.

Regimental Histories
I have as a general rule avoided regimental histories as they are often inaccurate as to facts, blinkered and slur over or conceal anything even remotely discreditable. The four quoted in the bibliography are notable exceptions, all being by practised hands. (Even so Fergusson has Masters withdrawing by the Kyunsalai Pass, Barclay has the orientation of the map of Blackpool wrong by 45° and Stevens omits the enforced withdrawal of the 4th/9th from Point 2171 and has the 3rd/9th making a counter-march of thirty-two miles which never took place.)

Select Bibliography
Alison, J. R., Symposium in the rôle of air power in counter-insurgency and unconventional warfare. *Chindit operations in Burma,* Rand Corporation for USAF, 1963
Anon., *Notes for Gunners in Far Eastern Theatres,* War Office, London, 1945
Anon., *Notes from Theatres of War,* No. 19 Burma 1943–1944, War Office, London, 1944
Barclay, C. N., *History of the Cameronians* (Scottish Rifles) Vol. III, 1933–1946, Sifton Praed, London, 1947
Boyle, P. and Wood, J. Musgrave, *Jungle, Jungle, Little Chindit,* Hollis and Carter, London, c. 1944
Calvert, M., *Prisoners of Hope,* Cape, London, 1952
Doorn, F., *Walkout,* Crowell, USA, 1971
Eldridge, *Wrath in Burma,* Doubleday, New York, 1949
Fergusson, B. E., *The Black Watch and the King's Enemies,* Collins, London, 1950
—— *The Wild Green Earth,* Collins, London, 1946
—— *The Trumpet in the Hall,* Collins, London, 1973
Hunter, C. N., *Galahad,* The Naylor Company, San Antonio, Texas, 1963
Hiroshi Fuwa, 'Japanese Operations in the Hukawng Valley,' *Military Review,* USA, January 1963

* Available in the Imperial War Museum.

Lewin, R., *Slim: The Standard Bearer*, Leo Cooper, London, 1976

Masters, J., *The Road Past Mandalay*, Michael Joseph, London, 1961

Mountbatten, of Burma, Vice-Admiral, the Earl of, *Report to the Combined Chiefs of Staff by the Supreme Allied Commander, South-East Asia 1943–1945*, HMSO, London 1951

Ogburn, C., *The Marauders*, Hodder and Stoughton, London, 1960

Pownall, Sir H., Chief-of-Staff, *Diaries*, Ed. Brian Bond, Vol. II, 1940–1944, Leo Cooper, London, 1974

Robertson, K. E., 'Indawgyi'. *The Royal Engineers' Journal*, Vol. LXII, September 1948

Romanus, C. F. and Sunderland, R., The US Army in World War II: the China India-Burma Theater. *Stilwell's Command Problems*, US Government Printing Office, 1951

Saunders, St G. H., *Royal Air Force 1939–1945*, Vol. III *The Fight is Won*. HMSO, London, 1975

Shaw, J., *The March Out*, Rupert Hart Davis, London, 1953

Slim, Viscount, of Yarralumla, *Defeat into Victory*, Cassell, London, 1956

Stevens, G. R., *The 9th Gurkha Rifles*, Vol. 2., 1937–1947, London, 1953

Stone, J. A. (Ed), *Crisis Fleeting*, Office of the Surgeon General, Department of the Army, Washington, 1969

Swinson, A., *Kohima*; Cassell, 1966

Sykes, C., *Orde Wingate*, Collins, London, 1959

Thorne, C., *Allies of a Kind: The United States, Britain and the War against Japan, 1941–1945*, Hamish Hamilton, London

Tuchman, B., *Sand Against the Wind: Stilwell and the American Experience in China*, Macmillan, London, 1971

Tulloch, D., *Wingate in Peace and War*, Macdonald, London, 1972

Woodburn Kirby, S., *The War Against Japan*. Vol. III, (History of the Second World War, United Kingdom Military Series), HMSO, London, 1961

White, T. E, (Ed), *The Stilwell Papers*, Macdonald, London, 1949

Underhill, W. E. (Ed), *The Royal Leicestershire Regt 1928–1956*, Privately printed, Plymouth, 1957

Notes to Chapters

1. PRELUDE
1. Fergusson, *The Trumpet in the Hall*, p. 180.
2. Sykes, p. 396.
3. Safely back in Imphal, it is said, he blurted out, 'I suppose that this means a court-martial'. Private communication. He thought he had failed badly, Mead.

2. THE TWO GENERALS
1. Mountbatten, personal communication.
2. Stilwell, diary. Tuchman p. 127. The British were also 'pig-fuckers'.
3. Doorn, pp. 99, 71, 95.
4. Romanus and Sunderland, p. 29.
5. A. C. Simonds, personal communication.
6. D. Whyte, ibid.
7. C. A. R. Nevill, ibid.
8. Simonds, ibid. Sykes, p. 250.
9. Mead. On joining he expressed regret that he had not attended Staff College. 'A matter for congratulation,' said Wingate.
10. Mead.
11. Piggott, personal communication.
12. D. N. H. Tyacke, ibid.
13. J. H. Marriot, ibid.
14. Lewin, *Slim* pp. 142–143.

3. PREPARATIONS
1. Wingate's 'Training Notes', PRO/WO/203/5216
2. War diaries of bns of 14 Bde, PRO/WO/172, 4864, 4900, 4870, 4934; also *Use and Employment of LRP Forces* (McCutcheon, Sources)
3. Ibid.
4. Vaughan.
5. PRO/WO/203/5216; Tulloch, p. 139; personal communication, Mountbatten. Later Tulloch alleged: 'Above all others, Mountbatten did NOT [sic] want Chindit II to be launched': letter December 8th 1969 to A. J. Barker. Tulloch appears to have been infected by Wingate's paranoid fantasies, for without Mountbatten's support THURSDAY might well have foundered, or been restricted to a mere raid.

6. PRO/WO/172/4261.
7. G. W. Symes, personal communication.
8. Tulloch, pp. 57, 127–128. Lord Ballantrae, personal communication.
9. Rhodes-James.
10. Carfrae.
11. Durant.
12. J. Hart, personal communication.
13. Tyacke, ibid.
14. H. T. Alexander, ibid.
15. A. J. Barker, ibid.

4. THE GENERALS MAKE THEIR PLANS

To disentangle the sequence of plans, cancelled, modified, approved, skeleton, suggested and discarded, would require a whole chapter. It was hard enough for Mountbatten and his staff to keep abreast. Pownall, *passim*. No wonder Wingate and Tulloch misunderstood the situation.

1. Sykes, p. 456.
2. Mead: Chindit HQ.
3. Hunter, p. 10.
4. Kirby, p. 177 and Appendix No. 17, p. 486.
5. Fergusson, lecture to Royal United Service Institution. London, August 1946.
6. Piggott, personal communication.
7. Tulloch, p. 194.

5. GALAHAD GOES TO WAR

1. Romanus and Sunderland, p. 149, but Hunter, p. 27, says that a proper written order with a precise objective was not issued.
2. Hiroshi Fuwa.
3. Romanus and Sunderland, pp. 200–203, p. 204; Hunter, pp. 85–86.

6. OPERATION THURSDAY

1. Alison (Rand Corp. Report), Mead, Tulloch, pp. 196–197. Claims vary from 30 to 100 aircraft destroyed, but whatever the correct figure it was a great contribution to the battle for air superiority being fought by Eastern Air Command.
2. Woodburn Kirby, p. 182. Personal communication, D. W. Wilson, then G SO2, Army Photographic Intelligence Section, Bengal/Burma.
3. Tulloch, p. 207
4. Tulloch, pp. 199–200; Calvert, pp. 21–23; Slim, pp. 261–2.
5. Full, valuable account in Mead.
6. Tulloch, p. 211.

7. EMPHASIS IN THE RAILWAY VALLEY

1. Correctly the 'Mu Valley'.
2. Patterson.
3. Durant.
4. Ibid.

5. Report annexed to Special Force war diary PRO/WO/172/4266.
6. Lack of observation baffled the 25-pounders of the artillery, but firing over open sights they destroyed a 70 mm infantry gun brought up by the Japanese.
7. There were junior liaison officers with Dah Force and later with Morris Force. They would have made no difference even if favourably impressed by the Chindit effort, owing to Stilwell's attitude and the timidity and toadyism of his staff. See Thorne, esp., p. 228.

8. ENTERPRISE AT INDAW

1. Needham.
2. Ibid.
3. Quoted in full, appx. to Calvert, *Prisoners of Hope.*
4. Fergusson knew what was in the wind by March 12th.
5. 3 Ind Div Op Order No 6 dated March 23rd.
6. And, as said, continued in this belief until well after the war was over.
7. Lord Ballantrae, personal communication.
8. Confirmed by Marriott, brigade major of 16 Bde. Ibid.
9. Sqn Ldr R. now Sir Robert, Thompson, who invented and perfected the system.
10. R. Tatchell, personal communication.
11. Marriott (himself a Royal Leicester), ibid.
12. War diary.
13. Excellent account in Underhill.
14. Letter of March 21st, Tulloch, p. 223.
15. Woodburn Kirby, pp. 176–177.
16. Symes, personal communication.
17. Tulloch, p. 209–210.
18. Marriott, personal communication.
19. 77th Brigade war diary for March.

9. LENTAIGNE SUCCEEDS WINGATE

1. Rhodes-James.
2. Shaw, p. 144.
3. Tyacke, personal communication.
4. Patterson, ibid.
5. Tulloch, pp. 236–237. (He makes no reference to Symes).
6. Symes, personal communication, diary entries.
7. Mead.
8. Rhodes-James; Masters; H. T. Alexander, personal communications.
9. Masters, pp. 199–200: 'I intended to feign sick, fly out of Burma and tell Wingate that he must come in himself and judge whether Joe was physically fit.'
10. Tulloch, p. 240.
11. Calvert, pp. 101–103.
12. The interrogation quoted in the sources says that the supply situation was 'very bad', but this was the result of a combination of the effect of

action west of the Chindwin, the almost non-existent roads, lack of bridges across the Chindwin and the raids of the Allied air forces, as well as the operations of the Chindit brigades.
13. Woodburn Kirby, pp. 214–216.

10. BLOCKING THE BHAMO ROAD
1. Herring's fascinating report, *passim*.
2. He was the son of the Macgillicuddy of the Reeks, and regarded as outstanding even by the standard of the Gurkha officers.
3. Masters, Rhodes-James, McCutcheon.
4. Gurkha opinion of Morris varied. Harper justly observed to the author that he should be judged by the magnitude of his responsibilities. No one could have done more to meet the demands of the Myitkyina Task Force commanders and at the same time preserve his columns from complete destruction.
5. Herring's account.
6. Cane, McCutcheon, war diary of 4th/9th G.R.

11. THUNDER AT THE WHITE CITY
1. All the troops of 69 Regt did well. 'X' tp at the White City records aircraft claimed destroyed and confirmed by infantry patrol 6, probable 7, damaged 8. PRO/WO/172/4733.
2. Pagagyi PoW Camp Interrogation Report No. 2.
For the fighting generally: Calvert, Carfrae, Nicholls, Sealy, Vaughan and Durant.

12. THE STRONGHOLDS ABANDONED: ALL MARCH NORTH
1. Alexander visited the White City after Gillmore had assumed command, and he is the only source of information on which Lentaigne could have formed an opinion. Contemporary opinion is that however the relief was made, the change was for the better. Private communications to author.
2. Ricketts, personal communication.
3. Fergusson, *The Black Watch and the King's Enemies*, pp. 243–249.
4. Mead, for all the air operations.

13. PROFOUND IN THE DEPTHS
1. Op Instr No. 8 of April 27th, 1944. PRO/WO/172/4266.
2. Ricketts, personal communication.
3. Stevens, war diary and personal communication from Ricketts.
4. For an agonising description of the march see Shaw, pp. 83–96.
5. Private communications.
6. Vaughan, Graves-Morris, personal communication from Ricketts.
7. War diary PRO/WO/172/4663, also original notes kept by Lieut. Swann with sketches, target numbers, ranges and bearings.
8. Stevens, also good war diary of the battalion, PRO/WO/172/5030.
For the march to Blackpool, Harper, personal communication.
9. Harper, personal communication.
10. J. Hart, ibid.

11. Rhodes-James.
12. Harper, personal communication.
13. Miller.
14. There is a detailed account of the fighting, omitting the misdirection of the columns and the shooting of the severely wounded, in PRO/WO/172/4267: Masters to Lentaigne: *Report on Ops 23–28 May, to Comd 3 Ind Div Secret and Confidential* dated May 28th. He blamed the 3rd/9th for allowing the perimeter to be breached, but pointed out that without air support, re-supply and strong floater columns to keep the Japanese from close investment his position was untenable. Masters' signal announcing his decision to withdraw handed to Rhodes-James early a.m. 25th is on the file dated 28th; clearly sent after arrival at Mokso Sakkan.

14. LACK OF AMITY

1. See note 14 – Chapter 13 above.
2. A discussion lies outside the scope of this book, but unconvinced pro-shooters and floggers can consult Robert H. Arhenfeldt, *Psychiatry in the British Army in the Second World War*; Routledge and Kegan Paul, London, 1958, Appendix B.
3. Except for aiding the enemy and mutiny.
4. Patterson, personal communication.
5. Vaughan, Diary.
6. *Henry V*, Act 4, Scene 3, aptly quoted by Calvert in personal communication.
7. Private communication.
8. Needham's narrative.
9. Masters, personal communication.
10. Masters, personal communication, but see also *The Road Past Mandalay*, p. 198, which implies a general use.
11. 2nd Y & L war diary (PRO/WO/172/4394) records 'Public punishment for two men caught pilfering rations', but does not mention type of punishment. If flogging, the number of known cases is increased by that number. This is the only *recorded* incident.
12. Recollection of Macgillicuddy, Asten.
13. Personal communication from Graves-Morris, who also kindly lent me the press cuttings of his court-martial.
14. Moffat, personal communication. He was present at the rout but stood his ground, helped collect the fugitives and recalls a sort of summary court-martial. Moffat served throughout the campaign until the final evacuation, and is intensely proud of being a Chindit, but took a dim view of HQ 14 Bde.
15. Barclay, pp. 153–154. When on July 2nd Masters ordered the Cameronians to lead the brigade attack Henning felt it his painful duty to report that his battalion 'was unfit for further offensive operations'.
16. Bower having been flown in as a replacement medical officer for the Beds and Herts had to march with the Black Watch from the vicinity of Aberdeen to Indawgyi.

17. J. H. Stone, pp. 283–288. This report was suppressed, but a copy passed through medical channels to the medical branch of the US China-Burma-India theatre found its way to the Surgeon-General's department in Washington and so to publication. The investigation was made at the rest camps immediately after evacuation in August 1944. No cases of psychiatric illness were diagnosed in any brigade, and the general morale of the Chindits was 'surprisingly good'. Predictably the officers of the 111th Brigade refuted the report when they learnt about it long after the event, but all the same, it should be treated with reserve. Of a sample of 273 from 111th Bde almost all were from the Cameronians and the King's Own, and the sweeping unanimity of the opinions, that *all* of the sample had lost confidence in *all* their officers, and that 184 would rather 'face detention' than serve in another Chindit campaign raises the question of how the interrogation was conducted. Blackpool was said to be the turning point for morale, not surprisingly: neither battalion had a successful action afterwards to act as a reviver. Rhodes-James' account indicates that while at Mokso Sakkan many officers and others eagerly awaited the order that they were to be flown out, and the resumed march to Sahmaw was a great disappointment. The reporting officer noted that men in those units who had never heard of the '90-day tour' were not ticking off the days in their mental calendar and their morale was correspondingly higher.

18. Robertson.

19. He was disappointed. In spite of the fact that the Japanese 56th Division had to send an equivalent regiment under its infantry group commander Mizukami to reinforce the garrison of Myitkyina, the Chinese offensive bogged down in mid-June. Romanus and Sunderland, *op cit*, Chapter IX.

20. Tyacke, personal communication.

21. Mead. Not all of the US staff officers were so obstructive. He soon found allies among the younger ones and managed to circumvent the inertia of Stilwell's headquarters.

22. Ibid.

I have used the expression 'Stilwell's HQ' for his establishment at Shaduzup as shorthand for HQ, Chinese Army in India, Chih Hui Pu, and Northern Combat Area command, all somehow combined. Boatner was Chief of Staff of CAI, and also commanding general of NCAC, when he was not task force commander at Myitkyina. Mead's adverse portrait of the HQ, supported by Tyacke and Alexander, is not any harsher than Hunter's. For the view from inside of the British, Mountbatten and so on, see Eldridge's sour account.

15. THE CHINDITS' LAST BATTLE

1. Romanus and Sunderland, pp. 228, 226–238; Hunter, pp. 114–128.
2. As before, Hunter was treated as the task force commander in the field, Merrill being unable to march.
3. Hunter, pp. 128–129.
4. Approximately. See Romanus and Sunderland, p. 233 and f.n. 73.
5. Ibid.
6. Cane. Stevens, p. 281.

7. Rome first flew in his light aircraft to locate the 114th Regiment, and found it happily bivouacked and not marching on Mogaung at all. On arrival at Shaduzup he had some initial difficulty in convincing Stilwell, and his son, that this was so. He, too, noted the subservience of the CAI/NCAC staff to Stilwell. Personal communication.
8. Durant.
9. Calvert, pp. 250–251. Stilwell seemed prone, when confronted, to blame his staff. Similarly, he affected to be unaware of conditions affecting Galahad which amounted to a military scandal. See Hunter, pp. 130–137.
10. The full transcript of this conference is available. PRO/WO/172/4268.
11. The total casualties were: killed, 1,034; wounded, 2,531; missing, 473; evacuated sick during the campaign, 5,000 plus. Many wounded were sick as well, and when the brigades returned to India medical examination revealed that one man in two was unfit for active service. Some of these never recovered completely.

16. EPILOGUE
1. See Tulloch, *passim*.
2. Personal communication from the late Major-General H. T. Alexander.

Index

T

Takeda, Maj-General, 195, 213; difficulties, 231-2; attacks Blackpool, 235-6; fails to pursue, 240

Tanaka, Lieut-General S., 18, 90, 209

TARZAN plan, 70

Templecombe landing ground, 79, 175. 178

Thetkegyin, action at, 145-7

Thompson, Sqn-Leader R., 65, 117, 123

Thompson, Lieut-Colonel, 237

THURSDAY, operation, 18, 25, Chapter 6 *passim*

TOREADOR plan, 70

Tulloch, Brigadier D., 42, 52, 55; character, 57, 105; advises on successor to Wingate, 160; Symes and Lentaigne's opinion of, 161, 164

Tulbahadur Pun, Rifleman, VC, 270

Twelvetrees, Major, 130

Tyacke, Major D. N. H., 43

U

Udai Bahadur, 262

U-Go, operation, 26, 71, 102, 139

United States Army
   10th Air Force, 255
   No. 1 Air Commando, composition, 64; successes against Japanese, 102, 104, 147; disbanded, 126, 169, 173, 184, 214; devastating effect of, 199
   5307 Composite Unit (Provisional), 61; *see also* Galahad
   Engineers, 108, 124, 142; at Blackpool, 228

Upjohn, Major G., comd. 6th Nigeria, 152, 197, 240, 242

V

Varcoe, Major R. A. S., 145

Vincent, Air Vice-Marshal, 154

Vaughan, Lieut-Colonel C. P., 198; attack on Mawlu, 201-2, 203; attack on Yawthit, 214, 232, 242; on discipline, 247

W

Wavell, General Sir A., 25, 60

Wavell, Major A., 268-9

Wakayuma, Major, attacks Broadway, 127 *et seq*

Walawbum, battle, 89-91

Wedemeyer, Maj-General A. C., 275

West Africans, as soldiers, 198

Weston, Lieutenant L., 88, 90, 95, 97

White City, 114; occupied, 119-120, 126, 192, 194; reinforced, 196, 198; successfully defended, 198-9; Japanese attack repulsed, 205; evacuated, 219-221

Wilkinson, Lieut-Colonel, 144; action at Inwa, 147

Wilson, Lieutenant S., USA, 87-8

Wingate, Maj-General O. C., 17, 18, 19, 20; former career, 23-7; at Quadrant conference, 26-7, 67-9; ambitions, 28; character, 36-44; clash with Kirby, 40; prone to violence, 41-2; dislike of staff, *ibid*; as leader, 41; military philosophy, 51-3; creates Special Force, 51-65; impact on troops, 62-3; intentions, 73; refused 26th Division, 74; threats to resign, 75; plans 'A' and 'B', 75; mission defined, 78; operational plan, 79; reaction to blocking of Piccadilly, 105-6; signals Churchill, 110-11; Order of Day, 113, 132, 135, 136; 'stronghold' directive, 137; orders Indaw attack, 137-9; role of 14th Brigade, 142; scheme to reorganise Special Force, 149-150; signals Churchill for more aircraft, 152; assessment of as comd., 148-155, 161; death, 155; reaction to by troops, 156-8; problems of succession, 159-160; assessment of effect Plan 'B', 171-4, 176, 187; disciplinary code, 136, 137, 245-9

Woomer, Lieutenant, USA, 90, 100

Y

Yawthit, action at, 214

Yembahadur, Lieutenant, 279

Young, Captain, Royal Artillery, 234, 235, 236